CONCISE ENCYCLOPEDIA OF

The Atom

CONCISE ENCYCLOPEDIA OF

The Atom

BY DR. PAUL MUSSET AND DR. ANTONIO LLORET

INTRODUCED BY SIR GEORGE THOMSON

COLLINS · GLASGOW **FOLLETT** · CHICAGO

Other titles in the series

Concise Encyclopedia of Astronautics
Concise Encyclopedia of Astronomy

and in preparation

Concise Encyclopedia of Electronics
Concise Encyclopedia of Exploration
Concise Encyclopedia of Mythology
Concise Encyclopedia of Ballet
Concise Encyclopedia of Modern Art

About this book. *The original French text was written by Dr Paul Musset, nuclear engineer and doctor of physical sciences and Dr Antonio Lloret, doctor of physical sciences. It has been translated and re-edited by Dr G. Wylie, Senior Lecturer in Natural Philosophy at the University of Glasgow. The Introduction has been written by Sir George P. Thomson, winner of the Nobel Prize for Physics in 1937.*

Printed in Great Britain by
Morrison and Gibb Ltd.,
London and Edinburgh.

INTRODUCTION / *SIR GEORGE THOMSON*

If one asked a non-scientist—and many scientists—what the word ' atom ' suggests, 90 per cent of the answers would be ' bomb '. But in fact the idea which the word conveys has a history not only older than nuclear warfare, but older than gunpowder. The Greeks had the idea of tiny particles out of which everything was built and which were indestructible, though they had parts. This very up-to-date view almost disappeared in the Middle Ages and the best statement of it, a long Latin poem by Lucretius, survived only in a single manuscript. Atoms came back to science in the early nineteenth century as a consequence of the application to chemistry of accurate measurement by weighing, and of the study of newly discovered gases. John Dalton, the son of a poor weaver from the mountainous English county of Cumberland, partly by intuition and partly as the result of experiment, put forward the germ of modern atomic theory, explaining compound substances by the union of small numbers of atoms of elements from what are now called molecules. Not without opposition this theory gradually came to dominate the rapidly growing science of chemistry, though even near the end of the century there were still some who held it unscientific to believe in bodies which had never actually been seen or counted.

Physics came later to atoms but with perhaps greater enthusiasm, leading to advances which make it as absurd to deny atoms as to believe in a flat Earth. But they are atoms with a difference, no longer indestructible. It was first proved by J. J. Thomson that they could lose small parts of themselves, electrons, which would in time be replaced by others. Then Rutherford and Soddy, studying the radioactivity discovered by Becquerel and the Curies, proved that the atoms of these substances undergo much more drastic changes spontaneously, which transform an atom of one element into that of another, or sometimes two others. He went on to produce analogous changes in ordinary elements, nitrogen first, using the alpha particles shot out by radium as shells to bombard the central nuclei of the lighter atoms. Cockcroft did the same with particles produced in an electric discharge. Already by 1939 a vast number of ' nuclear reactions ' had been discovered, largely in the USA where the work of E. O. Lawrence and others had made powerful accelerators, ' atom smashers ', common laboratory tools.

The discovery of nuclear fission, when it came in the first days of 1939, was exciting because it so quickly became clear that here at last was a possibility of releasing the large stores of energy which it had been known for years lay inside the nuclei of the heaviest atoms. This possibility had been discounted by many, including curiously enough Rutherford himself. Regarded as a discovery in pure science it was not of the highest importance, not equal to the discovery seven years earlier of neutrons by Chadwick, which indeed are needed to produce this fission of a heavy atom into two roughly equal parts. It was known that the very heavy atoms were mortal, this was just a new death they might die. But it is death from an infectious disease, which in certain circumstances can kill half the population, not in the billion years of such atoms' normal life but in a millisecond. Further, it can be controlled, which makes the power reactor possible.

The hydrogen bomb in contrast depends on the fusion of light elements which is much more important in the universe as a whole for it is the source of heat in many stars. It has not yet been usefully controlled on earth in spite of determined efforts for 20 years.

Atomicity has indeed proved one great feature of physical science in the present century, perhaps the greatest. Not only do the atoms themselves, and the molecules which feature in chemistry, show the passion of nature for mass-production, the creation that is of vast numbers of identical units, small indeed but *units*, no fractions allowed. This now applies to electricity, to magnetism, to electromagnetic radiation with the proviso that the energy of the unit depends on the frequency, to atomic structure where an integral number of electrons surrounds a nucleus which has an integral charge, a nucleus made of integral numbers of protons and neutrons, or of nucleons if you prefer to use the word coined to express their similar behaviour in a nucleus. Most fundamentally of all it applies to mechanical action. Considering all this, one is inclined to regard atomicity as the most fundamental discovery yet made about the material world.

This encyclopedia therefore deals with far more than the technical applications of nuclear energy, though it describes these at some length, naturally in view of the nationality of the authors, with special reference to those in France. It covers things such as carbon dating for archaeological purposes, dating by lead for geology, and the Van Allen belts, zones tied to the Earth by its magnetism, but far away, which hold for a time electrons and other particles coming from the Sun and from cosmic rays. Indeed readers will find reference to a large fraction of modern physics. It is up-to-date and includes such innovations as isotopic spin, and strangeness number.

Though some of the articles are long, this book is an encyclopedia not a text book. However, it will be very valuable in teaching and will make it reasonable to ask students to read books which contain unexplained references to matters they have not come across. If a student takes it down to consult he will probably keep it for some time. Turning over its pages he will acquire a knowledge of many interesting sides of physics, chemistry and technology which he might not otherwise meet. Knowledge so acquired is apt to last better than that derived from lectures where the need to make notes interferes with memory, and acquiring it bring a certain feeling of discovery which the ordinary text book does not always give.

On another side the book is well adapted for those who need a knowledge of the technologies of the nuclear age without being specialists in any of them or for specialists in one branch who want information about another. There will also be those who, with little or no formal training in the subject, wish to understand references in the press, or just to get some idea of discoveries which have had a profound effect on human life and which even those to whom science has little personal appeal cannot afford to ignore.

Dr Musset and Dr Lloret are to be congratulated on having done a very good job.

A

A, symbol of ●**atomic number** and **mass number** (qv).

ABRAGAM, Anatole (1915–) French physicist. He works at the Centre for Nuclear Studies at Saclay. His studies have dealt mainly with the solid state and with the phenomenon of magnetic resonance.

absorber, a body intended either to stop a radiation (it then absorbs the radiation particles) or to slow it down (in which case it absorbs the energy). In reactors, elements such as cadmium or boron are used, which capture neutrons. In nuclear physics, it is possible, by means of absorbers, to:
1) separate particles by absorbing those which are unwanted
2) estimate the energy of radiations by measuring the thickness of the absorbers through which they can pass
3) establish protective systems against the different radiations emitted by reactors and accelerators, to provide protection for personnel and for the detection apparatus.

●**total absorber,** see **opaque.**

absorption, a phenomenon which takes place when radiation passes through an absorber. Several effects may then appear, either separately or together:
a slowing down, that is to say a lessening of the energy of the radiation (it can even come to a complete stop),
an attenuation, which means that only part of the radiation passes through the absorbing substance,
a transformation of the radiation, which, acting upon the particles of matter of the absorber, induces the emission of a secondary radiation.
These phenomena have very different origins:
a) *Electromagnetic interaction of electrons:* charged particles which pass through the absorber undergo the electromagnetic action of electrons of the atoms of the absorber. The particles lose energy through **ionisation** and **excitation** (qqv) of the atoms of the absorber.
b) *Radiation:* the charged particles also react with the nuclei of the atoms of the absorber. There is then an emission of gamma rays.
c) Possible *nuclear reactions* which can absorb the radiation and, in certain cases, the emission of a secondary radiation.

●**resonant absorption,** takes place when the energy of the incident radiation is that which corresponds to a maximum probability of reaction with the material. Then the absorption is also at a maximum.

abundance, cosmic. The cosmic radiation which reaches the Earth's atmosphere contains a certain number of nuclei of elements such as helium and carbon. These are most frequently protons (hydrogen nuclei), the very lightest nuclei. *Cosmic abundance* is the name given to the proportions of these various elements, and is generally related to the abundance of a particular element (silicon, for example), the ratio giving the *relative cosmic abundance*. If there is twice as much carbon as silicon, it is said that the relative cosmic abundance of carbon is 2. *See two illustrations on p. 2.*

abundance of isotopes, relative. Atoms of a pure body all have the same number of protons in their nucleus. The number of neutrons is not always the same, and in nature different isotopes of a pure body are to be found.—Take chlorine for example: each of its nuclei contains 17 protons, yet nuclei are found which contain 18 neutrons, ie a total mass of 17+18=35, and nuclei which contain 20 neutrons, ie a total mass of 17+20=37. The proportion of the first isotope, chlorine 35, is 75 per cent, whereas the proportion of the second, chlorine 37, is 25 per cent. These percentages are the abundances of the isotopes. Abundance is said to be *relative* when it is related to that of a distinct isotope. Abundance of isotopes varies slightly according to the samples found. It is only approximately constant on Earth, and is very different in the stars because nuclear and thermonuclear reactions are still in progress there.

abundance of mass, relative, another term for indicating the relative **abundance** (qv) of isotopes.

abundance of uranium, see **uranium.**

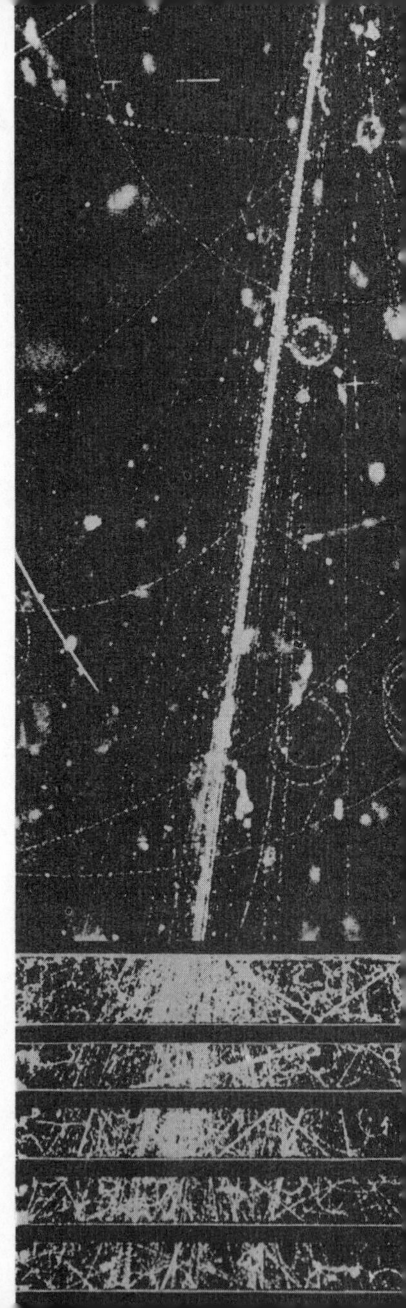

The interaction produced by a particle of cosmic radiation whose energy may be estimated at ten thousand billion electron-volts. This photograph was obtained in a first Wilson chamber. In the bottom picture the secondary particles of the same interaction may be seen passing through a second Wilson chamber which is fitted with parallel metallic plates. The experimental installation which enabled this remarkable photograph to be taken is reproduced in the article on the Wilson chamber. (Photo Ecole Polytechnique)

accelerator, an apparatus which enables particles to be accelerated. Many kinds of accelerators exist in different countries. Their development has enabled knowledge of the properties of matter to be considerably extended. To find how particles react upon one another and to understand their properties, target particles are bombarded with projectile particles, and the reaction of the first particle with the second is observed. From stationary particles the accelerator provides accelerated particles which possess a definite velocity. They will constitute the projectiles in the reaction. To accelerate them, the particles, which bear an electric charge, are passed through a strong electric field.

There are two groups of accelerators:

1) *Linear accelerators,* in which the speed of the particles is increased while always maintaining the same direction.

2) *Circular accelerators,* in which the particle track is coiled up to save space, the acceleration being repeated at each revolution.

In the latter case, it is a magnetic field which guides the particles on a circular orbit or trajectory. In this way it is possible to make these particles acquire very high speeds, which almost reach the speed of light, ie 300,000 km per second. This speed cannot be exceeded because of the principle of relativity. Thus, in the Saturn accelerator at Saclay, the protons travel round a circle of 16 m in diameter in a millionth of a second. In *electrostatic accelerators* there exists throughout the entire path of the particle an electric field which accelerates it. This field is produced by means of a considerable voltage source which varies between about 100,000 V and several million volts. Electrostatic generators are used to achieve this, in which the friction of an insulating substance induces the formation of electric charges at a very high voltage. These are usually *Van de Graaff* and *Felici generators*, etc. Another type of generator, the *Greinacher*, perfected by Cockcroft and Walton, is a voltage multiplier, in which the desired degree of voltage is worked up from a lower voltage supply. These two kinds of accelerators allow the study of low energy nuclear reactions. In the so-called *linear accelerators*, a low voltage is used, 20,000 V for example, but the acceleration of the particle is repeated several times throughout the length of its course. It is thus possible to use alternating currents (those changing their direction from positive to negative), which are easier to produce than continuous current. It is sufficient for the particle to pass through the electric field at the moment when its direction corresponds to the acceleration. The voltage sources, in this case, are high frequency ones.

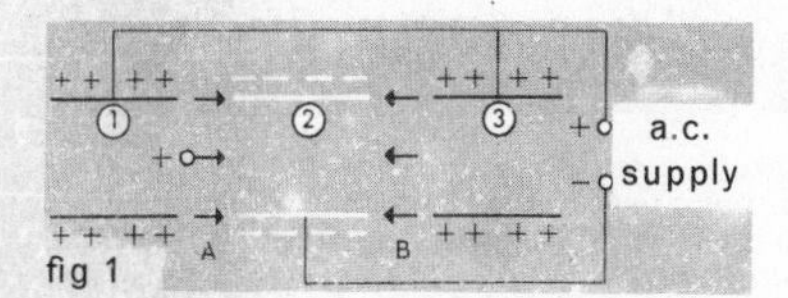

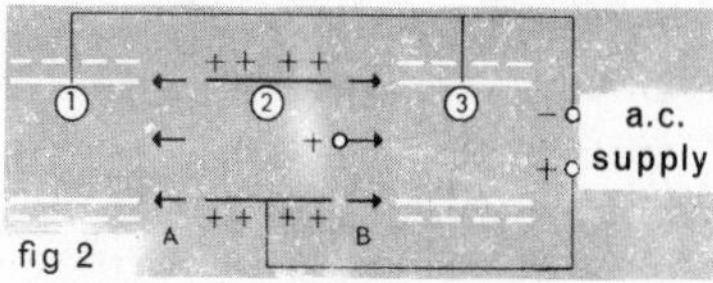

Linear accelerator

An electric field may be established in accelerating cavities by means of this source of alternating current. The operation of linear accelerators is shown in the diagram on p. 3. There is a positively charged particle in the accelerator gap A (figure 1). The electrodes 1 and 3 are positively charged. Electrode 2 is negatively charged, so that the electric field is directed towards the right in A and towards the left in B. The particle is therefore accelerated, it receives an impetus which increases its velocity in the gap A. While passing through electrode 2 it is not subjected to any force, because the electric field in it is zero. After a time, the particle reaches gap B (figure 2). The current source is alternating and in the meantime its direction has changed. It is now the electrode 2 which is positively charged, whereas electrodes 1 and 3 are negatively charged. As a result, the electric field is directed to the left in A and towards the right in B. The particle therefore is again accelerated

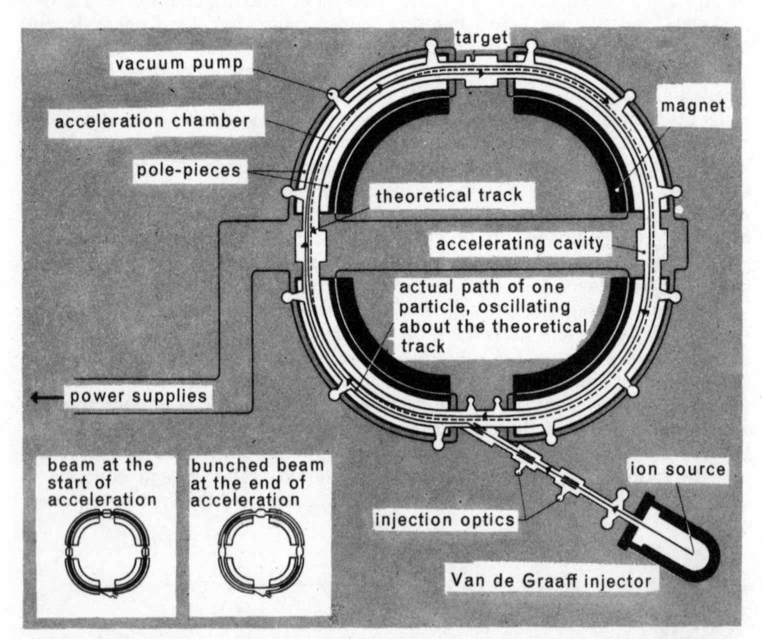

Principles of operation of the Saturn synchrotron at Saclay. In this accelerator, the protons circulate inside a toroid where a magnetic field keeps them on a single circular trajectory. At each revolution, the protons are acted on by an electric field which increases their energy by 1160 electronvolts. At the end of the acceleration, after having travelled 172,000 kilometres and having completed 2.5 million revolutions, some 10^{10} protons finally achieve an energy of 3 billion electronvolts (Diagram CEA)

Interior view of the Faraday cage, with the Haefeli Cockcroft-Walton generator of 500,000 V. Above, in the background is the source of protons which feeds the synchrotron at CERN. (Photo Ecole Polytechnique)

View of a part of the ring of the proton synchrotron at CERN. Each magnetic unit contains a pumping station, so as to guarantee a high vacuum in the accelerating cavity. (Photo Ecole Polytechnique)

in B and so on until the end of the acceleration. But as the particle gains speed it passes more and more rapidly from one gap to the other. The current changes direction at an invariable rhythm, given by its frequency. For the particle to arrive at each gap at the moment when the electric field is in the right direction it is necessary to increase the separation of these gaps. In this way the particle, having a greater velocity yet travelling a greater distance, will always take the same time to pass from one gap to the next. If a very high velocity is desired, it is necessary to line up a considerable number of accelerating gaps and to use very high frequencies so as to reduce the size of the apparatus. Acceleration is then produced in bursts, eg one burst per second. The particles in this case hit the target in bunches. Thus the mean electric power used by the machine is reduced, as well as the construction difficulties of the voltage source. With perfected techniques, accelerators giving energies equivalent to several billion volts can be made.

The *cyclotron* is the simplest of the *circular accelerators*. Charged particles are produced at the centre, by means of an ion source, and guided by the magnetic field of a large electromagnet. This consists of a conducting coil along which an electric current passes. Iron is placed in the middle for the purpose of increasing the magnetic field. Particles emitted by the ion source are accelerated by an electric field produced between the two electrodes, or Ds 1 and 2. As with the *linear accelerator*, an alternating current is used, which changes its direction each time the particle makes a half turn. In this way, the electric field is always found in the right direction in which to accelerate the particles. In fact, since the velocity of the particle goes on increasing, its trajectory is not a circle but a kind of spiral, because the radius of this trajectory increases with the increasing velocity. The particle therefore leaves the centre without any speed, undergoes two accelerations on each revolution, and after several revolutions shoots off the accelerator and hits the target. Twenty-five million volts for a proton can be attained with a *cyclotron*. In this way, the structure of nuclei can be studied, where the energies involved amount to some 10 MeV. Acceleration cannot be pushed beyond this point on account of a relativistic effect: the mass of a body increases with its velocity. Obviously this applies only to high speeds. It happens that the necessary frequency of the source of alternating current is narrowly determined for a given mass, so that when this relativistic effect appears there is no further acceleration. The remedy is simple; the frequency of the voltage source must be varied during acceleration so as to overtake this relativistic effect. The machine is then called a *synchrocyclotron* (qv) because the voltage source has been synchronised with the velocity of the particles. The radius of the trajectories is greater and the electromagnet consists of a series of smaller magnets assembled in the form of a crown along the trajectories. With this machine, protons can be accelerated up to 500 million volts, which makes it possible to obtain the fastest particles. Accelerators exist which produce 30,000 million volts and there are plans which foresee **synchrotrons** (qv) of several hundred billion volts. Acceleration is achieved by means of one or more resonant cavities excited by a high frequency alternating current. In a synchrotron the frequency of the source of the high alternating current and the magnetic field are both varied during the acceleration. These are complicated, gigantic machines possessing a radius of from 10 to 100 metres and consuming several thousand kilowatts of power. They are used for the study of fundamental particles, protons, neutrons, mesons, etc. The number of accelerators has considerably increased in recent years. There are more than a hundred of the *Van de Graaff* type in the range of energy of 0.5 to 5 million electronvolts. The accelerated particles are usually protons, but there are also deuterons, tritons and alpha particles (helium ions that have been twice ionised), helium ions once ionised and again more electrons. A certain number of them are used for medical treatment (in which case they are a source of X-rays). On a somewhat lower scale of energy, varying from 0.25 to 1 million electronvolts, there are some 30 accelerators of the Cockcroft-Walton type. Cyclotrons are accelerators of a higher scale of energy which varies from 3 to 30 million electronvolts for the protons. These

General view of the Van de Graaff accelerator which supplies protons with an energy of 5.2 MeV to be injected into the Saturn synchrotron, at the Centre for Nuclear Studies at Saclay. On the left of the machine is the proton source. (Photo CEA)

General view of the electron linear accelerator at Saclay, France (Photo Jean Biaugeaud CEA)

Proton linear accelerator at CERN. After passing through this accelerator, the protons are injected into the synchrotron with an energy force of 30 GeV. (Photo Ecole Polytechnique, Paris)

machines can also accelerate heavier ions (deuterons, tritons and alpha particles). In those of 20 to 700 million electronvolts some 15 synchrocyclotrons are to be found. The betatrons accelerate electrons (beta rays). There are 25 of them in existence, and their energy varies from 5 to 34 million electronvolts. There are also some 20 electron synchrotrons in a higher scale of energy from between 30 to 1200 million electronvolts. Of these two types of accelerators a few are used in medical research. There are also about 20 linear accelerators, of which the great majority produce electrons, others protons. Their energy, which varies greatly, is typically from 1 MeV to 1 GeV. The electron linear accelerator of 1 GeV at Stanford, USA, has made particularly important contributions to the determination of the distribution of electric charge within nuclei, including measurement of the effective electrical radius of the proton. There has now been constructed at Stanford an electron linear accelerator (linac), 2 miles long, of 40 GeV. Accelerators of even higher energy accelerate protons. The most important of these are, in the USA, those at Brookhaven (3 GeV, ie 3 billion electronvolts), at Berkeley, California (6 GeV) and at Brookhaven (33 GeV); in Europe, those at Saclay in France (3 GeV), Harwell (7 GeV) and at the *European Centre for Nuclear Research* at Geneva (28 GeV); in the USSR, that at Dubna (10 GeV). An accelerator designed for 70 GeV, at Serpukhov in the USSR, is in an advanced stage of construction. A study is also being made of storage-rings in which accelerated particles are stored and sent one against the other instead of being projected against a target of stationary matter. This process considerably increases the amount of energy available for the formation of secondary particles in collisions. Low energy accelerators are used for the study of nuclear reactions and the structure of the nuclei. Electron accelerators are mainly used to determine the electromagnetic properties of matter. Finally, the field of application for high energy is the physics of elementary particles, which are thought to be the ultimate components of matter, at least in the present state of our knowledge.

Actinides, a series of elements whose atomic number (number of protons in the nucleus) varies from 89 to 101.—These are successively, *actinium, thorium, protoactinium, uranium, neptunium, plutonium, americium, curium, berkelium, californium, einsteinium, fermium, mendelevium.* Elements beyond uranium are not to be found in nature; they are artificially produced. They have been made up to element 104. This has been made by Russian workers at Dubna, by bombarding plutonium nuclei with neon nuclei accelerated in a cyclotron. The nuclei fuse and four neutrons are emitted to give a nucleus of atomic number 104. This element decays by fission with a half-life of 0.3 sec.

actinium, first element of the Actinide series. Its atomic number is 89. It was discovered in 1899 by Debierne. It is known to have two isotopes, whose mass are 227 and 228; they are both radioactive, and can be produced artificially, by bombarding radium 226 with neutrons; radium 227 is obtained which, by means of beta disintegration, gives actinium 227.

actinium X. This is really a radium

(atomic mass 223). Its atomic number is in fact 88. It is so-called because it belongs to the radioactive series of actinium.

actinon, a radioactive gas, deriving from the radioactivity of actinium X, which splits up to produce an alpha particle and actinon. It is the isotope of radon of mass 219 and atomic number 86.

actino-uranium, a name occasionally used to describe **uranium** 235 (qv). This derives from the fact that uranium 235 is the parent of the radioactive family of actinium. All the elements of this family are produced from uranium 235.

action, a fundamental physical quantity.—It is known that momentum is the product of mass times speed. Action is the product of momentum by a length. It is used in classical mechanics in the *principle of least action* (minimal action). This principle makes it possible to determine the motions of a physical system. It has its equivalent in optics, which makes it possible to determine the course followed by a light ray. In microscopic systems (atoms, molecules, etc), it has been observed that action is quantised; this means that it can accept only certain values, eg 1, 2, 3, . . ., and cannot accept intermediate values. (See **quantum.**)

activation, a process by means of which a body is rendered radioactive. Take for instance a stable body (not radioactive): if it is bombarded (usually with a neutron) other bodies will be formed having a different mass and atomic number. These latter bodies may be unstable. Suppose neutrons are directed on to titanium. A titanium isotope is obtained which has one neutron more; its mass therefore passes from 28 to 29. But this isotope is unstable and emits an alpha ray upon disintegrating. It is then said that titanium has been activated. Bombardment can also be effected with the help of other particles such as protons, deuterons, alpha particles, etc. The radioactivity of a body thus formed is called *induced radioactivity*. Depending on the particles used, alpha, beta and gamma rays, etc, are emitted.

● **activated,** that which has been subjected to **activation.**

active, a synonym of *radioactive* (eg *active element*); synonym of fissile (eg uranium 235 is *active*). ‖ In a reactor the *active part* is sometimes referred to when speaking of the core which contains fissile material.

activity, a synonym of radioactivity (eg '*uranium* has an alpha *activity*'). Also, the number of atoms which disintegrate in one second. The unit of activity is the *curie*.—In a radioactive source whose activity is 1 curie, 37 billion atoms disintegrate per second. It is more usual to employ the millicurie, which has the value of one thousandth of a curie. It is also possible to speak of the activity produced by an accelerator or a reactor, since in a specific zone it is possible to measure the number of particles emitted by the accelerator or the reactor per second.

affiliation, radioactive, connection through a series of consecutive disintegrations leading from one member to the next of the same family or radioactive **series** (qv). There is a radioactive affiliation between radium 226 and lead 214 (called radium 13), both of the uranium family. This affiliation takes place through the intermediary of three consecutive alpha disintegrations.

age, when speaking of ores and terrestrial bodies, the period of time which has elapsed since their formation.—This period of time can be measured by the method of end-product. In an ore, the proportions of two bodies are measured—that of the radioactive body or parent, and that of a stable body produced by the radioactivity of the parent body. Now, the average lifetime of the parent is known, ie we know the proportion of atoms of the parent which disintegrate in, for example, one year. From this can be deduced how many years have passed since the ore was formed. (See **dating**).

●**age, Fermi,** see **lifetime, Fermi.**

agitation, thermal. In a gas, the molecules are in a permanent condition of disordered motion. They move about and gyrate. The higher the temperature, the greater the molecular motion. It is only at absolute zero (−273° C) that they are stationary. (It should be remarked that absolute zero has never exactly been achieved.) In liquids and in solids molecules are equally in motion. But they move about little in liquids, and not at all in solids; there is only *molecular vibration*. All these motions constitute what is known as *thermal motion*. Since motion is related to temperature, one can inversely attribute to particles of a known average speed a certain value of temperature. Neutrons whose velocity corresponds to normal temperature (20° C), may be called *thermal neutrons*.

albedo, the proportion of neutrons reflected off a surface. (A term used in reactor calculations and mainly for the reflector.) (See **reactor.**) If 100 neutrons reach the surface of the reflector and if, after all the scatterings have taken place, 60 neutrons pass across this surface while 40 neutrons remain on or return to the near side of that same surface, the albedo is 40/100=0.4.

algotron, a linear **accelerator** (qv) in which the acceleration of particles is effected in a wave guide.

allobar, a mixture of the different isotopes of an element in proportions which differ from the natural isotopic composition. (See **abundance of isotopes.**)

allotropy, the property possessed by certain bodies of existing in different forms because of different possible arrangements of the atoms or of the molecules of which they consist.

●**allotropic,** that which presents an **allotropy.**

alpha, α, a Greek letter used to designate a stable particle, consisting of two protons and two neutrons. The alpha particle may also be considered a helium nucleus stripped of its two electrons. It has a charge of two positive units; its mass number is 4. This particle belongs to the three natural radiations which were detected in the first studies of radioactivity; the alpha, beta and gamma rays. Many elements possess an alpha radioactivity: radium (which was the first radioactive body discovered by Pierre Curie in 1895), uranium, etc. (For the characteristics of this radiation see **disintegration.**) On the other hand, the alpha particle would appear to play a considerable part in the composition of the nuclei, on account of its great stability due to the strong forces which link two protons and two neutrons. Everything

Beam of alpha particles: in the centre, an elastic collision of an α particle with a nitrogen nucleus (Photo Proceedings of the Royal Society, A, vol. 134)

happens as though, in the nuclei, the nucleons (neutrons and protons) had a tendency to associate in groups of four; two protons with two neutrons. The alpha particle **model of the nucleus** (qv) is based on this idea.

● **long range alpha,** an alpha particle belonging to a higher energy group in natural radioactivity. Certain alpha-radioactive bodies have in fact the property of emitting particles with several energies. Thorium 228, for example, emits two groups of alpha particles of different energies: the first, of 5.4 million electronvolts, in a proportion of 72 per cent; the second, of 5.3 million electronvolts, in a 28 per cent proportion. The alpha particles of the first group, which are more energetic, travel a greater distance in matter than those of the second group; they are called *long range alphas.* It should be observed that the residual nuclei produced in such disintegrations, although of identical composition, are to be found in different energy states. (See **isomer.**)

aluminium, a metal with the atomic number 13, atomic mass number 27. Each of its nuclei contains 13 protons and 14 neutrons. It is used in the construction of reactors because it combines good mechanical behaviour with a weak propensity for the capture of neutrons. Moreover, the metal is plentiful in nature and easy to handle.

americium, artificial element with atomic number 95 and atomic mass 241. Each of its nuclei contains 95 protons and 146 neutrons. It was produced in 1945 by Seaborg, James and Morgan by bombarding uranium 238 with helium ions. In this way, plutonium 241 is obtained, which, through beta decay, gives americium. Americium 241 has an average radioactive life of 475 years. It can equally well be produced by the repeated bombardment of neutrons on plutonium 241.

anaemia, an illness in which the composition of the blood undergoes a change. This deficiency may be a diminution of haemoglobin or of red corpuscles in the blood. It can be induced by exposure to radiation.

ANDERSON, Carl (1905–) American physicist. Nobel Prize-winner 1936. He discovered the positive electron in a Wilson chamber, observing a particle of the same mass as the ordinary electron, but of opposite charge. Independently and simultaneously Dirac's theory prophesied the existence of such particles.

ångström, a minute unit of length which is used in optics and in atomic physics. It is 0.01 millionth of a centimetre. Its symbol is Å.

angular correlation, see **correlation, angular.**

anion, negatively charged **ion** (qv), particularly in solution.

anisotropy, the opposite of isotropy. This word is used in every case where a spherical symmetry is absent. It would be said that a reaction presents an anisotropy if the products of the reaction distributed themselves in a different manner according to the direction in which they are emitted. In the same way, every physical system will present an anisotropy if its properties vary according to the direction under consideration.

● **anisotropic,** that which presents an **anisotropy.** ‖ An *anisotropic beta emission* is a beta emission the intensity of which varies with direction.

annihilation. In a meeting of an electron and a positron, there is annihilation (disappearance or *dematerialisation*) of matter and production of energy in the form of gamma rays.—This gamma radiation was demonstrated by Thibaud and Joliot in 1933. It takes place whenever a positron in motion encounters a negative electron of any kind of substance. The appearance of energy in the form of gamma rays follows the law of the equivalence of mass with energy proposed by **Einstein** (qv). The energy of the gamma rays is proportional to the vanished mass, the constant of proportionality being always the same. The phenomenon of annihilation is possible each time a particle and a corresponding antiparticle start a reaction. A proton and an antiproton, for instance, can annihilate each other by giving gamma rays. But there is also usually a production of pions, which, unlike gamma rays, possess a **rest mass** (qv). This phenomenon enables Einstein's law, deduced from the special theory of relativity, to be thoroughly tested.

anticoincidence the opposite of **coincidence** (qv).—A system used in electronic techniques to signal that an event A (the passage of a neutron for example) has taken place where event B (passage of the decay electron from the neutron) has not taken place. It is said that the anticoincidence AB has been established. Or again, the coincidence $A\bar{B}$ (see diagram under **coincidence**). This system has also been used to study the disintegration of cosmic particles in a Wilson chamber. A counter A registers the arrival of the particle above the Wilson chamber. A meter B placed underneath the chamber and mounted in anticoincidence, permits the release of the chamber only if the particle does not come out (coincidence $A\bar{B}$). The manner in which it stopped or disintegrated in the chamber is then studied.

antielectron, a synonym of **positron** (qv).

antimatter, matter which contains only **antiparticles** (qv).—Despite its name there is no clash between matter and antimatter, their difference being due solely to different physical characteristics. For example, a proton has a positive charge. The antiproton has the same charge, but it is negative. The mass of the antiproton and that of the proton are equal. If a quantity of matter and the equivalent quantity of antimatter make contact over a sufficiently long period, an interaction of each particle with its corresponding antiparticle would be obtained. There would then be annihilation of matter with production of gamma rays. In fact, it would also be possible to have production of pions, K mesons, etc, but the disintegration of these mesons would ultimately produce only neutrinos, electrons and antielectrons. On the annihilation of these electrons and antielectrons we obtain, as the end-product of the reaction, gamma rays (of a nature similar to light rays) and neutrinos (particles of zero rest mass which travel with the speed of light, just as the gammas do). There would remain nothing from the reactions but radiation (which consists of particles without mass). There is at present no evidence which would allow the conclusion that antimatter exists in the world in the form of atoms, like matter, in an appreciable quantity. Antimatter is only observed in the form of isolated antiparticles, which are produced either by cosmic radiation or by large accelerators.

antineutrino, an antiparticle which corresponds to a neutrino. The neutrino has no charge, nor has the antineutrino. Its rest mass is zero. Having neither a rest mass nor charge, it is difficult to detect. The only possibility of detecting it consists in observing its reactions on charged particles, but they are very rare. Its existence is postulated to explain the negative beta disintegration. For example, a neutron gives a proton, a negative electron and an antineutrino. The only differences between the neutrino and the antineutrino would then be its *hand* or **chirality** (qv), that is to say the direction of the spin relative to the direction of the motion.

antineutron, an antiparticle corresponding to the neutron. Its mass is equal to that of the proton; its electric charge is zero. It is to be observed in cosmic radiation. It is then produced in very high energy nuclear showers. It has also been studied with the large accelerators, where it is produced by sending an antiproton against a target which contains protons. The products obtained from this reaction are a neutron and an antineutron.

antiparticle. An antiparticle corresponds to each existing particle. This fact has been verified experimentally for the great majority of particles. Particles and antiparticles have the same mass and opposite electric charges. They have the same spin and their magnetic moments are oppositely directed in regard to the direction of the spin, eg the proton and antiproton. Other quantum numbers are equally in opposition for particle and antiparticle. These are the baryon number, the lepton number and strangeness number. Some particles are at the same time their own antiparticles. For instance, the quantum numbers characteristic of the neutral pion are zero. Thus it is

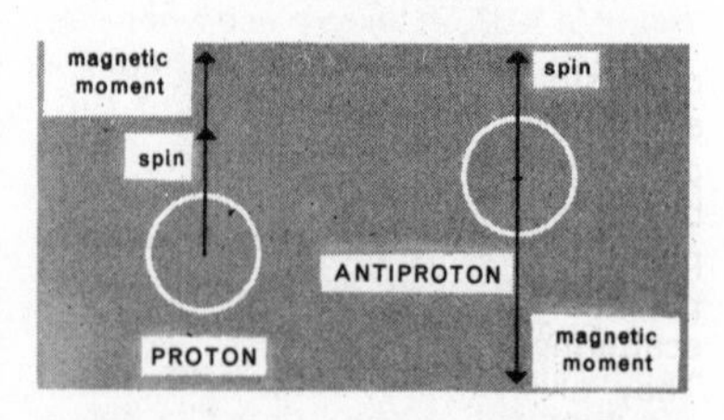

antiparticle	*proton*	*antiproton*
Charge	+	–
Baryon number	+1	–1
Strangeness number	0	0
Lepton number	0	0

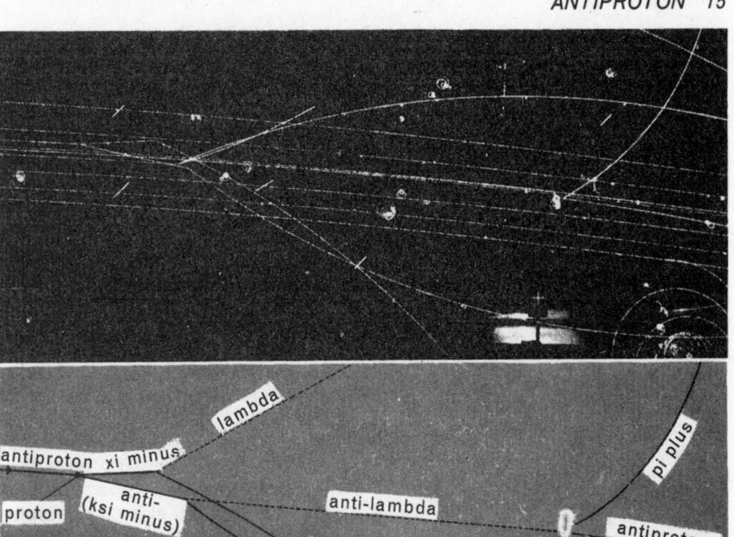

Discovery of the antiparticle of the negative xi hyperon. (The photograph was obtained with the hydrogen chamber CBH 81 belonging to Saclay and the Leprince-Ringuet Laboratory.)

understood that it can be its own antiparticle, the quantum numbers characteristic of the neutral antipion being zero, like those of the neutral pion. Reactions to which the antiparticles may be subjected are various: scattering, meson production, etc. They always end by disappearing, either by disintegration or by annihilation with the corresponding particle.

antiproton, an antiparticle corresponding to the proton. It has the same mass as the proton, but a negative electric charge. Its existence, foreseen by theory, was experimentally shown in 1955, at the California Institute of Technology, in the United States. To produce an antiproton, it is necessary to produce a proton at the same time, for the number of nucleons less the number of antinucleons must remain constant throughout the reaction. Such a reaction is expressed by the following formula:

proton+proton *gives* proton
1 + 1 = 1
+antiproton+proton+proton
−1 + 1 + 1.

One must therefore have fairly high sources of energy available to produce antiprotons. The accelerator of 6 GeV at the California Institute of Technology enabled this energy to be attained.

argon, a rare gas which is contained in air in a 1 per cent proportion. Its mass is 40, but there is an isotope of mass 41, formed by the absorption of a neutron by argon 40. Argon 41 is radioactive, and it cannot be subjected to chemical reaction, because it is inert. This gas also constitutes a danger in piles in which the air is irradiated by neutrons. This circumstance necessitates the taking of special precautions to avoid contamination by argon 41.

ASTON, Francis William (1877–1945) English physicist. His work on isotopes earned him the Nobel Prize in 1922. He was the first to separate two neon isotopes (20 and 22) in appreciable quantities.

atom (from the Greek word *atomos*, that which cannot be divided), the smallest part of a pure body.—The idea of a particle of matter has existed since Greek antiquity, although at that time nothing was known of its properties. About the year 500 BC especially, Greek thinkers, such as Leucippus and his better known pupil Democritus, set down their conception of matter. This was fairly close to our present conception of the molecule and the atom. The idea of the indivisible is actually applied nowadays to the elementary particles of which atoms are constructed, in a more or less complicated form of structure. The existence of the atom was essentially demonstrated by the progress which was made in chemistry during the nineteenth century. At that time it was observed that pure bodies combined together in constant ratios which could be related by not very high whole numbers. This could easily be explained by supposing that the chemical combination was carried out at the level of microscopic elements which assembled together in twos or threes, etc. At the same time Van der Waals was studying the behaviour of gases and establishing laws for them. The interpretation of these laws by the kinetic theory of gases, in which gas is considered to consist of a number of molecules travelling at different speeds in random directions, tended to confirm these preliminary ideas. It then became possible to have an idea of the Avogadro number, ie the number of molecules in a certain volume of gas. For a gas at normal temperature and at atmospheric pressure it is about 6.025×10^{23} for 22.4 litres. At the same time an idea of the size of the molecules was arrived at, ie some tenths of millionths of a millimetre. In 1908 Jean Perrin gave a precise value to the ● **Avogadro number** (qv) by measuring the Brownian movement of small grains in suspension in an emulsion, the motion of which is maintained by surrounding molecules. At the end of the nineteenth century a radiation was discovered, produced by electric discharges in a highly rarefied gas, and Perrin was able to demonstrate, in 1895, that it conveyed electric charges; these were electrons. Other phenomena, for example the photoelectric effect, were discovered to be electron sources. In 1896 Becquerel discovered radioactivity, having ob-

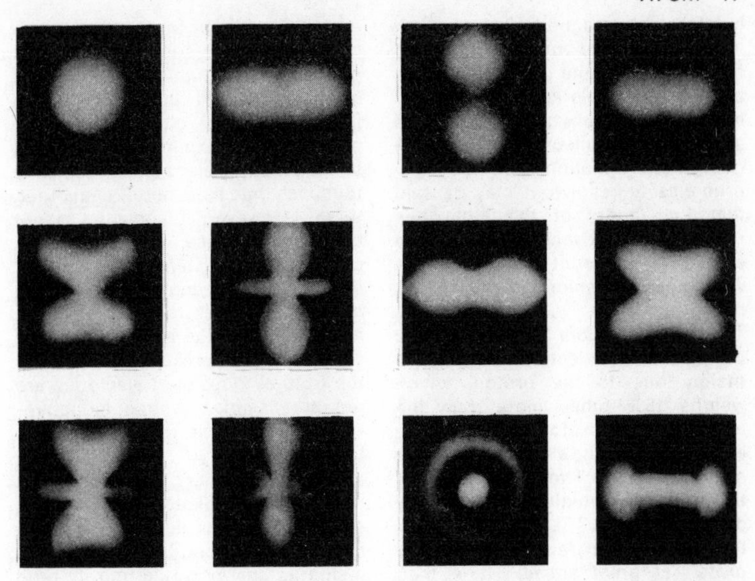

Different aspects of the probability density for the presence of an electron in a hydrogen atom for certain values of the quantum numbers. In ordinary terms, it would be said that the chance of finding an electron is greater the whiter the representative region.

served that photographic plates shielded from exposure to light had been marked by an ore, containing radium, left by chance in their vicinity. Research on this subject was the foundation of understanding of the nuclei of atoms. As for the atoms themselves, at the beginning of the twentieth century the masses of some of them were measured by studying the deviations produced by an electric and a magnetic field upon an ionised atom. It was still thought that the hydrogen atom was the basis of all the other atoms, but there were some hesitations before the true model of the atom was achieved. At first it was thought that the atom should be formed of protons and electrons mixed together. Rutherford, by studying the scattering of alpha particles by a thin sheet of material, was able to provide the first coherent model of the atom. An atom with the atomic number Z consists of a nucleus carrying Z positive electric charges, surrounded by Z negatively charged electrons. The greater part of the mass is concentrated in the nucleus. It is the peripheral electrons which explain the chemical properties of atoms. The nucleus plays no part in these properties. In 1913 Bohr introduced the quantisation of energy into a description of the atom, after Planck and Einstein had introduced it into electromagnetic radiation. It was with the development of quantum mechanics that the properties of the atom were explored in detail. If nuclear physics, whose field is the study of the nucleus, is still undergoing transformations and has many problems to resolve, it may be said that the theory of the atom has reached a very advanced stage, which enables an account to be given, in very precise fashion, of known experimental facts.

The *hydrogen atom* consists of one proton and one electron. Its mass is mainly due to the proton, which weighs 1836 times more than the electron. The proton has a positive electric charge, the electron a negative electric charge. These two particles, therefore, are mutually attracted. Why do they not meet? Let it be imagined that the electron revolves round the proton at great speed. It is then acted upon by a centrifugal force (the force to which a car is subjected when going round a bend), which tends to push it away and which exactly counterbalances the forces of attraction. This is no more than a picture; in quantum mechanics it can be demonstrated that the electron forms a kind of cloud around the proton. If, by experiment, one tried to localise the electron, it would be found at one time here, at another, there. However, its position is not a matter of chance. It is possible to calculate a *probability of presence* for the electron in each of the possible positions. To return to the *planetary model* in which the electron revolves round the proton like a planet round the Sun, all possible trajectories are not permissible. Bohr's model restricts the trajectories by means of two postulates:

a) When stationary, the atom does not emit any radiation. A revolving electron should emit an electromagnetic radiation. The electron thus losing its energy would find its orbit growing gradually narrower but, in fact, no such radiation is observed.

b) There is only a discrete set of orbits possible for the electron. Since

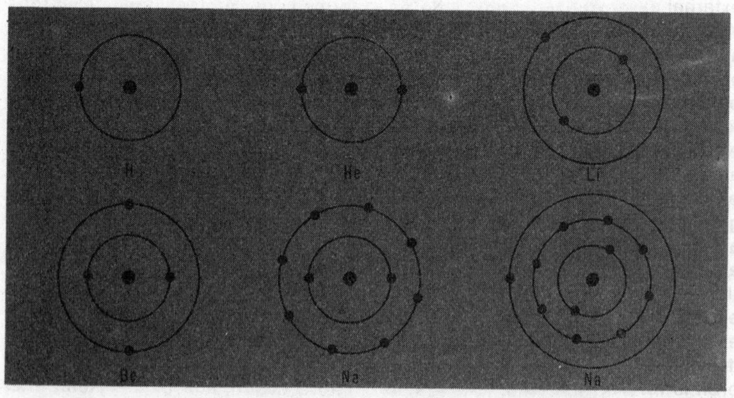

Position of electrons in the atoms of some elements

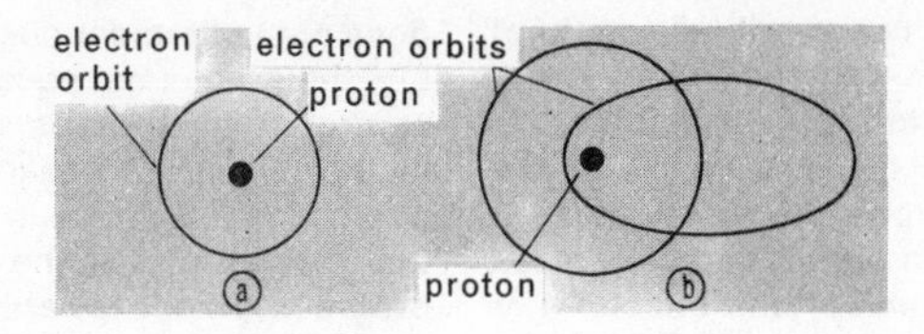

Bohr's orbits of the fundamental level (a) *and of the first excited level of the hydrogen atom* (b)

the energy of the electron depends on the orbit under consideration, the electron may have only a discrete set of energies. Energy is therefore quantised. The angular momentum, or moment of momentum, can only be a whole multiple of a constant. The same constant is to be found in Planck's theory of radiation. In Bohr's model, an electron can pass from one orbit to the next. If the energy of the first is higher than the energy of the second, the difference in energy is emitted in the form of an ultra-violet ray or an X-ray. If, on the contrary, the electron passes from a low to a higher energy, it is necessary for an external physical phenomenon, eg an X-ray to have provided the necessary additional energy. All these phenomena have been observed in detail by measurement of the radiation emitted by excited atoms, as, for example, when gaseous hydrogen is placed in an electric arc. The whole assembly of the radiations of the various energies is called the **spectrum** (qv) of an atom. The electron is bound in the atom by a certain energy. To extract the electron from the atom, this same energy must be provided for it. The electron is the more bound the closer its orbit to the proton. The size of an orbit is very large in comparison with the size of the proton. The radius of the proton is about one millionth of a millionth of a millimetre, whereas the radius of an orbit is 100,000 times greater. Thus it may be said, paradoxically, that matter is almost entirely composed of vacuum. In fact, the density of matter in the proton is much higher than the densities one is accustomed to encounter on the human scale. Two quantum numbers are associated with each orbit of the electrons; one characterises the angular momentum, the other, its projection on an axis. Energy depends generally on the first quantum number. The second can be discerned by placing the atom in a magnetic field. In this case, the electron revolving on its orbit is equivalent to a small magnet, whose orientation in the magnetic field corresponds to a magnetic energy depending on the second quantum number and on the value of the magnetic field. The spectrum of an atom in a magnetic field offers a multiplication of lines which correspond to the several possible values of the second quantum number. This is the normal Zeeman effect. An improvement was introduced into Bohr's atomic model by Sommerfeld. The rules of quantisation advanced by the latter are more general. In particular, they show that orbits of the electrons can be ellipses and not only circles. On the other hand, Sommerfeld introduced the idea of relativity into the description of the atom. Electrons revolving at high speed round a proton find their mass increased by relativistic effect. It is then found that the energy of the atom depends equally on the second quantum number, even in the absence of a magnetic field. From this it follows that the lines of emission of the atom split up. It is then said that the atom possesses a fine structure. Fine structure can only be fully explained if the spin of the electron is taken into account; the spin being a quantity which can be related to the intrinsic angular momentum of the electron, independent of its motion round the proton. Other more complex phenomena, eg hyperfine structure and the anomalous Zeeman effect, can also be calculated by means of the quantum theory, and these agree perfectly with the measurements.

Complex Atoms.—The hydrogen atom can exist in other forms. For example, the nucleus of deuterium, or heavy hydrogen, consists of a proton and a neutron. The neutron has practically the same mass as the proton, 1840 times the mass of the electron, but it has no electric charge. The negative electron is always present in the atom, balancing the charge of the proton. The neutron and proton are attracted to each other by nuclear forces, they are wedded in the nucleus. How are heavier atoms built up? The helium nucleus contains two protons and two neutrons; it has two peripheral electrons. In nuclei which grow heavier and heavier every time a proton is added to them, the nuclear forces strive to add a neutron as well. The nucleus remains stable and does not split under such conditions. On the whole an equal number of neutrons and protons will be found in the nuclei, and exactly the same number of electrons in the atom as there are protons in the nucleus. As progress is made towards the heaviest atoms, the relative number of neutrons in the nucleus increases slightly. Electrons are not distributed haphazardly in the atom. They accumulate in the form of shells, ie in electronic shells. The number of electrons present in each of these shells is limited. It cannot go beyond a value that is determined exactly by quantum electronic numbers. The first shell, known as the K shell, can accept two electrons. This shell is the only one to be found in hydrogen and in helium. The next shell, the L shell, which is outside the first shell, can accept eight electrons. It is complete for neon, which therefore possesses ten electrons. The following shell, or M shell, outside the two previous shells, can also accept eight electrons. It is complete for argon, which therefore has eighteen electrons. The sequence of atoms whose outer shells are closed possess 2, 10, 18, 36, 54 and 86 electrons. With these atoms there is a particularly stable symmetry in the distribution of the outer shell, so that the electric effects of nucleus and electrons compensate one another. This fact explains why these atoms are precisely those whose chemical affinity is practically zero. Their electrons in the outer shell are closely bound on account of this symmetry, and they cannot accept any other electron on the same shell. On the other hand, atoms in which the outer shell contains only one electron, and those in which an electron is absent in the outer shell, are chemically active. They correspond, respectively, to the alkali metals and to oxidising bodies. The absence of an electron on the outer shell of a body of the second type may be partially filled by the presence of the isolated electron on the outer shell of a body of the first type. The two atoms associate, and this phenomenon is the origin of chemical force. In general, by classifying bodies in this fashion, according to the number of electrons their atoms contain, it is possible to explain the chemical properties of matter. The structure of electronic shells also makes it possible to explain electric conduction in metals. The isolated electron on the outer shell of a metal atom is lightly bound, and can pass from one atom to the next. Free electrons of a metal in this way constitute carriers of electric current. The understanding of atomic structure is now very advanced, and the success of atomic theory is astounding, but the structure of the nucleus of the atom has not yet been so thoroughly investigated.

●**atom, bound state of,** see **bound state of an atom.**

●**mesic atom,** an atom having captured a negative mu meson, the mu being on an orbit similar to that of an electron.—This atom is not stable: the mu may either disintegrate while on the orbit, or react by weak interaction with the nucleus of the atom, according to the reaction:

negative mu+proton *gives* neutron+neutrino.

Disintegration is the most probable phenomenon for light mesic atoms, reaction being more probable for heavy mesic atoms; the two phenomena are equally probable for the carbon atom, atomic number 6. This difference is the result of two effects. On the one hand the orbit of the mu is closer to the nucleus when the electric charge of the latter is higher, the mu meson is therefore closer to the nucleus the heavier it is. On the other hand, the bulk of the nucleus increases with the number of protons and neutrons which it contains. These two effects favour mu reactions in heavy atoms to the detriment of its disintegration. Capture of the mu by the nucleus is used in the study of weak **interactions** (qv).

atomic, that which refers to the atom (eg *atomic energy*).

●**atomic bond,** see **bond, atomic.**

●**atomic furnace,** see **furnace, atomic.**

●**atomic mass,** mass of an atom of the isotope of carbon whose mass number is 12 is used as a reference. This consists of 1 nucleus containing 6 protons and 6 neutrons, and of 6 electrons; as it is due, above all, to the 12 nucleons (protons and neutrons) of the nucleus, the mass of the atom is fixed by agreement at 12. The atomic mass of other elements is not a whole number, but each nucleus is characterised by an integral **mass number** (qv).

●**atomic number,** number of protons of the nucleus of the atom (noted Z). (See **mass.**)

●**atomic sickness,** see **sickness, radiation.**

atomism, a physical theory founded on the idea of the atom, and in general, of the concept of matter which embraces the hypothesis of distinct particles, in opposition to the concept of continuous matter.

attenuation, lessening of the intensity of a beam of particles. It is produced by absorption (capture by an absorbent medium) or by scattering (change of direction in a scattering medium), both of which can take place simultaneously in the same medium.

● **attenuation factor,** the ratio of the intensity of incident radiation to the intensity of transmitted radiation. Only some of the radiation which enters a certain thickness of matter comes out of it again. The strength of the radiations is attenuated by passing through matter: eg, if 20 per cent of the particles pass through matter, the attenuation factor is 1/0.2=5.

● **attenuator,** a medium which induces **attenuation** (qv).

AUGER, Pierre (1899–) French physicist. His name is associated with the Auger effect, Auger electron and the Auger shower. His principal work deals with X-rays, neutrons and cosmic rays.

● **Auger effect,** a phenomenon by means of which an excited atom may be de-excited by emitting an electron. For instance, the atom may be excited by absorption of an X-ray and may also be de-excited by re-emitting an X-ray. The Auger effect and de-excitation by means of X radiation are therefore two phenomena competing with one another. The energy communicated to the electron emitted in the Auger effect is equal to that which the X radiation would possess under similar conditions, less the binding energy of the electron within the atom. Another case, frequent in practice, in which the Auger effect is observed is that in which one of the electrons of an inner shell in an atom has been ejected, for example, by a photon. Then, one of the electrons of an outer shell may come in to replace the electron of the inner shell, thus releasing a certain energy, since the electrons of an outer shell are less bound than those of an inner shell. This energy may be recovered in the shape of an X-ray, or again, it may eject an electron from the atom by Auger effect. It is under this last aspect that, in 1925, Auger discovered the effect which bears his name.

autoradiography, a method of radiography in which the source of radiation is distributed throughout the whole mass of the body to be radiographed. This is achieved by means of radioactive isotopes, whose radiation is detected as in ordinary radiography.

autunite, a uranium ore, fairly common in France, so called because of the deposit near the town of Autun. It is also found in Portugal and in North Vietnam.

avalanche, a phenomenon in which a charged particle (usually an electron), colliding with the atoms contained in a gas, knocks out electrons of the gas (ionisation). These electrons, in turn, reproduce the same phenomenon. In this way there is a multiplication of free electrons and, at the same time, formation of ionised atoms through the loss of electrons. This process develops particularly in the presence of a high electric field. The electric field, in fact, exercises forces of opposing directions upon the negatively charged electrons and upon the positively charged ions. It tends to separate them and in this way to prevent their recombining. This is also known as *Townsend's avalanche* (after the physicist Townsend who studied this phenomenon).

AVOGADRO, Amadeo (1776–1856)

Italian physicist. He formulated, with the hypothesis of gaseous molecules, a preliminary statistical interpretation of the behaviour of a gas.

● **Avogadro number,** a number frequently employed in particle physics. It permits calculation of the number of molecules present in a body when its weight is known. By definition, it is the number of molecules present in a **gram-molecule** (qv). There are 602,500 billion billion molecules per gram-molecule. What is, for instance, the number of atoms present in a mass of 2.7 g of aluminium? The gram-molecule of aluminium weighs 27 g. The mass of 2.7 g is therefore equal to 0.1 gram-molecule. On the other hand, it is known that the aluminium molecule is mono-atomic, that is to say that each atom consists of one molecule, because aluminium is a metal. The number of atoms present in 2.7 g of aluminium is therefore 1/10 of the Avogadro number, that is to say 60,250 billion billions.

B

background or **background noise,** a term which describes the parasitic phenomena which simulate the physical phenomenon being studied. In an electronic device in which the products of disintegration of a radioactive body are counted, the counter may be triggered by particles other than the disintegration products: eg natural radioactivity, cosmic radiation, etc. Evaluation of background, for the purpose of subtracting it from the number of bodies shown on the counter, is carried out by measurement in the absence of the radioactive body.

BALMER, Johann Jakob (1825–98) Swiss physicist. He discovered the formula which bears his name. This formula gives the wavelengths of the lines in the visible spectrum of hydrogen.

band, a set of radiations emitted by a pure body, for example when raised to a high temperature. These bands are characterised by allied frequencies (or wavelengths). There are several bands for each body. It is known that molecules are in a state of motion which increases with any rise in temperature—this is thermal motion. The energy of the molecule, which depends on the temperature, can be divided into three parts: translational energy (the molecule travels), rotational energy (the molecule revolves on itself) and vibrational energy (the molecule vibrates round a position of equilibrium somewhat after the manner of a leaf spring, one end of which is clamped). When a body is heated the molecules acquire energy of thermal motion. To each possible state of a molecule there corresponds a clearly determined level of energy (see **quantisation**). When a molecule grows cold, it passes from a higher to a lower energy, and the difference in energy is emitted in the form of luminous radiation. The word *luminous* should be understood in a wide sense: eg it may equally well be a question of invisible infrared or ultra-violet radiation. On decomposing this light according to its colour (which means according to its wavelength), bands may be observed which present radiations of closely allied colours with a well defined boundary on one side. These bands are associated into groups and the groups into systems so that the whole assembly is extremely complex. This may be explained by the different ways in which a molecule is able to store energy. In fact, on the one hand, electrons may pass from one orbit to the next, on the other, there may be slight variations in the vibrational energy. Finally, variations in rotational energy may be even smaller. These three types of bands may be expressed as follows: *electronic bands, vibrational bands* and *rotational bands* which correspond to ever decreasing energies and therefore to radiations which range from ultraviolet to extreme infra-red.

barn, a very small unit of area used in nuclear physics to measure **cross-sections** (qv). Its value is 10^{-24} cm^2, ie the surface of a square the length of whose side is 1 mm divided by 100 billions. Its name comes from the fact that, in the microscopic domain, this unit is still immense. It corresponds to large cross-sections. A thousandth of a barn (a *millibarn*) is more frequently used, or the millionth of a barn (*microbarn*). Indeed, the radius of protons and neutrons being of the order of 1 mm divided by 1000 billions, their apparent surface, which corresponds to the *geometrical cross-section*, is in the region of 40 millibarns, which is much lower than the barn.

barrier, porous, see **porous barrier.**

barrier, potential, a region in which the repulsive forces existing between two particles are predominant. Such a barrier exists around nuclei. These contain positively charged protons which repel positive particles. If one of these, a proton for instance, approaches the potential barrier, it will be repelled, but if its energy (or velocity) is sufficient, it may cross the barrier and penetrate inside the nucleus. In this case the potential barrier is called *Coulomb barrier*,

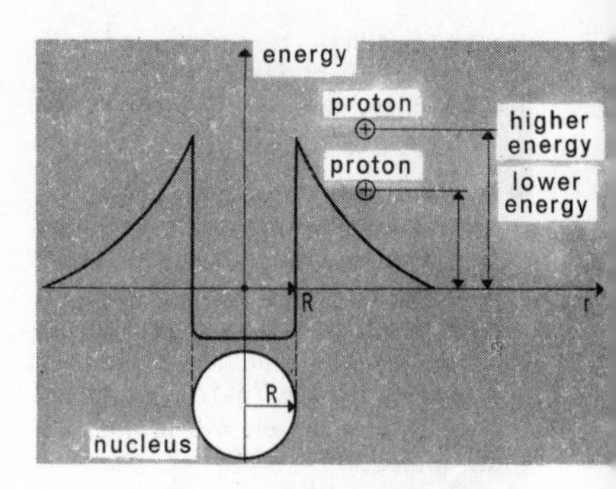

Potential barrier

because it is due to coulomb electric forces. A potential barrier may be penetrated even if the incident particle has a lower energy than the barrier—a phenomenon that is impossible in classical mechanics—and which may be explained only by means of quantum mechanics. (See ●**tunnel effect.**)

baryon, a fundamental particle with a mass equal to or higher than that of the proton.—This idea was first introduced so as to classify particles according to their mass. It turned out to be fundamental to the study of reactions. The number of baryons remains constant in all reactions. It should be understood as being diminished by the number of antibaryons. In other words, in a nuclear reaction no baryon can be formed without the simultaneous formation of an antibaryon. Let us observe the reaction of two protons. The initial number of baryons is (1+1=2). After the reaction, one can obtain two protons (1+1=2) or else 3 protons and 1 antiproton (3−1=2), etc. Three protons only cannot be obtained, as the number of baryons would then be

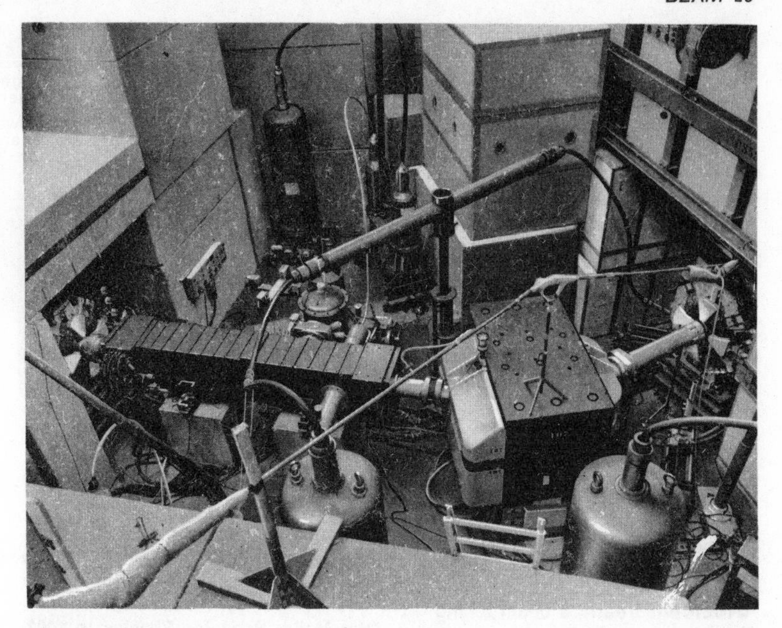

Part of the equipment enabling a beam of K mesons to be obtained in a target of the proton synchroton at CERN (Photo Ecole Polytechnique, Paris)

three, different from the initial number of baryons. This rule, the law of conservation of baryon number, has been experimentally tested in many reactions, and has never been faulted. It applies to all baryons. Among the baryons may be included:

Nucleons

Protons	with	a positive	electric	charge
Neutrons	,,	no	,,	,,

Hyperons

Lambdas	,,	,,	,,	,,
Sigmas	,,	a positive	,,	,,
		,, negative	,,	,,
		,, zero	,,	,,
Xi	,,	,, negative	,,	,,
	,,	,, zero	,,	,,

There is an antibaryon with an opposite electric charge which corresponds to each of these antibaryons.

beam, a group of particles animated by the same motion.—The particles of a beam travel with closely allied speeds and directions. The resolution of a beam indicates how closely the particles are grouped around an average speed. This is usually expressed in percentage of the momentum, product of mass and velocity. For example, the beam of a Van de Graaff accelerator may possess a 1 per cent resolution. The divergence of a beam indicates with what precision particles are grouped around an average direction. It may be expressed in degrees, since it indicates the maximal angle made by the particles with an average direction.

● **exit beam,** a beam which has passed through a target or a detection apparatus.

● **extracted beam,** in circular accelerators, the beam of accelerated particles inside the apparatus is generally sent on to a target placed in its path. In this case, most experiments employ the secondary beams which are produced by reactions of the beam on the target. For certain applications, the primary beam which circulates inside the accelerator has to be used; this requires some extraction device for the beam. The beam is then called an *extracted beam*.

● **incident beam,** a beam falling on the target or detection apparatus being used.

● **molecular beam,** stream of molecules with the same direction and the same velocity.—Its source is generally a receptacle containing gas, in which a hole has been made. A system of collimating apertures is used to determine the direction of the beam. Molecules belonging to the beam possess velocities of the order of a kilometre per second, which corresponds to the energy of thermal agitation with normal temperatures. Such beams are used in measurements of nuclear magnetic moments in transverse electric and magnetic fields.

● **polarised beam,** a beam in which an important percentage of the particles have their spin oriented in a certain direction. (See **polarisation.**)

Henri Becquerel

BECQUEREL, Henri (1852–1908) French physicist. In 1896 he discovered radioactivity through studying uranium salts, as well as the phenomenon of the ionisation of gases. His work was rewarded with the Nobel Prize for Physics in 1903, which he shared with Pierre and Marie Curie.

becquerelite, a uranium ore mainly found in the Republic of the Congo (Kinshasa).

belts of radiation. The Earth is surrounded by two zones in which radiation is particularly strong: the *lower* or *Van Allen* belt, and the *outer belt.* These zones are due to capture of cosmic radiations by the Earth's magnetic field. (This field, which retains ionic particles, is called a *magnetic bottle.*) The first experiments were carried out by Van Allen —from whom the first belt takes its name—by fitting rockets with counters and releasing them from balloons at an altitude of 80 km. Launching of the Russian and American satellites into

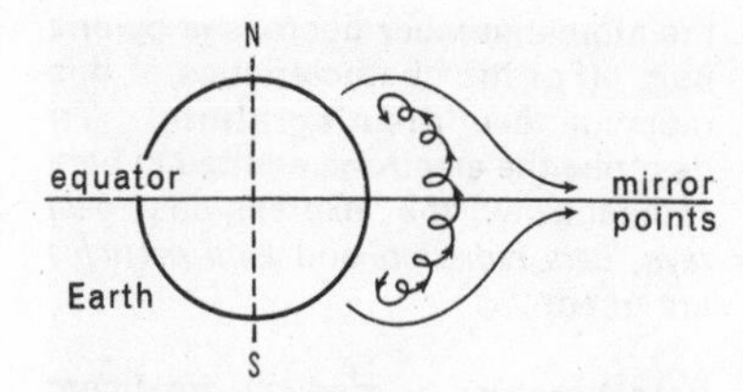

space enabled more complete measurements to be made. In this way, the first belt, known as the Van Allen belt, was discovered. It is located at an altitude of some 3000 km. In 1959, the second belt was discovered at an altitude of 16,000 km. By what means are the particles concentrated inside the belt? They follow trajectories similar to a spiral as they approach the Earth. But as they come nearer, the particles encounter an ever-increasing magnetic field and the spiral then tends to contract. As a result the particle is unable to pass beyond a certain point, called *mirror point* (see above) and it goes off again in the opposite direction, crosses the equator and re-encounters the symmetrical mirror point. It thus continues to oscillate between two mirror points. On the other hand, the spiral itself moves slowly round the Earth, to the westward for protons and eastward for electrons. For electrons of a million electronvolts the spiral goes round the Earth in about 30 minutes. Particles do not always remain imprisoned within the belts. A certain number enter it coming from cosmic radiation, whereas other particles, colliding with the atoms of the rarefied atmosphere, are deflected and escape from the belt. Thus it is calculated that electrons and protons of 1 million electronvolts remain at an altitude of 1000 km for several days. The *inner belt* is restricted to latitudes below about 30°. The particles of which it is formed, protons and electrons, appear to derive principally from neutron disintegration:

neutron *gives* proton + electron + neutrino.

The neutrons are derived from the interaction of cosmic rays with the atmosphere. However, it is possible that some of the injected protons may be of solar origin. Heavy ions are also detected in this belt. The *outer belt* extends up to latitudes of 50°. It consists mainly of low energy electrons. These electrons would be projected by the Sun into the belt simultaneously with magnetic storms, polar aurorae, etc. The outer belt is larger, and is located between 10,000 and 20,000 km. The interest in understanding these belts is obvious in the event of space flights in which the astronaut must be protected from the considerable biological effects of radiation.

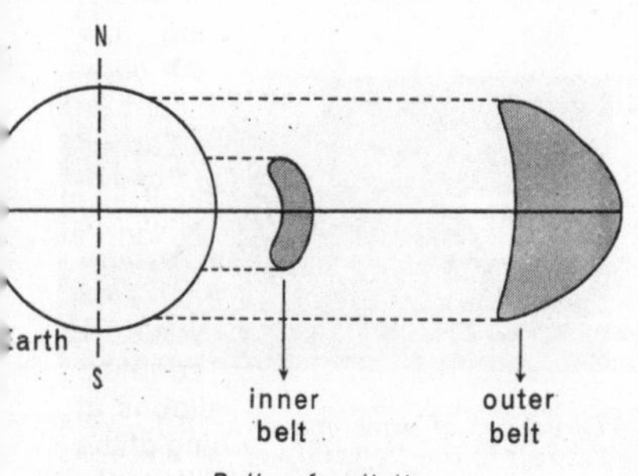

Belts of radiation

berkelium, an element belonging to the Actinide family, atomic number 97. It was obtained by Thompson, Ghiorso and Seaborg in 1950, by bombarding americium 241 with alpha particles. In this manner they obtained berkelium 243, two neutrons also being produced in the reaction. Berkelium 243 is radioactive with a half-life of 4.6 hours.

beryllium, an element with the atomic number 4 and atomic mass 9. Each of its nuclei contains four protons and five neutrons. It is very much used in reactor physics. Since it is the lightest of the metals, its slowing down power for neutrons is considerable and it is used as a **moderator** (qv), or as a reflector. Its absorption cross-section is weak; ie it absorbs few low energy neutrons. It is, moreover, a good heat conductor. Oxide of beryllium BeO, which is a ceramic, is also used for the same purpose. This metal, as well as its compounds, is highly toxic and its manufacture demands great precautions. The principal source of beryllium is a silicate of beryllium and of aluminium, $Be_3Al_2(SiO_3)_6$.

beta, β, a Greek letter used to indicate an electron when it is the product of radioactivity (eg iodine 137 emits a beta ray).—There exists both a beta plus radioactivity (positive electrons) and a beta minus radioactivity (negative electrons). Beta radiation belongs to the three natural radiations which were detected at the beginning of discoveries concerning alpha, beta and gamma radioactivity. In beta minus radioactivity the emitting nucleus loses a negative charge: ie its charge is increased by one unit. Since the number of nucleons does not alter, it means that a neutron has disappeared from the nucleus and a proton has appeared in it. The atomic mass, which is the number of nucleons, remains unchanged. The atomic number, which is the number of charges, increases by one unit. In beta plus activity it is obvious that the atomic number decreases by one unit. (For the characteristics of this radiation see **disintegration.**) To describe the electrons emitted in beta radioactivity, the expressions *beta rays*, *beta radiation* and *beta particles* are used.

betatherapy, a medical treatment which consists of irradiating an infected organ with beta rays. This method is used when the parts to be treated are fairly deep. Beta rays, in fact, penetrate a considerable distance through tissue and can exercise a relatively well localised action.

betatron, an electron accelerator.—This is a circular accelerator in which the electrons move round in a magnetic guide field which is perpendicular to their trajectory. But whereas, in general, acceleration of charged particles is achieved by means of a strong electric field, in the betatron the magnetic guide field itself is used for the acceleration of electrons. To obtain this, the magnetic field is varied during the acceleration cycle. An electromotive force resulting from the variation of the field acts along the path of the electrons. It is this electromotive force which accelerates the electrons and replaces the high voltage of normal acceleration. The

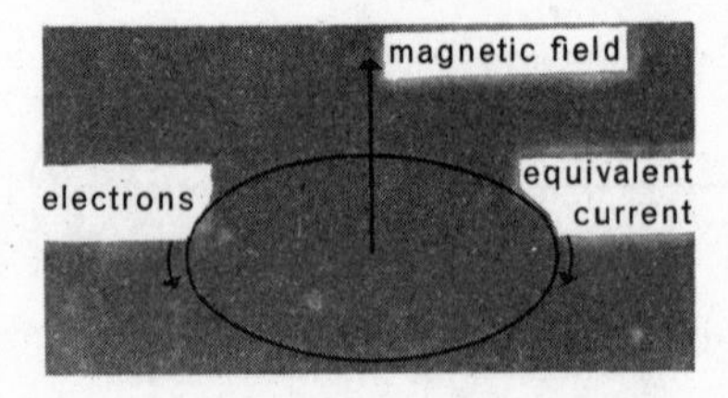

Direction of the magnetic field with respect to the trajectory of the electrons in a betatron

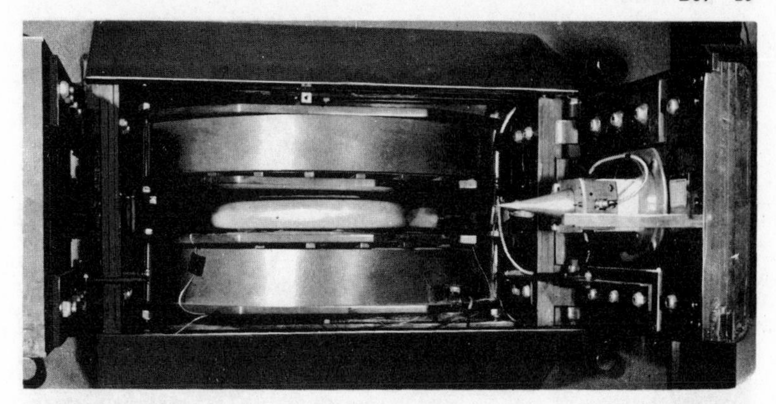

View of an American betatron accelerating electrons up to a speed corresponding to 24 million volts (Photo Allis-Chalmers)

principle of the betatron may be understood in another way by recalling that when a magnetic field varies, currents are produced in a conductor which tend to oppose this variation (*Lenz's* law). In the case of the betatron, the acceleration of the electrons corresponds to an increase in current, since they are electric charges circulating at a greater velocity. This increase in current creates a variation in the magnetic field which tends to oppose the variation of the magnetic guide field. Electrons may be accelerated with the betatron to a velocity corresponding to 20 million volts. There exists a perfected version in which the functions of the guiding and accelerating magnetic field are separated. A constant magnetic field is used for the guiding, on it a variable magnetic field is superimposed, the latter making it possible for the acceleration to be obtained. Thus the output of the apparatus is increased and electrons can be accelerated to a speed which corresponds to 300 million volts. The limitations of these devices arise from the fact that electrons when revolving emit a gamma radiation which increases with the speed of the electrons. This gamma radiation presents protection problems, and, most important, involves an equal reduction in the energy of the electrons.

BETHE, Hans Albrecht (1906–) German physicist naturalised American. Physics prize-winner at the University of Frankfurt (1928), he left for the USA in 1935 where from 1943 to 1946 he was Director of the Physics Division at Los Alamos, for research on the atomic bomb. He has mainly been responsible for the theory of cascade showers in cosmic rays (with Heitler) and the discovery of the Bethe cycle or carbon cycle (see thermonuclear **cycle**), and won the Nobel Prize for Physics in 1967 for his contributions to the theory of nuclear reactions.

BeV, abbreviation for billion-

General view of the bevatron at the Radiation Laboratory of California University. This machine accelerates protons to an energy of 6 billion electronvolts. (Photo USIS)

electronvolt, a unit with a value of 1 billion electronvolts. The notation GeV (gigaelectronvolt) stands for the same unit, and this has been officially adopted.

bevatron, an accelerator of the synchrotron type, in use at the Lawrence Institute at Berkeley, Cal. It accelerates protons to 6 BeV, whence its name. It has a nearly circular shape of 17 m radius. Until 1960, it was the largest accelerator in the world. Every six seconds, the bevatron produces 300,000 million protons. The protons, which are injected at the entrance to the bevatron, already possess a certain velocity which is supplied to them by two auxiliary *Van de Graaff* accelerators. At the end of the acceleration cycle, they are directed on to a target, and the properties of the secondary particles which have been produced by the interaction of protons with the nuclei of the target are then studied. It was by means of this accelerator that the existence of the antiproton, or negative proton, was established.

Bikini, an atoll in the Pacific on which was tested, in 1946, the first atomic bomb to be exploded after World War 2.

binary fission or **bi-partition,** a phenomenon in which the initial nucleus splits into two nuclei. The number of protons in the initial nucleus is equal to the total number of protons in the two nuclei produced. In consequence, the sum of the atomic numbers of the nuclei which have been produced is equal to the atomic number of the initial nucleus.

This is not so for the number of neutrons, since free neutrons are ejected along with the fission. In the bi-partition of uranium 235, this body when bombarded by a neutron undergoes fission. Its nucleus contains 92 protons and 235−92=143 neutrons. There are, therefore, including the incident neutron, 144 neutrons. Bi-partition produces, for instance, tellurium and zirconium, for which the number of protons in the nucleus is respectively 52 and 40. There is a total of 52+40=92 protons, as in the initial nucleus. If, on the other hand, tellurium is produced in the form of isotope 137 and zirconium in the form of isotope 97, in these two nuclei are to be found (137−52)+(97−40)= 142 neutrons. Since there were originally 144 neutrons, fission has released two neutrons. These two neutrons in turn may serve as projectiles, to induce fission of two uranium nuclei, whereas only one neutron was available to start with. This is the phenomenon known as chain reaction. Fission may lead to a great many nuclear pairs. It can form stable isotopes, but it usually leads to radioactive isotopes. The number of neutrons emitted also varies with each fission.

bi-neutron, see **dineutron.**

biophysics, the study of living organisms by means of physical techniques. This is a branch of biology in which the physical manifestations of life are studied. It is also a biological method in which biological phenomena are studied, starting with their physical causes. For instance, muscular or intellectual activity corresponds to electric voltages measured at the level of the brain or nerves. The physical study of the actions of atomic radiation upon living organisms has made progress, but there remains a great deal to discover. This is partly because living beings present great structural and functional complexities. Also, physical phenomena induced by radiation are produced on a microscopic scale, whereas biological phenomena are observed on an incomparably greater scale.

bismuth, an element with the atomic number 83. Natural bismuth contains only the isotope of atomic mass 209, which is stable. It is the heaviest bismuth isotope. Bismuth 209 is the end-product of the radioactive series of neptunium. Bismuth is a metal which melts at low temperature. It possesses a weak neutron capture cross-section and in consequence does not absorb many of them. On account of these two properties, bismuth is used as a coolant in reactors, either alone or in association with other metals. On the other hand, it is a good gamma ray absorber, because of its high atomic number. This property enables it to be used as a gamma ray filter to preserve transmitted neutrons. Bismuth is also used to detect high energy neutrons. In fact, bombardment of bismuth by high energy neutrons induces its fission and the ionised products of fission can be detected in an *ionisation chamber*.

black body, an idealised body which absorbs all and reflects none of the radiation falling upon it. The study of the black body led **Planck** (qv) to the idea of the quantum of energy.

BLACKETT, Patrick Maynard Stuart (1897–) English physicist. Nobel Prize-winner for Physics, 1948, for his work on cosmic rays. With the help of a Wilson chamber he confirmed the existence of the positron and, with Occhialini, he obtained the first photographs of the materialisation of a photon into two electrons. He was made President of the Royal Society in 1965.

blood count, a medical analysis which enables the number of red corpuscles and the number of white corpuscles in the blood to be observed.—It is systematically practised in atomic centres where the personnel is subjected to **radiation** (qv).

BOGOLYUBOV, N. N. (1908–) Russian mathematical physicist. He has made great contributions to the theory of many-particle systems and to quantum field theory.

BOHR, Niels (1889–1962) Danish physicist. Famous for the atomic theory which bears his name and which brought him the Nobel Prize for Physics in 1922. He is well known for his *correspondence principle*

Niels Bohr
(Photo Danish Embassy)

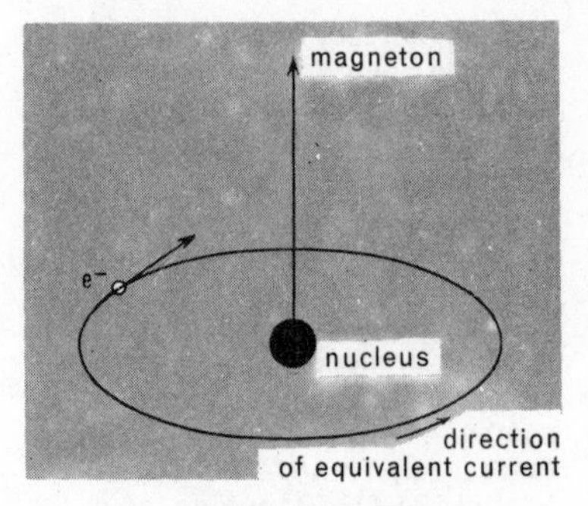

Bohr magneton

which allowed the passage from classical mechanics to quantum mechanics. He pointed out what a proper atomic theory should imply at a time when ideas were very confused. He also studied the problem of atomic nuclei, proposing the liquid drop model to explain nuclear disintegrations. (See **models of the nucleus.**)

● **Bohr magneton,** a unit of magnetic moment used in atomic physics.—In Bohr's theory of the atom, the electrons of an atom revolve round the nucleus at a certain speed. As an electron is negatively charged, its rotational motion is therefore equivalent to a circular electric current. In this way it forms a magnetic field perpendicular to its trajectory. From the magnetic point of view, the electron on its trajectory is the equivalent of a small magnet directed perpendicularly to the plane of this trajectory. The Bohr magneton is the magnetic moment corresponding to this magnet. It can only take certain quantified values, whose size is related to the azimuthal quantum number which fixes the rotational motion. In the expression of the magneton the following intervene:

—the elementary action or Planck constant,
—the elementary charge or electron charge,
—the mass of the particle.
The nuclear magneton, a unit employed for the nucleon (neutron and proton), is 1836 times smaller than the electronic magneton used for the electron, the proton being 1836 times heavier than the electron. The proton has a magnetic moment of 2.79 nuclear magnetons.

● **Bohr orbit,** the trajectory followed by an electron in Bohr's theoretical model of the atom.

● **Bohr radius.** The radius of the fundamental Bohr orbit is the hydrogen atom. (It has a value of approximately 0.5 ångström.) This radius of other orbits is occasionally called by this name, the value depending on the principal quantum number.

BOLTZMANN, Ludwig (1844–1906) Austrian physicist. His work on the kinetic theory of gases has contributed greatly to the development of particle physics. He linked thermodynamics to ordinary mechanics and clarified the concept of entropy by applying statistical ideas.

● **Boltzmann constant,** denoted by *k*. Relates the average energy of a particle of a gas to the temperature of the gas.

● **Boltzmann statistics,** a group of laws which regulate the distribution of a great many systems (the molecules of a gas, for instance) over their possible positions and velocities. Boltzmann's statistics, which made great advances in thermodynamics possible, are classical statistics which do not take **quantisation** (qv) into account. They may be understood as an approximation of quantum statistics in the limiting use where the elementary quantum or Planck's constant may be considered small.

bomb. The name *atomic bomb* is given to an appliance in which the explosive power is derived from nuclear forces. It is therefore more accurate to call it a *nuclear bomb*, since in this case the structure of the atom plays a secondary part. The first two bombs, the only ones to be used against people, at Nagasaki and Hiroshima, were exploded by the USA at the end of World War 2. Since then, hundreds of tests have been carried out by the atomic powers: the USA, the USSR, Great Britain, France and China. It is necessary to distinguish two types of atomic bomb: the *nuclear bomb* in which heavy nuclei undergo *fission*, and the *thermonuclear bomb* in which light nuclei undergo *fusion*. Weight for weight, the second type of bomb is considerably more powerful than the first.

● **nuclear bomb.** In this type of bomb uranium 235 or plutonium 239 is used. In natural uranium extracted from the ore, it is uranium 235 which is fissile. When acted upon by a neutron, its nucleus divides into two or more fragments which form elements of lower atomic mass, and there is also ejected a number of neutrons which varies according to the light bodies formed. These neutrons induce new fissions with emission of fresh neutrons; this is a chain reaction which develops in an explosive fashion inside the atomic bomb. (For the rapidity of this phenomenon, figures mentioned are of the order of a millionth of a second.) In the fission reaction nearly all the

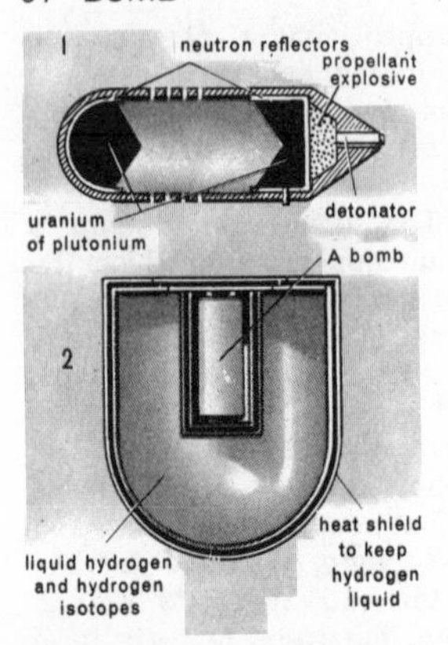

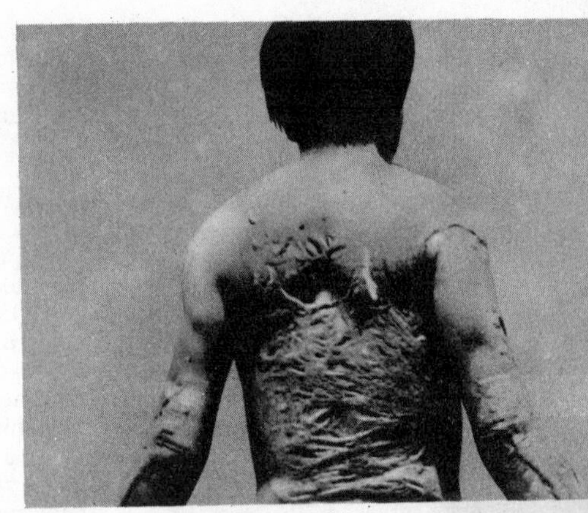

(top right & bottom). *Effects produced by the atomic bomb. Atomic energy is one of the most important discoveries of humanity. Unfortunately, it can also be the origin of the greatest disasters.* (top right) *The effect of burns produced by the atomic bomb which destroyed Hiroshima, August 5th 1945.* (photo AFP) (below) *The ruins of Hiroshima.* (Photo USIS) (top left) *Possible structures: 1 nuclear bomb; 2 thermonuclear bomb.*

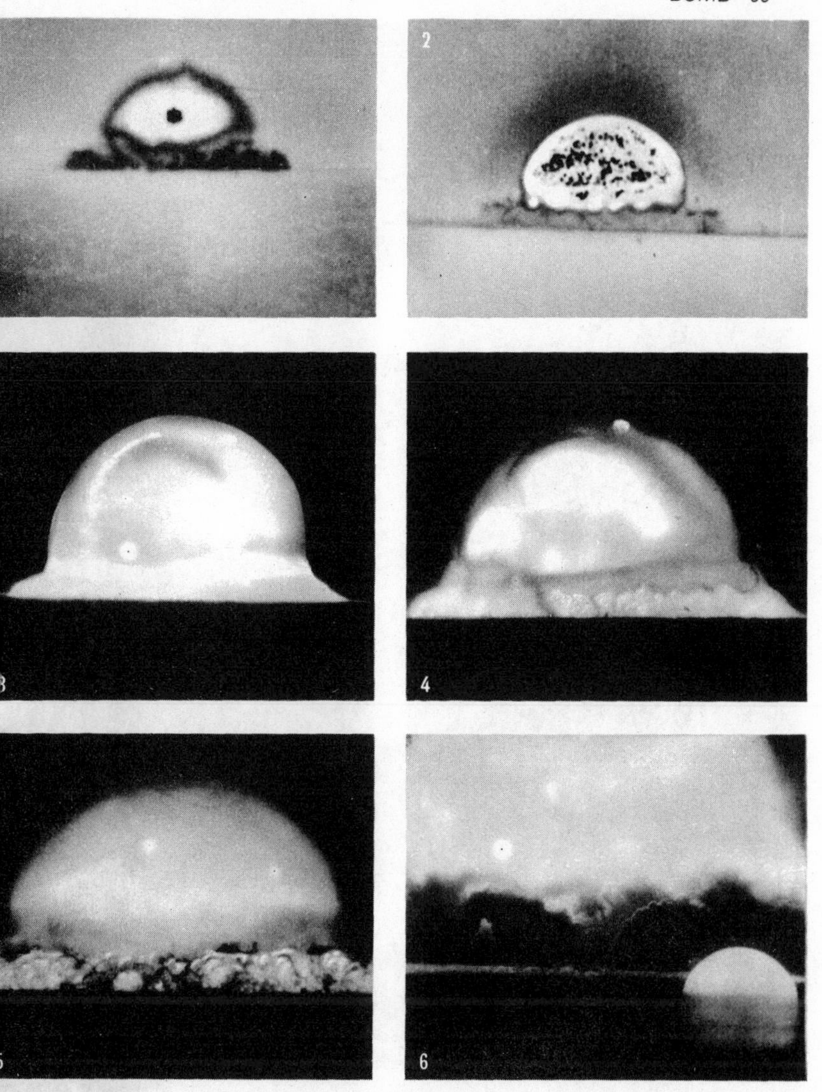

These photographs of the first atomic bomb to be tested were taken from a distance of 13 km (New Mexico, July 1945). Numbers show the chronological order of the pictures.

View of the mushroom cloud from an atomic bomb. The ships in the foreground indicate the relative size of the cloud. (Photo USIS)

protons and neutrons in the initial nucleus are re-encountered in the nuclei which have been produced. The energy released derives essentially from the fact that the binding energy of protons and neutrons in the initial nucleus is not as high as in the nuclei formed. Thus the total mass of the nuclei formed along with the neutrons ejected is lighter than the mass of the initial nucleus plus the initial neutron; this difference of mass is transformed into energy according to Einstein's relation of the equivalence of mass and energy. This energy first appears as a heat release. The heat flux (which is a flux of electromagnetic radiation) is produced by the de-excitation of matter excited by the radioactivity of the bodies formed. Part of the energy also reappears in the form of the kinetic energy of the radiation emitted. Neutrons escape from the bomb at a certain speed and there is emission of an important gamma radiation. For a chain reaction to be possible, with uranium as well as with plutonium, it is necessary to possess a certain *critical mass*, below which the phenomenon is not divergent and dies out progressively by the escape of neutrons from the surface of the bomb. This critical mass is of the order of a few kilos of uranium 235 and plutonium 239. Although the processes used are secret, several systems for priming an atomic bomb can be envisaged. The simplest consists in joining two fragments, each of which has separately a mass inferior to the critical mass, yet which together possess a mass superior to this same critical mass. It is possible also to place between two fragments a neutron absorber which can be withdrawn at the desired moment of explosion; or else suddenly drive in a neutron source. The two main effects of an atomic bomb at the moment of explosion are: the effect of blast, which can destroy buildings over an area of the order of a kilometre; and the considerable amount of heat given off which produces an effect similar to that of a gigantic fire; this is the fireball. Everything combustible is burned over an area of the order of a kilometre and at the heart of the explosion molten rock can be seen. At the moment of explosion a flash of light is produced capable of blinding anyone who keeps their eyes open or looks in the direction of the explosion. This damage ceases at a distance of about 10 kilometres. However, after the explosion, there are still emissions of all kinds of radiation, mainly of gamma radiation, which last for several minutes. Finally, a great many of the bodies formed in the fission are radioactive. Radioactive bodies, whose mean life is long, contaminate the area of the explosion for many years. The explosion throws up tens of tons of earth, or, if it is an underwater explosion, many tons of water. Not all the energy available in the critical mass is released during the explosion, because part of the fissile fuel fails to undergo fission. There is, therefore, an output from the bomb which at present is thought to be of the order of 10 per cent. This type of bomb is restricted to a power equivalent to several tens of thousands of tons of trinitrotoluene, a traditional explosive. In fact, after a certain mass, the power of a bomb does not increase much when more fuel is added.

● **thermonuclear bomb.** The thermonuclear bomb is realised by the use of light bodies. Let us consider, for example, the fusion of a light

Explosion of the first American hydrogen bomb in August 1952, in the Eniwetok Atoll of the Marshall Islands (Photo USIS)

hydrogen nucleus, consisting of one proton, with a tritium nucleus (heavy hydrogen) consisting of one proton and two neutrons. Thus a helium nucleus is obtained, consisting of two protons and two neutrons and this reaction gives out an energy of 20 million electronvolts. The mass of the two hydrogen nuclei being about 4000 million electronvolts, this fusion reaction makes it possible to transform 20/4000=0.5 per cent of the initial mass into energy. This percentage is higher than in the fission reaction, where it is of the order of 0.1 per cent. It is therefore understandable that the thermonuclear bomb should be of higher power than the nuclear bomb. The energies attained are of the order of tens of millions of tons of trinitrotoluene: ie a thousand times higher than for the nuclear bomb. In spite of this, the destruction induced by a thermonuclear bomb is not felt over a distance a thousand times greater than that of a nuclear bomb, since some of the energy is released into the atmosphere, but the zone affected would be, for instance, ten or twenty times larger. For a fusion reaction to take place, the hydrogen nuclei must be endowed with high velocities, so as to be able to overcome the coulomb repulsion due to their electric charges. These speeds are attained by thermal motion; the nuclei being raised to a temperature of several million degrees. In the thermonuclear bomb this temperature is obtained by means of the preliminary explosion of a nuclear bomb, which acts as a detonator.

bombardment, the action produced by a high particle flux on a target.—Bombardment is said to be *electronic*, *neutronic*, *protonic* or *ionic* according to whether the incident particles are **electrons, neutrons, protons** or **ions** (qqv). Electronic or ionic bombardment is used commercially for certain applications such as metal welding, homogeneity tests, etc.

bond, atomic, term for the valence linkage between atoms through their electrons.

BORN, Max (1882–) British physicist, born in Germany. His conception of probability in quantum theory prevailed over L. de Broglie's deterministic point of view. He has contributed to most branches of theoretical physics. Awarded the Nobel Prize for Physics with Walter Bothe in 1954.

boron, an element with atomic number 5. Much used in nuclear physics and in reactors on account of its great powers for neutron absorption, it presents the following absorption reaction:

boron (5 protons, 5 neutrons)
+neutron *gives*
helium (2 protons, 2 neutrons
+lithium (3 protons, 4 neutrons).

Boron 10 is present in a proportion of 19 per cent in the natural isotopic mixture; the other natural isotope being boron 11. This reaction is the more frequent the lower the speed of the neutrons. Boron is therefore a more effective absorber the slower the neutrons. This property is used to control thermal neutron (slow neutron) reactors. Boron is also used as a neutron absorber in shields and, finally, as a neutron detector in ionisation chambers or in counters. In the latter case, fluoride of boron (BF_3) is generally used as a filling gas, or else boron is deposited on the electrodes.

BOSE, Sir Jagadish Chunder (1858–1937) Indian physicist. The author of a statistical mechanical theory which Einstein perfected some years later. It constitutes a very powerful instrument for the study of atomic and nuclear physics.

● **Bose statistics,** Bose-Einstein statistics. A statistical law governing the distribution of an assembly of particles over the possible values of their energies and positions.—These are quantum statistics, ie they take into account the quantisation of possible energy states. Particles which obey these statistics may find themselves, in whatever number, in the same quantum state, in contrast to those particles which obey ● **Fermi-Dirac** (qv) statistics. In quantum statistics, a wave function describes the assembly of particles. Thanks to this function, the probability of finding particles in a certain quantum state is known. An assembly of particles obeys Bose statistics if the wave function remains unaltered when all the co-ordinates, including the spin, of a couple of particles are interchanged. In the Fermi-Dirac statistics the wave function changes sign. In both cases the probability of the presence of particles remains unaltered under the exchange, as it is proportional to the square of the wave function. The idea of quantum statistics is necessary because the particles are indistinguishable. For example, there is nothing to distinguish one neutral pion from another. If two mesons started a reaction, it would be impossible to distinguish the first from the second by the end of the reaction. When the number of possible quantum states is very great, Bose's statistics merge with the classical statistics of Boltzmann.

boson, a particle which obeys Bose statistics.—Pions, K mesons and photons are bosons. ‖ This word is more generally used to describe a particle system which obeys the statistics of Bose. The carbon nucleus, considered as a whole, is a boson, despite the fact that it is not composed of bosons.

bound state of an atom, state in which the energy of the atom is well defined and negative.—The electrons of the atom are tied to it and cannot escape without external interaction.

BRAGG, Sir William Henry (1862–1942) English physicist. In 1915 he shared the Nobel Prize for Physics with his son (Sir William Lawrence Bragg), for his work on the diffraction of X-rays by crystalline bodies.

braking, the English word for *Bremsung*. ‖ *Braking radiation*, photons emitted during the **bremsstrahlung** phenomenon (qv).

branching ratio, see **ratio, branching.**

breeder, a reactor which produces more fissile material than it consumes. (See **reactor.**)

bremsstrahlung (from the German *Bremsung,* braking and *Strahlung,* radiation), a phenomenon whereby electrically charged particles are slowed down during their passage through matter.—A charged particle which approaches fairly closely to a nucleus is deflected from it by the action of the electric field of the nucleus, which contains positively charged protons. Change in the direction of the incident particle is accompanied by a decrease in energy. A gamma ray is emitted simultaneously with an energy equal to that lost by the slowed particle. To be exact, the nucleus also carries off a very small fraction of the energy in the phenomenon. Bremsstrahlung is the more effective the faster the particle and the heavier the nucleus. For electrons with an energy higher than 100 million electronvolts, this phenomenon occupies the leading place in slowing down by matter. The energy of the rays emitted varies according to the distance of the nucleus to which the particle passes. Brems-

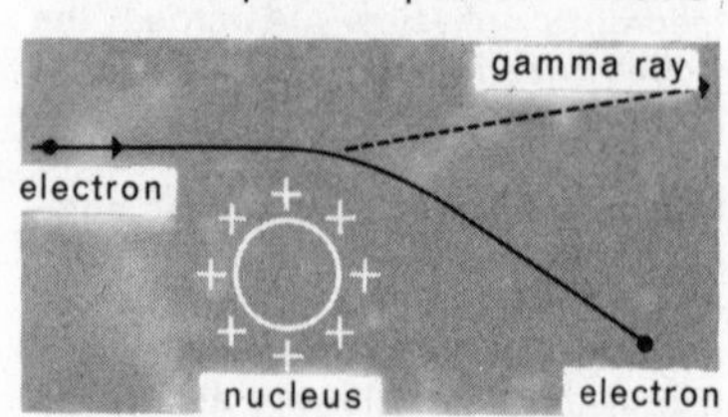

Bremsstrahlung

strahlung is also produced, though in a weaker proportion, by collision with the atomic electrons, since they are charged.

BRILLOUIN, Léon (1899–) French physicist, who has worked on quantum statistics, wave propagation in periodic structures and information theory.

broadening of spectral lines, see **line.**

Brownian movement, irregular random thermal motion of particles in a fluid.

C

C, the symbol representing the speed of light, 2.9979×10^{10} cm/sec.

cadmium, metallic element with atomic number 48. A metal much used on account of its great capacity for the absorption of slow neutrons. It is used in the control rod, the introduction of which enables the flux of neutrons to be reduced inside a reactor. It is also employed in the neutron shielding of measurement and control devices. It is obtained as a by-product of zinc, since cadmium minerals are scarce. Natural cadmium contains several isotopes. Cadmium with mass number 113 (48 protons, 65 neutrons), present in natural cadmium in a 12 per cent proportion, is the isotope which offers a high **• absorption cross-section** (qv) for slow neutrons.

californium, an artificial transuranian element with the atomic number 98.—It was obtained in 1950 by Thompson, Street, Ghiorso and Seaborg, by bombarding curium 242 with alpha particles, in the form of the californium isotope 244. Eleven artificial isotopes of californium have since been discovered. They are all unstable, which explains why they are not found in the natural state. Californium 251 is the least unstable; it has a mean life of seven hundred years.

calutron, an isotopic separator built on the principle of the mass spectrograph.—Uranium 235, which may undergo fission in a reactor, possesses a lower mass than that of uranium 238, which is not fissile. Uranium ions are produced to separate them, these are uranium atoms from which an electron has been torn. These ions have, therefore, a positive charge and may be accelerated by an electric field. Deflection of the uranium ion 235 is greater than that of the uranium ion 238 in a magnetic field when both types of ions are subjected to the same accelerating voltage. This method of separation was used at California University in 1941, by Lawrence, who used the electromagnet of the cyclotron to produce the magnetic field. Hence the name of this device. The calutron made it possible to obtain only a few micrograms of uranium 235 a day. It was then perfected so as to make commercial production possible: ie a few kilos a month!

capture, a phenomenon in which a particle becomes built in to an atomic or nuclear system. It may be produced by a variety of interactions.

• capture of an electron by an ion. An ion is an atom which has lost one or more of its electrons; in consequence it is positively charged. When an electron finds itself in the vicinity, the electrostatic force of attraction between the positive ion and the negative electron may bring about the recombination of the ion with the electron to form an atom. In this case, electromagnetic interactions are responsible for the phenomenon through the medium of electrostatic force.

● **capture of a nucleon by a nucleus.** Some nuclei may capture a neutron or a proton. The incident particle in this case is attracted into the nucleus by nuclear forces. These forces are much stronger than electromagnetic forces, and the distance at which they can act is restricted. When a neutron is captured by a nucleus, the mass number of the nucleus increases by one unit, whereas its charge remains unaltered, the neutron having no electric charge. The atomic number of the nucleus therefore remains unchanged, and an isotope is formed from the initial nucleus. Example:

cadmium 113 (48 protons, 65 neutrons)+neutron
gives cadmium 114 (48 protons, 66 neutrons).

When a proton is captured by a nucleus, the mass number of the nucleus increases by one unit, and its charge as well, because the proton possesses a unit positive charge. Therefore, the atomic number of the nucleus increases by one unit. Example:

lithium 7 (3 protons, 4 neutrons) +proton
gives beryllium 8 (4 protons, 4 neutrons).

In both cases, the incident proton or neutron possesses a certain kinetic energy (due to its velocity) whereas the target nucleus is in a stable energy state corresponding to its equilibrium. After reaction has taken place, the incident neutron, which has been captured by the nucleus, is bound. Therefore, there is an excess of energy ΔE available. Two things may take place:

a) The excess energy is emitted in the form of gamma radiation simultaneously with the capture. This is what happens in the first example (beryllium+gamma).

b) The excess energy is absorbed into the final nucleus. The final nucleus is then called an *isomer*. The excess energy is released in the form of a gamma radiation, though only after some delay. The isomer generally has a short mean lifetime. De-excitation is rapidly produced. In both cases, the capture is called *radiative*. The energy levels of a nucleus are quantised. They can only accept certain well-defined values. To them therefore corresponds a distinct kinetic energy of the incident nucleon. Reaction will take place more readily if the incident nucleon possesses this energy exactly. The capture is called *resonant*,

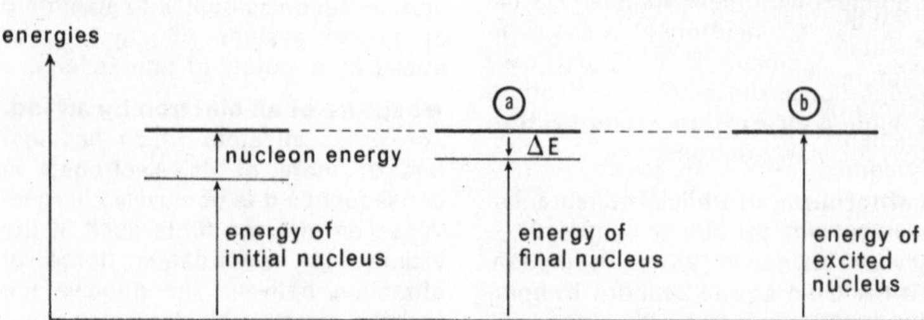

Capture of a nucleon by a nucleus

and the cross-section, which is low for other energy values, is particularly high for the resonance energy.

● **electronic capture,** a phenomenon in which an electron of an atom is absorbed into the nucleus of the atom. The electron having a negative charge, the positive charge of the nucleus (its atomic number) decreases by one unit. The total number of neutrons plus protons in the nucleus (its mass number) remains unchanged. In this phenomenon the electromagnetic forces play a part, since both the electron and the nucleus are charged. However, the final reaction is due to weak interactions. These are responsible for the fundamental reaction

proton+negative electron *gives* neutron+neutrino,

which is a reaction symmetrical to the beta disintegration of the neutron;

neutron *gives* proton+negative electron+antineutrino.

Another phenomenon may compete with electron capture: eg the beta+ disintegration of the proton, also symmetrical,

proton *gives* neutron+positive electron+neutrino,

cannot take place directly, because the proton has a lower mass than the neutron. It is only produced in nuclei. The necessary energy is borrowed from the nucleus in which the beta+ disintegration takes place. Electron capture takes place generally in elements of a high atomic mass (heavy elements), whereas the beta+ disintegration takes place generally in elements of low atomic mass (light elements). There is a neutrino emitted in electronic capture. The neutrino carries off the difference in the energies of the final and the initial nucleus. It is known that the electrons of an **atom** (qv) are distributed on shells which are more or less distant from the nucleus. The closest shells are called K, L, M, N, shells, etc. K capture is the name given to the capture of an electron of K shell; L capture, that of an electron of L shell, etc. When the capture takes place on K shell, it dominates the L, M, N, captures. But the electrons of K shell are the most closely bound to the nucleus, and the available energy is not always sufficient for K capture to be possible. There may then be L capture. For some elements, we find simultaneously electron capture and a beta+ emission, with clearly defined proportions according to the element. In the case of metal, some electrons are no longer bound to the nucleus (*conductivity electrons*). Capture of these free electrons is also possible. Example:

vanadium 49 (23 protons, 26 neutrons, 23 electrons)
gives titanium 49 (22 protons, 27 neutrons, 22 electrons)+neutrino.

carbon, an element with atomic number 6. Each of its nuclei contains 6 protons. A light element, it is used as a moderator and reflector in nuclear reactors. The capture cross-section of slow neutrons being low, it only slightly absorbs the neutrons of the reactor. On the other hand, it is easy to obtain in large quantities. Carbon 14 (6 protons, 8 neutrons) is an active isotope used in **dating** methods (qv) in archaeology.

carnotite, a uranium ore which has been discovered in the USA.

cascade, a name given to multiplicative phenomena induced by high-energy cosmic rays (see **shower**).

● **cascade separation of isotopes.** The separation of isotopes cannot be achieved by one single element. Each element of an installation can only separate a fraction of the initial product. So as to improve the separation many elements are connected together. To increase the output of separated isotopes, they are connected in parallel, and to increase the degree of separation, they are connected in series. A cascade is said to be *ideal* when the number of elements is such that the quantity of the initial product used is the smallest possible for the degree of separation desired.

castle, lead, a closed lead chamber in which a strong radioactive source is sealed, so as to protect personnel and material, and to prevent the source from influencing outside detection apparatus. The chamber is provided with doors, which enable the source to be introduced and if necessary permit the use of counting apparatus and screens.

cation, positively charged **ion** (qv).

cavitron, suggested accelerator which would consist of a single resonant cavity inside which the particles would be accelerated. To reduce the radius of curvature of the trajectories, and therefore the bulk of the apparatus, a strong magnetic field would be produced by a cooled coil, the loss of power due to electric resistance being decreased by the lowering of the temperature. It should be observed that superconducting coils are actually being developed, and some types are commercially available. In these the electric resistance is strictly zero, and the power required to maintain the magnetic field is very low. In this case, nearly all the power consumed goes to the compressors of the refrigerant. The temperature of the coil must be kept at a value dependent on the conductor used for the coil, though always lower than 200° C below zero.

cavity, a closed metallic enclosure in which an oscillating electromagnetic field is maintained. In nuclear physics this has several uses. Particles may be speeded up by means of an acceleration cavity. When passing across the cavity the particles are subjected to forces due to the field and as a result, their velocity is increased, if the field has a suitable structure in time and space (see **accelerator**). Cavities are also used to deflect particles in a beam and especially to separate them, since particles of different masses will be deviated in different directions by the cavity. The cavity is called *resonant*; ie little energy is required to maintain the field. This resonance phenomenon is the same as in the case of a cord which vibrates at a certain frequency; a low force which acts with the same frequency upon the cord is enough to maintain vibration. The structure of the field in the cavity is the same as that of a taut cord which vibrates. For example, the electric field is zero on the walls and maximal in the middle. It is also possible to obtain one, two, three . . . minima of the field to the interior of the cavity.

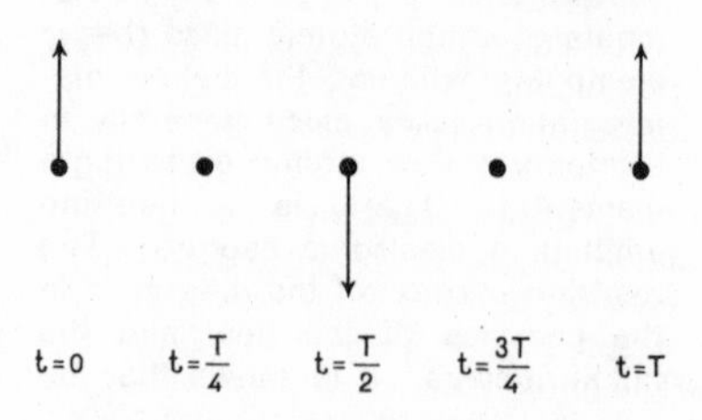

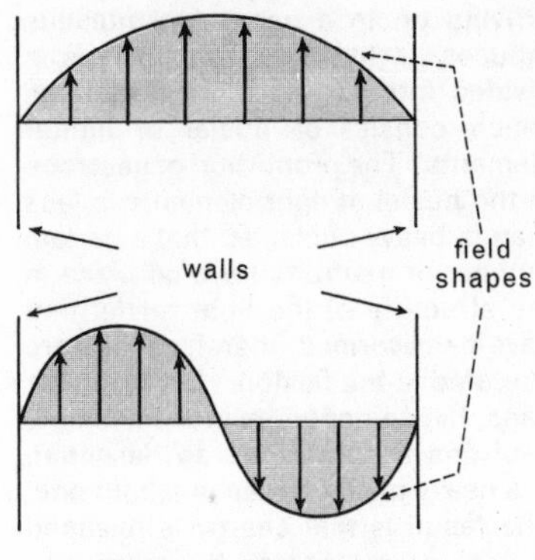

Shapes of a field in a cavity

At each point, the field oscillates round zero with a certain period T. If the field is maximal at the moment t=0 (see diagram) it is zero at the moment t=T/4, maximal (but reversed) at the moment T/2, zero at the moment 3T/4, and finally recovers its initial value at the moment T. One uses the term *stationary waves*. In this case there are fixed points at which the field is constantly zero. For some applications, cavities are constructed in which *progressive waves* are produced. Not only does the field oscillate at any point of the cavity, but the whole pattern moves at a certain velocity. In such cavities, those points at which the field is zero, move. These cavities are called *wave guides*. The frequencies used are generally fairly high and may reach some hundreds of megacycles per second; ie some hundred million oscillations per second.

cell, photo-electric, an apparatus in which incident light produces an electric current. Its functions are based on the photo-electrical effect. The photon, or constituent particle of light, may, on passing into matter, eject an atomic electron. The mass of electrons, ejected by this phenomenon from one electrode into a photo-emissive cell, form the photo-electric current. Each photo-electric cell is sensitive to a band of light of a distinct colour corresponding to the metal used. In fact, the electrons in the metal are bound with a given energy in the atom. To extract them, the photons must have a comparable energy; ie must possess a given colour. There are many uses for photo-electric cells such as photography, automatic control, production of current, etc.

centrifugation, a process for the **separation of isotopes** (qv).

CERENKOV, Pavel (1904–) Russian physicist. In 1958 he received the Nobel Prize for Physics for the discovery of the Cerenkov effect which is used in counter techniques.

● **Cerenkov effect.** When a charged particle passes through a transparent substance at a speed higher than the speed of light in that substance, there is an emission of visible light. This occurs with refracting substances (water, glass, gas under pressure) as soon as the speed of the particle becomes sufficient. In glass, for instance, the speed of light is 0.66 times the speed of light in a vacuum. To produce the Cerenkov effect in glass, it is enough for the speed of a particle to be at least 0.66 times the speed of light in a vacuum. Light is emitted on a cone co-axial with the trajectory of the particle, the opening angle of which is related to the speed of the particle and to the refractive index of the medium through which it passes. In Cerenkov counters this effect is used to measure the velocity of the particles. This phenomenon offers some analogy with the shock wave produced by an object moving at supersonic velocity through air, the energy of sound being replaced, in this case, by the electromagnetic energy of light. *See illustration p. 63.*

CERN, European Organisation for Nuclear Research (originally called European Council for Nuclear Research). The aim of the organisation is basic research on high-energy physics. The research centre is at Geneva. The member States are: Austria, Belgium, Denmark, France, German Federal Republic, Greece, Italy, Netherlands, Norway, Spain, Sweden, Switzerland and United Kingdom.

chain disintegration, successive disintegrations of the elements of the same radioactive series (see **series**).

chain reaction, an assembly of fission reactions which are produced in a reactor or in a nuclear bomb.—In a reactor, for instance, a neutron arriving on to a heavy fuel nucleus induces its fission. The nucleus is divided into two or more fragments which consist of nuclei of lighter elements. The proportion of neutrons in the nuclei of light elements is less than in heavy nuclei, so that a certain number of neutrons have no place in the structure of the light nuclei that have been formed, therefore they are liberated in the fission. On the other hand, the components of the nucleus, neutrons and protons, are less tied in a heavy nucleus than in a light one. The result is that energy is released in fission; the fission fragments are speedily brought to rest in matter, whereas a neutron may travel some distance, act upon a fuel nucleus and in turn induce fission. The phenomenon is multipliable: if each fission releases more than one neutron, each neutron in turn induces fission. In reactors, chain reaction is controlled, so that the number of neutrons released may be equal to the number of fissions induced. The number of fissions per second remains clearly defined and the quantity of heat produced which corresponds to it remains constant. In a bomb, on the contrary, the chain reaction is explosive. It develops freely until the fuel is exhausted or, more precisely, until part of the fuel has been used. The mass of fissile material being of necessity limited, some neutrons produced in the fission escape from it through the walls. Calculations have demonstrated that a certain minimal quantity of fuel is necessary for chain reaction to develop. This minimal quantity is said to be *critical*. Chain reaction is very rapid. In a bomb, the fuel is used up in a few thousandths of a second. In a reactor, the neutrons are decelerated in the moderator, so that their energy may be

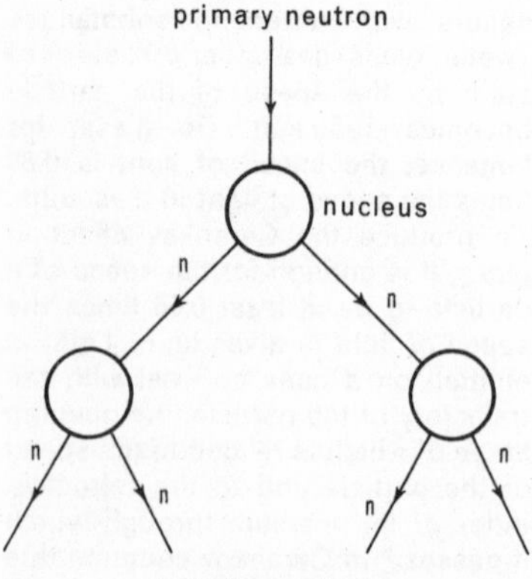

primary neutron
nucleus
n n
n n n n

Chain reaction

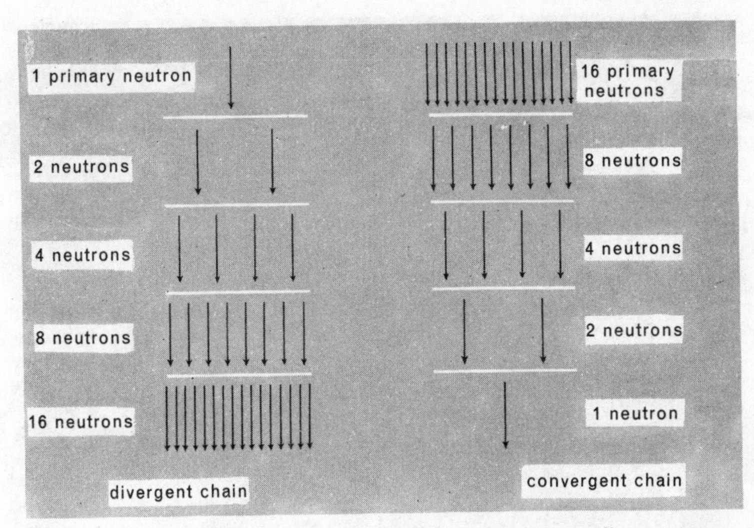

Diagram showing convergent and divergent chain reactions

optimal for the production of fission. The mean life of the neutrons is also of the order of a thousandth of a second, but the percentage of nuclei undergoing fission per second is considerably less in the case of the reactor.

chalcolite, a uranium ore which is found in England and in Portugal.

chamber, enclosure, frequently one maintained in a **metastable** condition (qv) for the detection of radiation.

● **bubble-chamber,** an apparatus for detection of particles, used in high energy physics.—Under certain conditions, a particle passing through liquid produces ebullition throughout the length of its trajectory. The bubble-chamber consists essentially of an enclosed volume of liquid held under pressure. About a hundredth of a second before the particle passes through it the liquid is decompressed, its pressure being reduced to a value lower than that at which it normally boils. When there is no particle, the liquid takes some time to boil, of the order of 50 thousandths of a second in an enclosure whose surface has received an ordinary polish. When a particle is present, a necklace of bubbles forms along the particle trajectory. After a thousandth of a second, these bubbles become large enough—some tenths of a millimetre in diameter—to be photographed. The bubble-chamber is then recompressed before ebullition takes place in the bulk of the liquid. Bubbles formed along the length of the trajectory are due to the energy lost by a charged particle which passes through matter. The particle ionises the atoms of the liquid, and separates them into ions and electrons. Recombination of these ions releases energy which, when absorbed into

General view of the heavy liquid bubble chamber BP3 at the Leprince-Ringuet Laboratory of the Ecole Polytechnique, Paris. In the foreground, the portholes which enable photographs to be taken. (Photo Ecole Polytechnique)

the vicinity of the trajectory, occasions a localised heating-up, which is the source of the ebullition. The bubble-chamber is not only a detecting apparatus, it is also a target; nuclear reactions being studied are produced on the nuclei of the liquid itself. Tracks of the incident particles as well as tracks of the secondary particles produced in the reaction are therefore detected simultaneously. The bubble-chamber is generally used in the presence of a magnetic field produced by an electromagnet. The magnetic field curves the trajectories and enables the particle momentum to be measured; this physical quantity is the product of the mass and velocity of the particle. In some cases, measuring the number of bubbles per centimetre, or measuring the range between the bubbles, provides information about the energy loss in relation to the speed of a particle; this particle can then be identified. The two main types of bubble-chamber are:

1) *The hydrogen chamber.* This per-

mits the study of reactions on the simplest nucleus: ie the hydrogen nucleus, with only one proton. Physical analysis of the results is made easier. It works at a temperature of 246° C below zero and at a pressure of 6 atmospheres. The most important technical problem in this case is the refrigeration of the chamber.

2) *The heavy liquid chamber* (propane, freon, etc). This machine makes it possible to obtain a larger number of nuclear reactions because the density of the liquids employed is distinctly higher. It permits the detection both of photons, which materialise in dense media (photon *gives* positive electron +negative electron) and of neutral pions which disintegrate into photons. Analysis of the results obtained is less easy than in the case of the hydrogen chamber. Heavy liquid chambers operate at temperatures of the order of 30° C and at pressure of the order of 25 atmospheres. The important technical problem is that of pressure.

The bubble-chamber is particularly

General view of the hydrogen bubble-chamber CBH 81 of Saclay and the Leprince-Ringuet Laboratories (Photo Ecole Polytechnique)

well adapted to the study of particles produced by the big accelerators. In this case, the beam of particles produced enters the chamber after it has been decompressed. The length of time before the chamber is again ready to function is generally less than the time taken to repeat the acceleration of the particles. The bubble-chamber can work on each pulse of the accelerator; which is not the case with the Wilson chamber. A dense liquid medium is, moreover, more favourable than a gaseous medium for the production of nuclear reactions. The working principle of this apparatus was discovered in 1952 by the American physicist Glaser. The technique of these chambers has, since then, been greatly developed. From early chambers, a few cubic centimetres in size, one has passed progressively to larger chambers, some of which reach 2 m in length. Information obtained by measuring photographs has been considerable in the field of fundamental particles. Masses, mean lives and decay modes have all been intensively studied recently.

● **diffusion chamber,** a detecting apparatus based on the same principle (ie formation of liquid droplets along the trajectory of the particle) as the Wilson chamber.—Whereas a state of supersaturation is obtained in a Wilson chamber by reducing the gas pressure, this condition is sustained in continuous fashion in the diffusion chamber by means of a difference in temperature, established along the vertical axis of the apparatus. A constant electric field sweeps out the ions formed along the track, so that the chamber remains sensitive. The principal disadvantage of the diffusion chamber is its restricted sensitive volume. In the first apparatus to be used with cosmic rays, the sensitive zone extended vertically over only a few centimetres. Progress was made with the installation beside accelerators of high pressure diffusion chambers. High pressure gas provided a greater density of matter than gases at atmospheric pressure, without, however, achieving density comparable to that of a liquid. The sensitive zone was raised to a vertical extent of 10 or 15 cm. This was sufficient for beams of particles which are produced by an accelerator, practically on a horizontal plane. The horizontal dimensions extended to 2 m, enabling exact measurements to be taken, principally on those particles called mu **leptons** (qv).

● **ionisation chamber,** a detector of charged particles.—Like the Geiger counter, it consists of one cathode and one anode. The cathode is frequently shaped like a cylinder on the axis of which is placed a threadlike anode. The chamber is filled with gas (air, nitrogen, hydrogen, bromine, etc). Between the electrodes a voltage of some hundred volts is applied. The particles which pass through the gas induce an ionisation phenomenon in it. Gas atoms are dissociated into ions and electrons; the ions, which have a positive electric charge, are attracted by the cathode, the electrons, with a negative charge, by the anode. From this displacement of charges results an electric current which is proportionate to the number of ions produced by the passage of the particle. The ionisation chamber works on a lower voltage than a Geiger counter. In the latter, the voltage between the electrodes induces avalanches, so that the electric current does not depend on the initial number

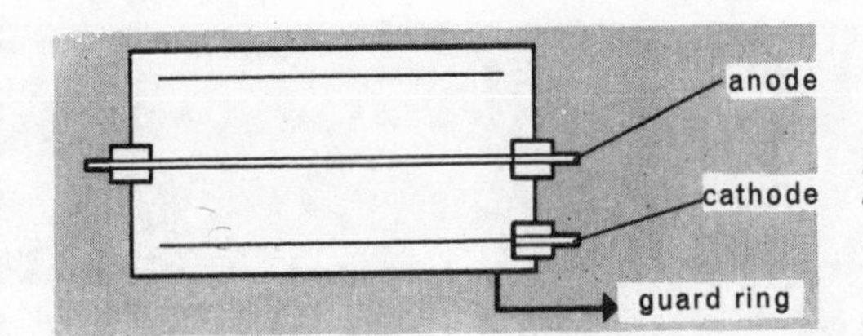

Diagram of a cylindrical ionisation chamber.

of ions, but only on the voltage used. The ionisation chamber may work in two ways:

a) If a flow of particles passes through the chamber, the ionisation which is produced by all the particles which pass per second, is measured. The chamber works on direct current.

b) It is also possible to count the particles one by one by using the electric pulses produced on the electrodes. In this case, the current enables the loss of energy, through ionisation, of the particles passing through the gas to be measured. The chamber is then working on pulses.

The current provided by an ionisation chamber is always very low; in the order of a millionth or a billionth of an ampere. To be able to measure or to use this current it must be amplified. Techniques for amplifying such currents are very delicate. Ionisation chambers are mainly used for electron beams and the sources of beta or alpha rays.

● **spark chamber,** an apparatus which makes it possible to localise the paths of particles through observing sparks produced in gas.— This is the most recent form of detection apparatus perfected for the study of particles produced by accelerators. Its main advantage is that its recovery time is very short. After its first release, it takes only a few thousandths of a second for the apparatus to be ready to operate again. This characteristic is especially valuable in beams of particles produced by an accelerator, for it then becomes possible to spread these beams over a period of time—some tenths of a second, for instance. Furthermore, it is possible to trigger the chamber on an event already selected by a system of counters. This second characteristic is useful for research into rare events. Although a great many particles pass across the chamber, this is not actuated and photographed unless the incident, whose type is defined by the geometrical lay-out of the counters, has already been detected. The simplest type of spark chamber is composed of two smooth, thread-like electrodes placed 1 or 2 cm apart, the interval between them being filled by gas. A counter placed in front of the chamber detects the particles and operates a very rapid increase of voltage between the electrodes. This amounts to several thousand volts within the space of a few billionths of a second. A spark explodes at the point at which the particle passes across the chamber. The initiation of the spark is due to the ions formed by the particle. The position of the spark may be found by means of an

An experimental device containing a spark chamber (on the right) *at Saclay. To the left is a liquid hydrogen target.* (Photo J. P. Sudre CEA)

oscilloscope, by an electronic circuit or by a photograph. The electric voltage decreases in a thousandth of a second and a lower voltage (some hundreds of volts) is applied to *scan* the ions produced in the gas. The chamber is then ready to function again. The geometrical structure of the spark chamber can easily be adapted to the phenomenon to be studied. The number of electrodes may be multiplied as desired. The distance between two consecutive electrodes, on the other hand, remains limited since the spark does not follow the trajectory exactly but has a tendency to be perpendicular to the electrodes. It is also possible to place screens of solid material in the middle of the electrode network, so as to study nuclear reactions produced in matter, or else to detect the materialisation of photons, which produces two charged electrons that can be observed. Experiments have already been carried out by means of large spark chambers. The main ones concentrate on the study of the disintegration of **strange particles** such as **hyperons,** lambdas and sigmas, and interactions of the **neutrino** (qqv).

● **Wilson chamber,** an apparatus for detecting charged particles.—It was mainly used in the study of cosmic radiation and is still so used occasionally, with the accelerators. The functional principle was discovered by C. T. R. Wilson in 1911. The Wilson chamber consists of a closed volume of gas, in which there is a saturated vapour, generally alcoholic. This volume is suddenly depressurised by means of a piston. From this results a cooling of the gas and the alcoholic vapour condenses. If a charged particle is passed into the chamber before the pressure is released, it induces the break-up of a certain number of gas atoms into ions and electrons. These, on which alcoholic vapour forms fine liquid droplets, constitute condensation nuclei. Condensation of alcohol is therefore preferably in the wake of the particle. The chamber is triggered, on the passage of a suitable particle, by a system of counters. The droplets are lit by a flashlight, and photographs are taken at the same time (see figure, p. 54). After expansion, an electric sweeping field removes the ions formed, so that the chamber may be ready for a fresh release. In some cases a few small releases, or sometimes supercompression, are applied to the chamber to speed up the cleansing process. The period of recovery, at the end of which the chamber is clean and ready to function again, is fairly long; of the order of minutes. This is one reason why the bubble-chamber has replaced the Wilson chamber for use with accelerators. Another important reason for the decline of the Wilson chamber is its gaseous density, which is low in comparison with the liquid density of a bubble-chamber. Operation of a Wilson chamber is delicate. It requires a regularity of temperature in the order of a hundredth of a degree. Great precautions have to be taken to avoid the introduction of impurities when setting it up. Since the discovery of the Wilson chamber many have been operated using different gases. Some have been as large as 2 m in length. A magnetic field was usually added and occasionally metal screens as well, which enabled reactions with matter or the materialisation of photons to be studied. The results achieved by these chambers were fundamental in elementary particle physics, for example the discovery of the positive electron, mu, lepton, strange particles, lambda and K mesons.

CHAMBERLAIN, Owen (1920–) American physicist. He shared the Nobel Prize for Physics in 1959 with Segré, for their experimental detection of the antiproton.

channel, a pipe which enters the interior of a reactor and is used in irradiation of material to be studied. This channel may also, on occasion, be used as a stock-room.—Radioactive bodies produced by the reactor are placed in it so that they do not contaminate the surrounding atmosphere, until such time as their radioactivity shall have decreased sufficiently. Protection against radiation is frequently achieved by a water filling, which acts as a screen and enables products placed in the channel to be freely handled.

charge. The idea of an electric charge is deduced from study of the forces taking place between two electrically charged objects. This force depends on distance, but it is greater the higher the charges. Unit charge being defined, it may be said that an electric charge is of 2, 3, . . . units if

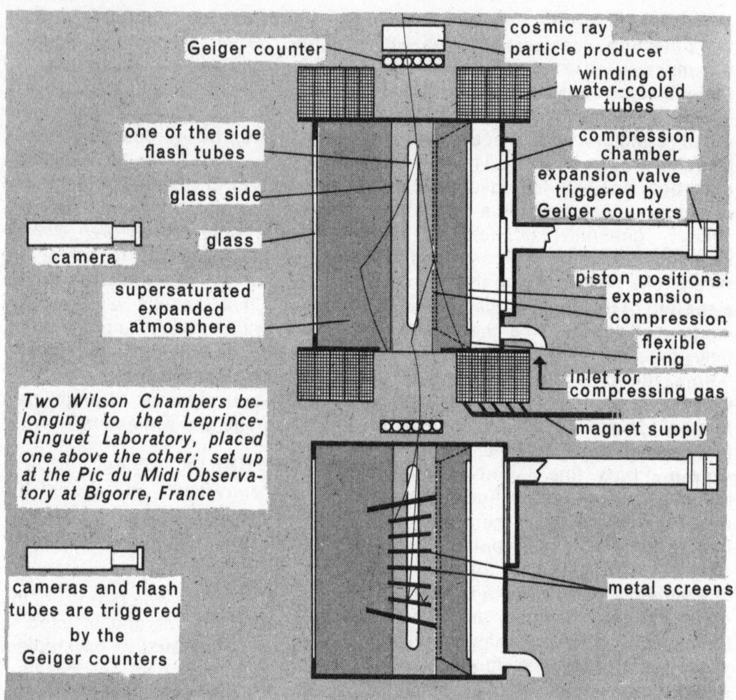

Two Wilson Chambers belonging to the Leprince-Ringuet Laboratory, placed one above the other; set up at the Pic du Midi Observatory at Bigorre, France

the force to which it is subjected is 2, 3, . . . times stronger than that on the unit charge under the same conditions: ie in the same electric field. It plays the same role in electricity as gravitational mass in Newtonian mechanics, the difference being that there is only one kind of mass but two kinds of electric charges.

● **charge exchange,** see **exchange of charge.**

● **charge independence,** the independence of the nuclear forces, acting between two particles, of the electric charges which they carry. The nuclear forces which bind a proton or a neutron inside a nucleus are similar. Research on *mirror nuclides*, in which a proton replaces a neutron, has demonstrated that they possess very similar properties. For example, the binding energies in lithium 7 (3 protons, 4 neutrons) and in beryllium 7 (4 protons, 3 neutrons) are almost identical. The deviations between them may be explained by the actions of the electric charges (positive for the proton, zero for the neutron) and not by differences in the nuclear forces. It is said that there is a charge symmetry between a proton and a neutron. The analogy of this behaviour appears to extend to nuclear reactions which bring into play proton and neutron or proton and proton, so that one comes to think that the nuclear forces between a proton and a proton, between a proton and a neutron and between a neutron and a neutron are identical, the only difference being their particular electric charges. This is the hypothesis of *charge independence*. The neutron and proton are therefore to be considered two different manifestations of one and the same particle. The nucleon may appear in two states of electric charge, ie the proton with a positive charge and the neutron with a zero charge. A quantum number called *isotopic spin* is introduced, the projection of which can only take two values associated with the two possible values of the electric charge. The neutron and the proton form a doublet of isotopic spin. Charge independence appears to be a property common to all particles capable of undergoing nuclear forces. For instance, all the pions, negative, positive and neutral, appear to have the same nuclear characteristics. They are said to form a triplet of *isotopic spin*, since the pion can exist in three states of charge. The hypothesis of charge independence enables numerous physical quantities to be predicted, for instance, the strength of nuclear reactions. All the results of present day experiments confirm these predictions.

● **elementary charge.** No electric charge smaller than the electron has ever been observed. The electron charge is therefore called the elementary charge. All the elementary particles possess either a zero charge, an electron charge or an opposite charge of the same value. For example, a proton has a positive elementary charge; the electron a negative elementary charge; the neutron a zero charge.

● **nuclear charge.** The electric charge of a nucleus. Since the nucleus is composed of positively charged protons and of neutrons with a zero charge, the nuclear charge is due to the electric charge of the protons. By taking the elementary proton charge as unity, it can be expressed by the number of protons in the nucleus; this is called the **atomic number** (qv).

● **radioactive charge eliminator,** a device used to eliminate electric charges which accumulate on objects subjected to friction. A slight deposit of radioactive substance induces ionisation of the air. Ions formed in this way enable the electric charges to flow away. This method is used to get rid of charge accumulation by air friction on aeroplanes, fuel-transporting tank trucks or in the textile trade (fibre friction, etc).

chemistry, radiation, the chemistry of reactions induced by ionising radiation, eg polymerisation reactions, peroxidation, etc.

chirality, term used to characterise the orientation of the intrinsic spin of a particle with respect to its momentum. The two basic states of chirality correspond to left- and right-handed screw motion.

chronotron, an apparatus which is used to measure very short intervals of time.—Standard valves do not function below a few tens of billionths of a second. A process for measuring very short periods of time consists in making an electric pulse correspond to each of the two events whose interval it is desired to measure. Both these pulses are sent to the end of a transmission line. At a certain point along this line the two events meet one on top of the other. An electric circuit detects this superposition and enables the point to be located. The time interval to be measured is deducted from the position of the superposition point of the electric pulses.

cleveite, an ore which contains uranium and is to be found in Norway and in the USA.

cobalt, a metallic element with atomic number 27; atomic mass 59. The artificial isotope, atomic mass 60, is used in medicine for the treatment of cancer. The apparatus, which is called a *cobalt bomb*, consists of a radioactive source of cobalt 60, surrounded by a shield and provided with a collimating system. (See **collimator.**) In this way, the radiation emitted is concentrated in a specific direction. Radiation remains steadily directed on to the region to be treated, while the source may rotate around the patient. In this way, one avoids excessive **irradiation** (qv) of parts of the body other than that which requires treatment.

COCKCROFT, Sir John Douglas (1897–) English physicist.—With E. T. S. Walton he was the first research worker to make a study of atomic transmutations by means of artificially accelerated particles. In 1951, with Walton, he received the Nobel Price for Physics.

● **Cockcroft-Walton accelerator,** an accelerator in which the voltage source is of the type invented by these two researchers. (See **accelerator.**)

coincidence, simultaneous production of two or more events.

● **accidental coincidence.** This is a coincidence produced by accident and which has no connection with selected phenomena.

● **coincidence circuit,** an electronic circuit which makes it possible to detect the simultaneity of two or more events. (Coincidence is called respectively, double, triple, etc.) Each event is associated with an electric pulse provided by a detection device. The coincidence circuit only provides an electric pulse if the events considered are produced simultaneously.

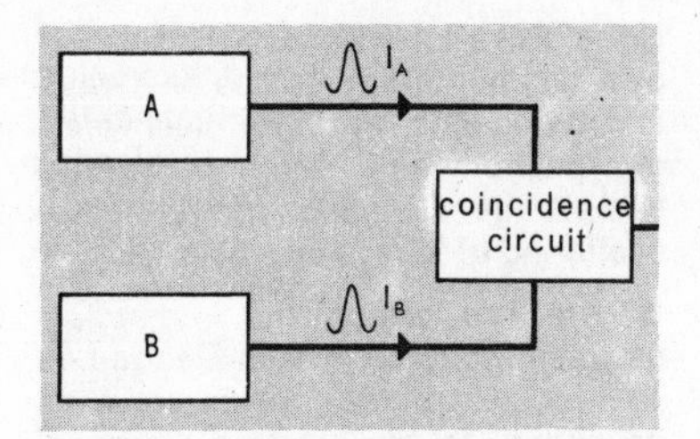

The presence of event A or B (for instance the passing of a particle into a counter) may be shown by an electric signal I_A or I_B. A coincidence circuit releases signal I when A and B events overlap in time. An anti-coincidence circuit emits a signal when A and B events do not overlap.

Coincidence circuits made it possible to release Wilson chambers on very special events. If one wishes to study the nuclear interactions of cosmic particles, the circuit will release the chamber when the pulse provided by the counter placed above the chamber, which indicates the arrival of a particle, coincides with 1, 2 or more counters placed beneath the chamber indicating that 1, 2 or more particles have been produced by nuclear interactions inside the chamber.

● **delayed coincidence.** Instead of requiring simultaneity of two events, the coincidence circuit may require that a certain interval of time shall pass between two events. The most frequent use of this technique is for the separation of particles of differing masses in a beam produced by an accelerator. The particles, having passed through magnets, have a selected momentum, but in this case their velocity is greater the lighter the particles. By fixing, in the coincidence circuit, a time interval which corresponds to the length at whose ends the counters are placed, particles are selected with a predetermined mass. Delayed coincidences are also used in the study of disintegration.

collimator, an apparatus usually consisting of a heavy material (concrete, iron, lead), intended to limit the size of a beam of particles. The collimator absorbs particles found outside a chosen area, as well as those which deviate too widely from the axis of the beam. It frequently has the form of a hollow cylinder.

collision, the impact of two particles, two nuclei, two atoms, two molecules. —More generally speaking, it is the interaction of any two of these microscopic objects, during which either some energy is transferred from one to the other or only the initial directions of the particles are altered. This interaction may be electromagnetic, nuclear, or weak. Collision is termed **elastic** (qv) when objects entering reaction retain their natural state. The only quantities altered by impact in this case are the speed and direction of the two objects. It can then be said that it is an elastic scattering. Collision is called **inelastic** (qv) if part of the energy is transformed into radiation (a photon, for example), or into matter (emission of particles formed by the impact). Collision is also inelastic if the nature of one or both of the objects is modified. For instance, the nucleus of an atom may be raised to an excited state in which it is heavier. In this case, the difference in mass is borrowed from the energy of the incident particle, according to the law of equivalence of mass with energy. Collisions play a very important part in microphysics. Their study is often the only way of knowing what are the interactions between particles.

combustion in a fission reactor, a reaction in which fuel undergoes **fission** (qv), giving off heat. When a certain proportion of fissile nuclei have been consumed, the fuel is exhausted and the reactor is recharged.

commutation. Two processes commute if the result of performing them in one order is identical with that of performing them in the reverse order. Shooting at oneself and putting on a bullet-proof waistcoat are processes unlikely to commute. The physical impossibility of simultaneously defining the position and momentum of a microparticle is mathematically expressed by representing the position and its corresponding momentum by non-commuting operators.

component, one of the parts of cosmic radiation which consists of two parts:

1) *The hard component* penetrates matter. A thickness of 10 cm of lead is selected to define this criterion. The hard component consists principally of mu leptons, which undergo few reactions in matter; protons, electrons and pions of high energy can also pass through a piece of lead 10 cm thick.

2) *The soft component* is stopped by the same thickness of lead. It contains all the low-energy particles and more generally, particles with strong interactions (also called *nuclear interactions*) which undergo numerous interactions in matter.

compound nucleus, see **nucleus.**

COMPTON, Arthur Holly (1892–) American physicist. In 1927, with C. T. R. Wilson, he received the Nobel Prize for Physics. To him we owe very important studies on X-rays and on cosmic rays. He discovered the phenomenon which bears his name: the *Compton effect*, elastic scattering of X-rays by electrons.

• Compton effect, the interaction between a photon and an electron.— The incident photon yields some of its energy to the electron which is assumed to be free. The electron is therefore set in motion, whereas the photon, having lost energy, has its frequency decreased. The photon and the electron emerge from the interaction with certain angles relative to the direction of the incident photon. Klein and Nishina calculated this effect within the framework of quantum mechanics. Their calculations agree admirably with the experiment.

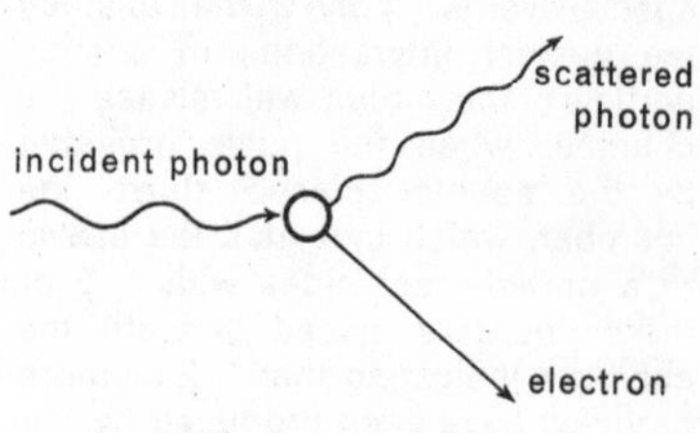

The Compton effect

• Compton wavelength, a length determined by the mass of a particle, varying in inverse ratio to the mass.— The Compton wavelength of an electron is 2.4 billionths of a millimetre. That of a proton is 1.3 thousandths of a billionth of a millimetre.

conservation, laws of. A certain number of basic physical laws arise from the conservation, over a lapse of time, of the measurable quantities of an isolated system. The amount of electric charges remains constant in an isolated system whatever the internal phenomena which may be produced in it. In the same way, total energy (the energy equivalent of the total mass) remains constant for an isolated system. The same applies to momentum. A conservation law is another way of saying that physical laws remain the same when a system undergoes certain transformations of its co-ordinates of space, time, etc. For instance, the fact that physical laws are unaltered by a simple movement of translation, enables the conservation of linear momentum to be deduced. If a system remains unaltered by rotation, the conservation of angular momentum follows. Conservation laws enable a large number of experimental facts, provided by nature, to be co-ordinated.

constant, Fermi, see **Fermi.**

contamination, state in which a substance finds itself which contains a certain proportion of an undesirable radioactive body. || State in which a radioactive substance has reached a zone in which its presence may be harmful to persons or to the equipment.—Rupture of the metallic envelope on a fuel rod induces *contamination of the reactor*. A fuel leak in the cooling circuit of a reactor contaminates this circuit.

control, an action which enables characteristic quantities of an installation to be given a fixed value in advance.—In a reactor, the most important control is that of the reactivity, which determines its divergence. It can be achieved by varying the amount of neutron absorbers or the geometrical arrangement of fuel rods in the reactor. (See ● **control rod.**)

conversion, internal, a phenomenon in which an atom whose nucleus is excited emits an electron. The nucleus of an atom may be raised to an excited state of higher energy, for example by a gamma ray. This energy may be transferred directly from the nucleus to an atomic electron. One part of it is used to eject the electron attached to the atom, the other, to give kinetic energy to the electron. Therefore, an internal conversion electron is expelled from the atom with a definite speed. The phenomenon of internal conversion is produced over the various atomic shells K, L, . . . with different percentages. On the other hand, the excited nucleus can always de-excite itself by re-emitting a gamma ray. The *internal conversion coefficient of the K shell* is the name for the ratio of de-excitation by emission of a K shell electron to de-excitation by emission of a gamma ray. A coefficient of internal conversion is defined in the same way for the other shells L, M, etc. The *internal conversion ratio K/L* is the name given to the ratio of the number of electrons emitted by the K shell to the number of electrons emitted by the L shell. The internal conversion is followed by a rearrangement of atomic structure, from which results an emission of X-rays or Auger electrons, the place left vacant by the internal conversion electron being taken by an electron from another shell.

converter, a reactor which transforms fertile material, which cannot undergo fission, into fissile material.—In general, a reactor consumes uranium 235, which is fissile, and also contains uranium 238, which is non-fissile. Uranium 238 is transformed into plutonium 239 by neutron ab-

The star-shaped core of the Dounreay reactor (Photo *l'Energie nucléaire)*

sorption. Plutonium 239 is fissile and may be used as a fuel in another reactor.

core, the part of the reactor wnich contains the nuclear fuel. In a *heterogeneous reactor* it is the area containing rods of fissile matter. In a *homogeneous reactor*, it is the place in which both fissile matter and, at the same time, the moderator appear. The core does not contain fuel found outside the active zone, if the fuel itself circulates in the heat exchanger.

corpuscular, that which presents itself in the form of particles of matter rather than in the form of waves.

correlation, angular. In a nuclear reaction the particles produced are ejected in certain directions with respect to that of the incident particle. The angles which measure these directions may have some relation among each other or with other quantities; the direction of spin, for example. It is then said that there is *angular correlation*. From the study of correlation, certain properties of the interaction may be deduced.

cosmic abundance, see **abundance, cosmic.**

cosmic rays, see **abundance, cosmic.**

cosmotron, a proton accelerator with an energy of 3 GeV at Brookhaven (USA).—It was so called because it was one of the first accelerators to provide particles with an energy comparable to that of cosmic rays. Its beam gives 200 billion accelerated protons every three seconds.

COULOMB, Charles Auguste de (1736–1806) French electrophysicist and mathematician who invented the torsion balance for measuring the force of electric and magnetic attraction. The law called *Coulomb's law* is mathematically similar to Newton's law of gravitation.

● **Coulombian,** that which refers to the electrostatic forces operating between two electric charges. These forces follow *Coulomb's law.* The positively charged nucleus exercises a coulomb attraction on negatively charged electrons.

counter, an apparatus able to detect the passage of an ionising particle through it.—The many types of counters correspond to different requirements. Generally speaking, they provide an electric pulse used in electronic circuits to measure the energy, time of passing and the speed or mass of the particle.

The 3 GeV cosmotron at Brookhaven Laboratory (USA) (Photo USIS)

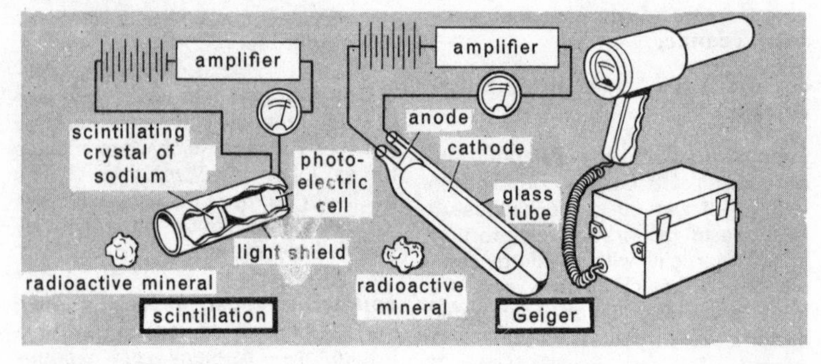

Scintillation counter and Geiger counter

● **Cerenkov counter.** This counter is based on the Cerenkov effect. When a particle passes through a body at a speed greater than that of light within that body, luminous radiation is produced. This phenomenon offers a certain analogy with the shock wave produced by bodies being displaced at a speed higher than the speed of sound in the air, the sound vibrations being analogous with electromagnetic vibrations (light). This phenomenon may be observed in glass, water or in compressed gases, and in general in transparent and refractive bodies. The luminous radiation is emitted on a well defined cone centred on the path of the particle. The opening angle of this cone is correlated with the speed of the particle and the refraction index of the medium through which it passes. The light emitted is detected by a photomultiplier tube which delivers an electric pulse. In consequence, the main use of the Cerenkov counter resides in the measurement of the velocity of particles. Placed in a beam of particles of different natures yet having the same momentum, it makes it possible to sort the particles according to their mass. It gives an electronic signal which releases the rest of the detection apparatus only if the particle has the required mass.

● **crystal counter,** a detecting apparatus based on the following principle: some insulating substances become electric conductors when an ionising particle or a photon passes through them (eg the diamond, silver chloride). These counters require a very low working temperature (liquid air) and are little used.

● **efficiency of a counter.** For a counter intended to detect certain types of radiation, efficiency is the fraction of the radiation which has actually passed the counter which is detected.

● **Geiger-Müller counter** or **proportional counter,** a detector of structure similar to the ● **ionisation chamber** (qv); a cylindrical cathode on the axis of which a threadlike anode is placed. The charged particle passing through the counter induces ionisation in it. Negatively charged electrons and positively charged ions are attracted respectively to the anode

Core of the homogeneous reactor Siloé at Grenoble. The Cerenkov effect may be seen at the bottom of the vat. (Photo CEA)

and the cathode, between which an electric voltage is established. If the voltage is high enough, the electrons are accelerated by this voltage and of themselves induce a secondary ionisation. In a certain range of voltage, the number of ions formed in this fashion is proportional to the number of ions released by the initial particle. The electric pulse is proportional to the ionisation induced by the particle; in this case the counter is called a *proportional counter*. If the electric voltage is even higher, the number of ions formed increases further because of two phenomena:

Detecting natural radioactivity with a Geiger counter (Photo P. Jahan CEA)

1) By recombining with the electrons the ions emit photons which, in turn, are capable of ionising gas and also of tearing the electrons from the cathode by photo-electric effect.
2) Ions, accelerated by the electric field are able, on reaching the cathode, to knock out other ions from it. This multiplicative effect is limited by the electric charges produced (space charge) which cancel the electric field produced by the electrodes. The electric current does not in this case depend on the initial particle, but only on the characteristics of the apparatus. This is called a Geiger-Müller counter. To reduce the phenomena which restrict the current, the counter is sometimes provided with a grid which surrounds the anode and is raised to a negative voltage, so as to reduce the effect of the space charge. The counter is called self-quenching if the cutting off of the electric discharge is effected within the counter itself, independently of the outside electric circuit. The addition of certain gases in the counter enables this quenching to be realised. A Geiger-Müller counter can detect several thousand particles per second. It has enabled many studies to be carried out in the fields of radioactivity and cosmic radiation. It is also used for prospecting for uranium ores, and for the detection of radioactivity by the protection services.

● **scintillation counter,** a detection apparatus consisting of a scintillator and a photomultiplier.—The scintillator is a body capable of emitting light when an ionising element passes through it. The light emitted is detected by a photomultiplier which provides an electric pulse. It is necessary for the scintillator to be a transparent body, so that the light emitted may reach the photomultiplier. This is the case with certain organic compounds such as naphthalene, anthracene and sodium iodide. Zinc sulphide, an almost opaque scintillator, may only be used in small thicknesses. One of the great advantages of the scintillating counter is the precise measurement of time. There are only a few billionths of a second between the passing of the electric particle and the electric signal. This type of counter is much used with fairly high-energy particles.

● **spark counter,** a detection apparatus consisting of electrodes which are subjected to electric voltage.—The passage of a particle produces the ionisation phenomenon in gas. (See the **Geiger-Müller counter.**) The phenomenon of electric discharge, which is controlled in the Geiger counter, is in this counter carried, on the contrary, up to the break-down with a spark, whence its name. Development of this technique has led to a more perfected apparatus—the ● **spark chamber** (qv).

coupling, a term which expresses the possibility of an exchange of energy between two physical systems. The neutron and the proton have a nuclear coupling; the electron and the proton, an electromagnetic coupling.

● **coupling-constant,** a quantity appearing as a factor in the interaction energy of a physical system. It characterises the intensity with which two particles interact.—For particles with nuclear interactions, protons and neutrons in the nucleus for example, its size is of the order of one unit. The coupling constant of particles with *electromagnetic interactions*—electrically charged particles—is 137 times lower. That of particles having *weak interactions*—beta disintegration for example—is of the order of one ten thousandth of a billionth. The constant corresponding to gravitation is still lower and it is expressed by a fraction, the numerator of which has a value of two and the denominator a value of one followed by 39 zeros. The values of these constants establish the relative order of strength of the four kinds of interactions at present known. (See ● **Fermi constant.**)

creation, see **pair creation.**

critical, used to describe a substance that has reached a state in which chain reaction becomes possible.—In fissile material, a neutron may induce the fission of a nucleus, which splits up into fission fragments, ie lighter nuclei and neutrons. The nucleus undergoing fission releases a certain number of neutrons. This number depends upon the method of fission: 2.5 on average for uranium 235 and 3 for plutonium 239. Each of the released neutrons may, in turn, induce the fission of another nucleus of fissile material, and chain reaction develops. However, not all the neutrons released are usable; some are absorbed into matter, while others escape outside the fissile material. The number of usable neutrons is therefore inferior to the number emitted by fission. When the number of those produced by fission and used again to produce a second fission is on average one per fission, a chain reaction is just maintained. If this number should be inferior to one, chain reaction gradually dies out. If the number is more than one, chain reaction diverges. It is said that a material satisfies the critical state when its number is equal to one. To this critical condition corresponds a mass of fissile material called *critical mass*. However, the critical mass depends on the one hand on the concentration of fissile material, on the other on the nature and placing of non-fissile materials inside a reactor. The critical mass is lower the greater the concentration of fissile material. In the case of a bomb in which fissile material is practically pure—uranium 235 or plutonium 239—the critical mass amounts to a few kilos. In a reactor using natural uranium, which is a mixture of fissile uranium 235 and non-fissile uranium 238, including a moderator and cooling circuits, the critical mass amounts to several tons.

● **critical dimensions,** dimensions at which a mass of fissile material may begin to undergo chain reaction.

CROOKES, Sir William (1832–1910) English chemist and physicist. Nobel Prize for Chemistry 1907. He discovered thallium, invented the electronic tubes which bear his name and demonstrated the electrified character of the particles of which cathode rays are composed.

cross-section, a concept which makes it possible to relate the number of reactions produced by particles when passing through matter to the number of particles and to the thickness of the matter traversed.—When a particle passes through matter, it has some chance of reacting with the nuclei of the atoms. The cross-section may be imagined as a surface associated with each of the nuclei, these being distant from one another, each particle has a certain chance of passing between the associated surfaces without inducing a reaction as well as through the associated surface, then inducing a reaction. When the matter is not very thick, the number of reactions is proportional to the number of nuclei, to the cross-section and to the number of incident particles as well. When the matter is thick, the associated surfaces overlap each other on the path of the particle so that the number of reactions does not change as fast as the number of nuclei but always remains proportional to the number of incident particles.

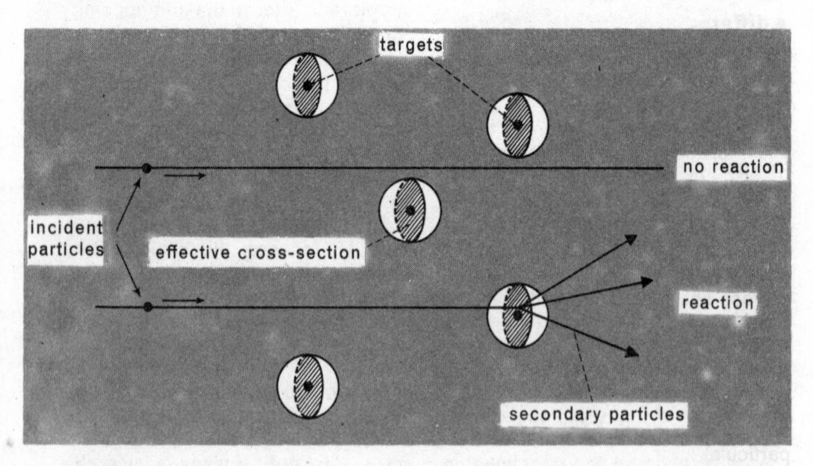

The cross-section is represented by the area of the circle which is cross-hatched. A reaction may be imagined to occur whenever the incident particle passes through this section.

The idea of *cross-section* is also valid for reactions which are produced on the electrons of the atom. The cross-section obviously depends on the kind of particles present and on the energy of the incident particle. Cross-sections which are very small are expressed in **barns** (qv), the surface of a square of

0.000000000001 cm

side length or again in millibarns (thousandths of a barn).

● **absorption cross-section,** a cross-section which corresponds to the absorption phenomenon, in which the nature of secondary particles is not identical with that of primary particles.

● **activation cross-section,** a cross-section referring to the formation of a radioactive nucleus in a nuclear reaction.

● **capture cross-section,** a cross-section for the capture of an incident particle by the target particle.

● **differential cross-section,** a cross-section measured per unit of solid angle around a given direction for secondary particles having directions close to that given. The differential cross-section is said to be *forward* for particles emitted in the same direction as the incident particle; it is said to be *backward* for those emitted in the opposite direction.

● **elastic scattering cross-section,** a cross-section referring to the process in which the particles emitted are of the same nature as the primary particles present.

● **partial cross-section,** a cross-section referring to a process of one particular kind.

● **total cross-section,** a cross-section referring to all processes arising in a given reaction. It is the total of all ● **partial cross-sections** (qv).

crystal counter, see **counter.**

curides, a series of elements contained between curium (atomic number 96) and mendelevium (atomic number 101) belonging to the Actinide family.

CURIE, Marie (1867–1934) born Sklodowska, married to Pierre Curie. A French physicist of Polish extraction. In 1903 she shared the Nobel Prize for Physics with her husband and H. Becquerel, and received the Nobel Prize for Chemistry in 1911. With her husband, she discovered polonium and radium. She demonstrated the radioactivity of thorium at the same time as the German physicist Schmidt. She isolated pure radium with Debierne. *See illustration p. 68.*

CURIE, Pierre (1859–1906) French physicist. With his brother, he discovered piezo-electricity and studied the relations between temperature and the magnetic properties of bodies. Upon the discovery of radioactivity by H. Becquerel, he and his wife Marie concentrated on the study of pitchblende radiations. Together they succeeded in isolating polonium and radium. With his wife and H. Becquerel, he received the Nobel Prize for Physics in 1903.

curie, a radioactive unit which has been defined as the quantity of a radioactive body in which the number of disintegrations is 37 billion per second.—This unit was originally chosen to represent the radioactivity of the radon in equilibrium with 1 g of radium. One curie represents a very high degree of radioactivity. Such concentrated sources are rare,

Pierre and Marie Curie

and the millicurie is generally used. 1 g of natural uranium has a radioactivity of approximately 1 millicurie.

curium, an artificial element with the atomic number 96.—It was discovered in 1944 by Seaborg, James and Ghiorso by bombarding plutonium 239 with alpha particles. The curium isotope 242 which they produced (96 protons, 146 neutrons) possesses an alpha radioactivity. Other curium isotopes have also been discovered.

cycle, thermonuclear, a very high temperature of several million degrees is to be found on the Sun and stars. Spectroscopic measurements have established that light nuclei are to be found there in greater quantity on average than on Earth. Thermonuclear reactions take place on the Sun and stars, which give off tremendous energy. In these thermonuclear reactions the light nuclei fuse together to produce heavier nuclei. Protons and neutrons in very light nuclei (deuterium, tritium) are not closely bound, while the proton of light hydrogen is completely free. The heavier nuclei are the most closely bound and when light nuclei fuse together to produce heavier nuclei, there is a corresponding release of the energy binding the heavy nuclei. The very high temperatures of the stars may be explained by the liberation of energy produced in these reactions. The existence of two kinds of cycle has been assumed to explain this emission of heat. These are the *carbon cycle* put forward by the physicist Bethe and the *proton-proton cycle*. In both these cycles, the lightest nuclei, the hydrogen ones, disappear in the reactions, while heavier nuclei, helium ones, appear.

● **carbon cycle,** a thermonuclear cycle whose different phases are as follows:

carbon 12 (6 protons, 6 neutrons) +hydrogen (1 proton) *gives* nitrogen 13
(7 protons, 6 neutrons), by thermonuclear reaction;
nitrogen 13 (7 protons, 6 neutrons) *gives* carbon 13 (6 protons, 7 neutrons)
+positive electron+neutrino, by beta radioactivity
carbon 13 (6 protons, 7 neutrons) +hydrogen (1 proton) *gives* nitrogen 14
(7 protons, 7 neutrons), by thermonuclear reaction;
nitrogen 14 (7 protons, 7 neutrons) +hydrogen (1 proton) *gives* oxygen 15 (8 protons, 7 neutrons), by thermonuclear reaction;
oxygen 15 (8 protons, 7 neutrons) *gives* nitrogen 15 (7 protons, 8 neutrons)
+positive electron+neutrino, by beta radioactivity;
nitrogen 15 (7 protons, 8 neutrons) +hydrogen (1 proton) *gives*
carbon 12 (6 protons, 6 neutrons) +helium 4 (2 protons, 2 neutrons), by nuclear reaction.

It is evident that, for the entire cycle, a carbon nucleus and four hydrogen nuclei are used, while a helium nucleus is produced. Carbon, therefore, is not consumed, while helium is obtained. The three thermonuclear reactions which come into play give out energy in the form of gamma rays and of the speeds of the products of the reaction.

● **proton-proton cycle,** a thermonuclear cycle the phases of which are the following:
hydrogen (1 proton)+hydrogen (1 proton)
gives deuterium (1 proton, 1 neutron) +positive electron+neutrino;
deuterium (1 proton, 1 neutron)

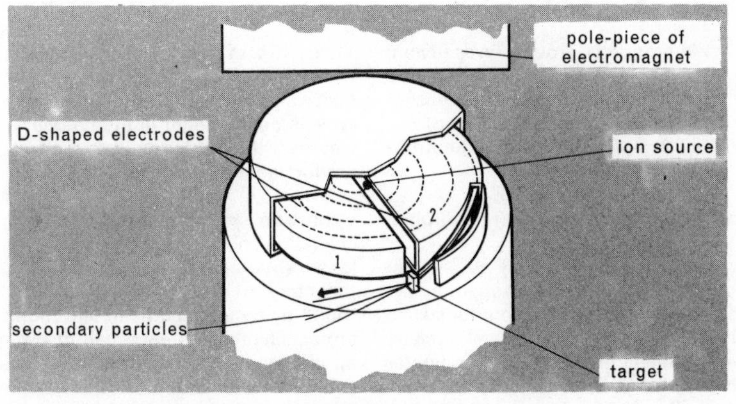

Diagram of a cyclotron

The cyclotron at the Centre for Nuclear Research at Saclay (Photo J.-P. Sudre-CEA)

+hydrogen (1 proton) *gives* helium 3
(2 protons, 1 neutron)+neutrino;
helium 3 (2 protons, 1 neutron)
+helium 3 (2 protons, 1 neutron) *gives* helium 4
(2 protons, 2 neutrons)
+hydrogen (1 proton)+hydrogen (1 proton).

An entire cycle produces one helium nucleus, while six hydrogen nuclei are absorbed and two produced, so that in all one heavier helium nucleus is obtained in place of four lighter hydrogen nuclei. These reactions give off energy as in the carbon cycle. These two cycles appear to play an important part in the Sun. It is generally thought that the *carbon cycle* is predominant in the hot stars, whereas the *proton-proton cycle* is predominant in the cold stars.

cyclotron, an apparatus for the acceleration of protons and positive ions. (See **accelerators.**) In it the trajectory of the particles is bent round by a magnetic field, and these are accelerated on each half-turn by an electric field maintained by a high voltage electric source. The cyclotron accelerates protons up to an energy of 25 million electronvolts. The energy is doubled, tripled, etc . . . when the electric charge of the ions is two, three, etc . . . times the charge of the protons. It is used in the study of nuclear reactions produced by accelerated particles. *See also diagram on p. 69.*

D

D, the symbol for **deuterium** (qv).

DALTON, John (1766–1844) English chemist whose physical researches included work on mixed gases, the force of steam and the expansion of gases by heat. He gave grounds for the hypothesis of atoms.

danger coefficient. The reactivity of a reactor is a number connected with the multiplication of neutrons produced by chain reaction.—The *danger coefficient* is the change in reactivity produced by a body introduced into the reactor. This change may be due, for example, to neutron absorption.

dating, measuring the **age** (qv) of a material.—The most commonly used method of determining the age of the remains of living organisms is that of dating by means of carbon 14. This is an artificial carbon isotope. It is produced in the Earth's atmosphere, which consists of oxygen and nitrogen, by neutrons of cosmic radiation according to the reactions:

nitrogen 14 (7 protons, 7 neutrons) +neutron *gives* carbon 14 (6 protons, 8 neutrons)+hydrogen (1 proton)

Carbon 14 possesses a beta radioactivity:

carbon 14 (6 protons, 8 neutrons) *gives* nitrogen 14 (7 protons, 7 neutrons) +negative electron+neutrino,

with an average life time of 5670 years. Living organisms absorb carbon in the shape of carbonic gas, and, in consequence, there exists in every organism a certain ratio of carbon 14 to ordinary carbon 12. Carbon 14 ceases to be absorbed at the moment the organism dies, while the quantity which was present in the organism slowly disintegrates and its proportion progressively decreases, which makes it possible to determine the time that has elapsed since the death of the organism. This method is especially effective for measuring ages of a few thousand, or some tens of thousands of years.

DAVISSON, Clinton Joseph (1881-1958) American physicist. With L. H. Germer, he confirmed the wave mechanics of de Broglie by discovering the phenomenon of interference in nickel crystals irradiated by electrons. He received the Nobel Prize for Physics in 1937, with the English physicist G. P. Thomson.

DEBIERNE, André Louis (1874–1940) French chemist. He isolated radium in the metallic state with Marie Curie; discovered actinium and studied the radiations of radioactive bodies.

DE BROGLIE, Louis (1892–) French physicist. In 1924 he invented wave mechanics, proposing to associate a wave with each particle. In 1929, he was awarded the Nobel Prize for Physics.

●**de Broglie wavelength.** De Broglie has advanced the hypothesis that a wave may be associated with a particle of matter in motion. (See **wave-particle duality.**) Quantum mechanics, which enables the behaviour of microscopic systems to be

Louis de Broglie

foreseen, has been constructed starting from this hypothesis. The de Broglie wavelength associated with a particle in motion is smaller the higher the mass and velocity of the particle.

decay, spontaneous **disintegration** (qv).

● **alpha decay,** a spontaneous disintegration in which a nucleus composed of protons and neutrons, emits an alpha particle consisting of two protons and two neutrons; these four particles, being linked, form a helium nucleus. The residual nucleus contains two neutrons and two protons less than the original nucleus. The first measurement of the mass of alpha particles was made by Rutherford in 1903, by deflecting them in electric and magnetic fields. In 1909 Rutherford was able to collect a sufficiently large number of alpha particles to analyse them spectroscopically and thereby demonstrate their identity with helium nuclei. The emission of nucleons (neutrons and protons) take place preferably in the shape of an alpha particle principally because alpha particles are particularly stable conglomerates of nucleons. Some theories even assume their existence already formed inside the nucleus. The mass of the alpha particle is smaller than the sum total of the mass of its components, the difference being equal to the energy linking the four nucleons. In alpha disintegration, the mass emitted is minimal by comparison with the number of nucleons, so that a very great deal of energy is released. Other stable, heavier, formations could be emitted, but it can be shown that they would be extremely rare. The energy possessed by the alpha particles amounts to some million electronvolts and they are able to travel some centimetres through air before being slowed down and stopped. The theory of alpha emission was developed by Gamow in 1928 and enables the rate of alpha emission to be predicted, as a function of the size of the nucleus. This theory has been used mainly to determine nuclear radii from experimentally measured periods. Rosenblum has observed that the energy of alpha particles is not always the same. The residual nucleus, which remains after the original nucleus has expelled the alpha, may be formed in an excited state; the energy necessary for this is taken from the alpha. The nucleus returns to a stable condition, its ground state, by emitting a gamma ray. This phenomenon is called the *fine structure* of alpha emission. Many elements among those of high atomic mass, are alpha active, such as the uranium isotopes contained in the natural mixture.

● **beta decay,** a spontaneous disintegration in which a nucleus emits a beta particle, the name given to the electron in this phenomenon. A neutrino is also emitted. Its presence is very difficult to detect but it is required to explain beta disintegration. The electron carries an electric charge, either positive or negative. The neutrino carries no electric charge. The opposite process to beta decay is the capture of an electron of the atom by the nucleus (see **capture**). Unlike alpha particles, beta particles emitted may take all the possible energies contained between two boundaries. In this case there are three particles present at the end of the disintegration: the residual nucleus, the electron and the neutrino. Energy is distributed in variable quantities between these three particles; on the other hand, the energy can take only a fixed amount for each of the two particles in the event of two only being present after the disintegration. The residual nucleus has lost a positive charge in the event of the emission of a positive electron; its atomic number has decreased by one unit, its mass number remains unchanged. In the event of the emission of a negative electron, its atomic number increases by one unit, its mass number remaining unaltered. To study the energy of electrons emitted in beta radioactive elements, a beta spectrometer is used. In this the electrons are deflected by a magnetic field, more sharply the lower their velocity. The maximal energy which an electron may attain varies with radioactive elements from some tens of thousand electronvolts to several million electronvolts. A theory of beta decay was advanced by Fermi in 1934, reviving the neutrino hypothesis proposed by Pauli. This theory, which has since been greatly developed, enables decay periods to be calculated, as well as the form of the spectrum, ie the proportion of electrons emitted with a given energy, since this is variable in beta disintegration. Neutrons undergo beta decay: one neutron disintegrates into proton, electron and neutrino with a mean life of about 13 minutes. This disintegration may be observed when free neutrons are produced by nuclear reactors or accelerators. On the other hand, neutrons contained in a nucleus cannot decay spontaneously because their mass is decreased by the energy binding them to the nucleus, so that the mass of the proton augmented by that of the electron is higher than the mass of a bound neutron, contrary to the case of a free neutron. This explains the fact that the nuclei are stable.

● **gamma decay,** or better **gamma emission.** An excited nucleus may lose its excitation energy by emitting a gamma ray or a photon. The photon possesses an electromagnetic nature, like visible light, but with a much higher energy. (Although this phenomenon consists in the division of an initial particle into two final particles, the expression *gamma disintegration* is little used.) An excited nucleus may also communicate its excitation energy to one of the electrons of the atom to which it belongs. In this case the electron is emitted with a speed corresponding to the difference: the excitation energy less the binding energy of the electron in the atom. This phenomenon is called *internal conversion*. It should be observed that an excited nucleus may also emit a beta or an alpha ray. In gamma radiation, the nucleus takes a small fraction of the energy in recoiling. An excited nucleus has generally a very short mean life, about a millionth of a millionth of a second. The nucleus is generally raised to an excited state by nuclear reaction, and it is difficult to make a distinction between instantaneous emission of a gamma ray in nuclear reaction and the emission of a gamma ray by an excited nucleus when the latter has a short mean lifetime. The difference is clearer when the excited nucleus has a long lifetime. In some cases this may reach several years. The excited nucleus and the nucleus in its fundamental state are called **isomers** (qv) and the gamma emission is called *isomeric transition*. The energy of gamma rays may be measured by several methods: diffraction of the gamma by crystals; measurement of the energy of an electron pair formed by the materialisation of a gamma; scintillation counters, etc.

● **radioactive decay.** In a radioactive body the number of disintegrations per second at a given moment is proportional to the number of nuclei not yet disintegrated at that moment. As a result of this property, it can be shown that the number of radioactive nuclei is an exponential function of time. Assuming there were originally 1000 nuclei of a radioactive body whose half-life was one hour, the number of radioactive nuclei remaining after an hour would be 500; half of the radioactive nuclei would have disintegrated in a time equal to that period. By the end of two hours, the number remaining would be 250; at the end of the third hour 125, etc. Strictly speaking, there would be slight fluctuations around these figures, fluctuations which would be the more negligible the greater the number of nuclei under consideration. In theory, a radioactive body remains so indefinitely. However, by the end of several half-lives the proportion of radioactive nuclei has been considerably reduced. At the end of three half-lives radioactivity may be divided by 8; after seven half-lives by 128, and by 1024 at the end of ten half-lives, and so on.

decay product, a particle produced in the disintegration of a nucleus or of an unstable particle.
In the alpha disintegration:
radium 226 (88 protons, 138 neutrons)
gives alpha (2 protons, 2 neutrons) +radon 222 (86 protons, 136 neutrons).
The alpha particle and radon 222 are called *decay products*.
In the neutron disintegration:
neutron *gives* proton+electron +neutrino.
The proton, the electron and the neutrino are called *decay products*.

decontamination, elimination of radioactive elements from material which is required in a pure state (eg withdrawal of radioactive waste from an exhausted uranium rod). ‖ Elimination of radioactive products on clothing, instruments or personnel, etc. Contamination due to dust or traces of radioactive bodies is detected on material and on personnel by counters at the very place where it exists, such as on hands or shoes. The most efficient method of decontamination therefore, is by washing in plenty of water to which organic

or mineral solvents have been added. In the case of air contamination, circulation of filtered air enables radioactive dust to be eliminated. The *decontamination factor* is the ratio of final radioactivity to intial radioactivity in a decontamination process.

dee, letter D. Sometimes used to indicate the accelerating electrodes of a cyclotron because they are shaped like a D.

defect, mass, see ● **mass defect.**

deflection, an action to which a beam or particle is subjected in a deflector. ‖ A change of direction in the trajectory of a particle.

deflector, a device which changes the path of a beam of particles.— This apparatus is used, for example, to direct the beam of a Van de Graaff

(top) *Decontamination of the interior of a basin for stockpiling radioactive effluents.* (Photo CEA) (bottom) *Moving an irradiated metal block for decontamination* (Photo J.-P. Sudre-CEA)

accelerator on to a chosen area. There are several different types.

● **electrostatic deflector.** In this device forces due to an electric field act on a charged particle. The deflective force is directed along the direction of the field when the particle is positive, and in the opposite direction when the particle is negative. The electric field, perpendicular to the trajectory of the particle, is formed by two conductor plates between which a high voltage is applied.

● **magnetic deflector.** In this device the properties of a magnetic field are used to bend the trajectories of charged particles. When a charged particle penetrates into a constant magnetic field perpendicular to its path, its trajectory is a circle. When the field is not directed in any special way, its trajectory is a helix. The magnetic field is usually formed by an electromagnet. These two kinds of deflection may be combined in the same apparatus.

degeneracy, expression used in quantum mechanics when a system possesses more than one state for the same energy.

● **Fermi degeneracy.** A fermion gas is said to be degenerate when the lower levels accessible to the fermions are fully occupied.

degradation of energy, the loss of energy to which a beam of particles or an isolated particle is subjected when passing through matter, by interaction with the atoms of the matter through which it has passed. ‖ Transformation of energy capable

A magnetic deflector (Photo CEA)

of producing work into energy useless for the production of work (eg, mechanical energy is degraded into heat by friction).

delta, δ, a Greek letter which stands for an electron ejected from an atom by a charged particle passing through matter.—The delta ray derives its name from the fact that the electron has a sinuous trajectory like the Greek letter δ, on account of the multiple scattering which it undergoes in matter. This phenomenon is produced more frequently the lighter and swifter the charged particle. It is therefore frequently met with if the incident particles are high-speed electrons. Delta rays are frequently to be observed in Wilson and bubble-chambers. Measurement of the angle made by the trajectory of the delta ray at its start with the trajectory of the incident particle, and measurement of the energy of the delta ray, enables the mass of the incident particle to be calculated whenever exact measurements are possible. This method is sometimes used in Wilson and bubble-chambers. The letter δ sometimes stands for a charged particle, whatever its nature, ejected by an incident particle (eg a proton may be ejected from a nucleus by an incident proton).

delta ray, an electron ejected from an atom by a charged particle in motion.

dematerialisation, see **annihilation.**

DEMOCRITUS (*c* 460 BC–*c* 370 BC) Greek philosopher. With his master, Leucippus, he was one of the first to describe matter as being composed of atoms or indivisible particles which are eternal and constant.

denaturant, a non-fissile isotope which may be added to a fissile element so as to render it useless in a nuclear weapon. Plutonium 239 is a fissile element with which bombs are made. Isotope 238, whose nucleus contains one neutron less than isotope 239, is non-fissile, but both isotopes have the same chemical properties. The addition of isotope 238 in sufficient quantity in the manufacture of a bomb may render it useless.

deposit, active, an assembly of disintegration products deposited on a surface, eg by radon, also called emanon 222, a radioactive gas of the uranium series. (The successive derivatives of the uranium series are alpha and beta radioactive.) An active deposit is also formed when a surface is exposed to actinon, known as emanon 219, a radioactive gas of the actinium series, or again when it is exposed to thoron, also known as emanon 220, a radioactive gas of the thorium series. In all three cases, the deposit possesses a high radioactivity of fairly brief duration, the mean life of the elements contained in the active deposit being short. ‖ In a wider sense, products of radioactive disintegration deposited on a surface by any kind of radioactive gas. ‖ A deposit of radioactive elements on a surface.

detailed balancing, very useful principle in quantum theory. It states that in a complex equilibrium situation the rate of any particular transition is equal to the rate of the reverse transition. Even if a cycle of the type A→B→C→A is involved, the rate of B→C is equal to that of C→B in the equilibrium situation.

detector, an apparatus which indicates the passage of a particle or of a flux of particles.—Certain types of detectors also enable measurements to be made on the flux of particles (intensity and energy, for instance), or on the particle (charge, mass, speed, for example). Electrically charged particles are detected by their electromagnetic effects on the matter through which they pass (ionisation, for instance). Neutral particles are detected by the reactions which they induce on the nuclei of the medium through which they pass, or else by observation of the charged particles produced in their disintegration. A list of the principal detection devices follows. Their theory and characteristics will be found at the corresponding word.

• **detectors of charged particles.** 1) *Electronic detection* by means of an electric signal: ionisation chambers, proportional counter, Geiger-Müller counter, scintillators, spark counter, crystal counter, Cerenkov counter. See **counter.**
2) *Visual detection* by means of the traces left by the particles: Wilson chamber, diffusion chamber, bubble-chamber, spark-chamber, photographic emulsion. See **chamber.**

• **detectors of neutrons,** boron detector, fission ionisation chamber, collision counter, artificial radioactivity (see **neutron**).

deuterium, an element possessing the simplest structure after hydrogen. —The deuterium atom is composed of a nucleus called deuteron which consists of a proton and a neutron, and of an electron. Its atomic mass is 2; it is a hydrogen isotope. It is found in natural hydrogen, extracted from water for instance, in 1 part in 6500. Gaseous at normal temperature, it only liquefies at 250° C below zero under atmospheric pressure. Deuterium molecules, composed of two deuterium atoms, or molecules composed of one hydrogen atom and one deuterium atom, lend themselves, on account of their simplicity, to many spectroscopic studies. Molecules excited by an external source present bands of radiation enabling the following phenomena to be observed:
1) interaction of the nuclei with an outer magnetic field, determination of the magnetic moment of the deuteron;
2) study of the intrinsic angular momentum of the molecule;
3) interactions between the rotation of the molecule and the magnetic moment of the nucleus.
Deuterium is also used as a target, for example in bubble-chambers, to study reactions on the neutron. The deuterium neutron is less bound than neutrons of other nuclei. Its binding energy in the ground state is 2.23 million electronvolts. The binding energy of a neutron in heavier nuclei is generally 8 million electronvolts. On the other hand, interaction at a heavier nucleus is usually complicated by the fact that products of reaction frequently react inside the nucleus before leaving it. Deuterium is present in heavy water, one molecule of heavy water containing two deuterium atoms in place of the two hydrogen atoms present in ordinary water.

deuteron, nucleus of the deuterium atom. It consists of one proton and one neutron bound by an energy of 2.23 million electronvolts.—This nucleus has been intensively studied because of the simplicity of its structure. Independently of its use as a target (see **deuterium**), it may also be used as a projectile. Projected on to a nucleus at moderate speed, it gives rise to the phenomenon of

stripping (qv) discovered by Oppenheimer and Phillips. When the deuteron approaches the nucleus, the electric field of the latter repels its electrically charged proton. There is fission of the deuteron, the neutron being absorbed into the nucleus, the proton being repelled. This interpretation enables one to understand the characteristics of interaction between a deuteron and a nucleus: cross-section, angular distribution, etc. The link between the two nucleons, neutron and proton of the deuterium nucleus, provides a simple field for the study of nuclear forces. The theory which assumes a central force, that is to say, one independent of direction, does not lead to satisfactory results, and it is necessary to bring more complex forces into play. These depend on the spin orientations, and on the relative angular momentum of the proton and neutron. This explains the electric quadrupole moment of the deuteron, which may be imagined, in a very approximate manner, as being due to the oval shape of the deuterium nucleus. The symbol of the deuteron is the letter d.

deuton, another name for the **deuteron** (qv).

diamond counter, a diamond used as a detector.—The impurities, contained in a very small quantity in the diamond, are rendered radioactive through bombardment. This process, proposed by Nahmias in 1936, has enabled a flux of low energy neutrons to be detected.

diffraction, a very small light source, called a point source, should give a sharp shadow of an object. In reality a little light may be observed in the interior of the shadow, which derives from the outer contour of the object. The diffracted light has undergone a deflection in the immediate vicinity of the object. It may also be said that the light is diffused by this edge. The term *diffraction* is, however, usually reserved for phenomena in which interferences are observed. These are periodic variations of luminous strength. It is also used for nuclear reactions which offer some analogy with the diffraction of light.

diffusion, molecular, a phenomenon by means of which two gaseous or liquid substances interpenetrate one another by reason of the thermal movement of the molecules.—It restricts the effectiveness of separation of isotopes. Calculation shows that the mixing of two gases is quicker the greater the density. Thus certain installations for the separation of isotopes are designed to function at low gas pressure, corresponding to a low density.

dineutron, a set of two neutrons which can exist in transient fashion and which are invoked to explain certain nuclear reactions.

dipole, an assembly of two poles. An *electric dipole* is an assembly of two opposite electric charges placed a short distance from each other. A *magnetic dipole* is a set of two opposite magnetic poles, placed a short distance from each other. A magnetic dipole is equivalent to a small loop of electric current. Fundamental particles possess the characteristics of a magnetic dipole, as does a small magnet. On the other hand, none appear to possess the characteristics of an electric dipole moment.

DIRAC, Paul (1902–) English physicist. A specialist in theoretical

Paul Dirac (Photo Mazenod)

physics, he was one of the creators of quantum mechanics. He invented relativistic quantum theory. He inferred the existence of antiparticles and clarified the notion of intrinsic spin. He also developed quantum statistical mechanics. (See ● **Fermi-Dirac statistics.**) He predicted the existence of the positive electron. He shared the Nobel Prize for Physics with Schrödinger in 1933.

● **Dirac electron,** an electron which obeys Dirac's equation.

● **Dirac equation,** an equation which describes the motion of an electron.—Dirac constructed it so as to respect the principles of relativity, and to give an account of the existence of *spin*, which is the intrinsic angular momentum of the electron. It enables the wave function of the electron to be calculated, from which may be deduced the probability of finding the electron at a given place and moment. At that time, only one electron was known: the negative electron. Dirac's equation contains solutions corresponding to negative energy and positive electric charge; yet the energy of a particle cannot be negative. However, discovery of the positive electron enabled these solutions to be interpreted by imagining a multitude of them, called the *Dirac sea*, and that the appearance of a positive electron corresponds to the expulsion of an electron from the *sea* with sufficient energy, ie a positive energy, for it to be observable. It is known as the *hole theory* and is now outdated. It is more fashionable to regard a positron as an electron travelling backwards in time.

disintegration, transformation of the structure of a nucleus or of a particle which leads to a final number of particles greater than the initial number. *Spontaneous* disintegration of a nucleus or of a particle is said to be *radioactive*. Disintegration resulting from the action of another particle is called *induced*. In natural disintegrations all the nuclei of a body do not disintegrate at the same time, yet the same proportion always disintegrates per second. Since the number of non-disintegrated nuclei decreases, the number of disintegrations also decreases with time. In a radioactive sample half the nuclei have disintegrated by the end of a time called *period* or *half-life*. By the end of double that time half of the remaining nuclei have disintegrated, so that finally a total of three-quarters have disintegrated. By the end of triple that time there will be $\frac{3}{4}+(\frac{1}{2}\times\frac{1}{4})=$ 14/16, or $\frac{7}{8}$ of the nuclei have disintegrated, etc. The quantity known as *mean life* is also used, which is the average lifetime of a disintegrating body. The period is equal to the mean

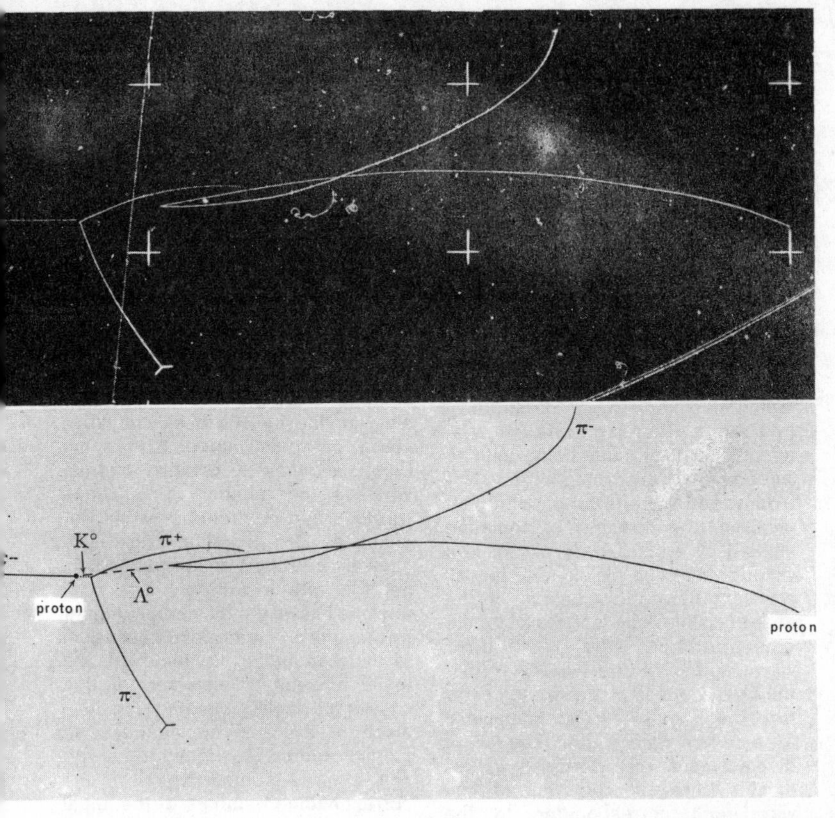

A neutral K meson (K°) and a lambda hyperon (Λ°) are produced in the interaction of a negative pion of 6 GeV/c on the proton of a hydrogen nucleus. The K° disintegrates, after travelling a very short distance, into two pions (π^+ and π^-). The Λ° in turn disintegrates into 1 proton and 1 negative pion. The photograph was obtained by means of the heavy liquid chamber BP3 at the Ecole Polytechnique, Paris.

lifetime multiplied by the factor 0.693. Three natural forms of disintegration of the nucleus may be observed: *alpha decay*, *beta decay* and *gamma emission*.

● **disintegration of fundamental particles.** Of the thirty-two fundamental particles actually known, four only appear to be absolutely stable: the proton and its antiparticle, the antiproton, the negative electron and its antiparticle, the positive electron. The question does not arise as to whether a photon or a neutrino are stable; as both these types of particles move at the speed of light, the theory of relativity tells us that any interval of time measured by an accessible observer corresponds to zero time in a geometrical system bound to the particle. All other fundamental particles are unstable. Their mean life is very variable. The longest mean life is that of the neutron which is of the order of 13 minutes. The shortest mean life is that of the neutral sigma hyperon, which is less than a millionth of a billionth of a second.

displacement. The law of displacement due to Wien, demonstrates how radiation emitted by a **black body** (qv) varies according to its temperature. The black body being defined as completely absorbing all the electromagnetic radiations which it receives, the strength of radiation emitted by a black body placed in a vacuum may be calculated for all wavelengths of the radiation. In the case of visible light, long wavelengths correspond to the red, short wavelengths to the violet. When the black body is at a given temperature, the intensity emitted is maximal for a certain wavelength. The law of displacement (or Wien's law) indicates that the product of the wavelength corresponding to the maximum with the absolute temperature is constant. Qualitatively it may be expressed by saying that the greater the increase in temperature of a black body, the shorter the wavelength of the radiation emitted. With visible light when the temperature increases, there is a displacement towards violet.

● **law of radioactive displacement.** When a nucleus disintegrates, a change takes place in one of the two, or in both of the numbers which characterise it: the atomic number (number of protons) and the mass number (number of protons plus number of neutrons). The law of radioactive displacement was established by Soddy and Fajans for the various transformations:

1) *Alpha disintegration*—the nucleus emits an alpha particle which consists of two protons and two neutrons. The final nucleus has, in consequence, an atomic number lower by two units and a mass number lower by four units than the corresponding numbers of the initial nucleus.

2) *Beta disintegration*—the nucleus emits an electron. If it is a negative electron, the nucleus loses a negative charge or, which amounts to the same thing, acquires a positive charge, whereas the number of nucleons (protons and neutrons) remains unchanged. Disintegration is therefore equivalent to the transformation of a neutron into a proton. The final nucleus has an atomic number higher by one unit and a mass number equal to corresponding numbers of the initial nucleus. Conversely, in the case of the nucleus emitting a positive electron, the final nucleus has an atomic number lower by one unit and a mass number equal to the corresponding numbers of the initial nucleus.

3) *Gamma emission*—the nucleus emits a gamma ray or photon, which carries no charge. In this case the final nucleus has an atomic number and a mass number equal to those of the initial nucleus.

dissociation, a phenomenon by which a high-speed particle induces the departure of a particle belonging to an assembly. (An electron is torn from an atom, a nucleon from a nucleus).

distillation, fractional, successive evaporation of a mixture of two liquids of which one is more volatile than the other.—The vapour evolved at successive stages contains an increasing ratio of the first to the second. This process may be used for the **separation of isotopes** (qv).

distribution law, term used in statistical mechanics.—It is a function defined for a set of identical particles giving the number of particles to be found within a certain range of energy. There are three important distribution laws:
1) *Maxwell-Boltzmann law* for classical particles;
2) *Bose-Einstein law* for bosons (eg photons);
3) *Fermi-Dirac law* for fermions (eg electrons).
These all refer to the case of ● **thermodynamic equilibrium** (qv)

Doppler effect, variation of the frequency of radiation emitted by a transmitter according to its velocity.—If a body which emits light is set in motion at a velocity appreciable compared with the speed of light, the radiation it emits changes frequency, eg visible light changes colour. When the transmitting body approaches the observer, the light observed moves from the red to violet; when it moves away from the observer, the light moves from the violet to red. The Doppler effect has enabled the fantastic speed at which remote galaxies move away from our Galaxy to be calculated. The same applies to radio waves which are used to measure the speed of fast appliances such as rockets. This effect has a certain analogy with an everyday phenomenon, the drop in pitch of the sound of the horn of a car as it overtakes a pedestrian. The sound frequency appears higher when the car is approaching the pedestrian than when it is moving away from him.

dose, the amount of radiation received by a body (see **dosimeter**).—It should be specified whether the dose has been received on the surface or throughout the whole volume of the body, for absorption of radiation by matter causes variations in its strength. The dose is defined differently for physical uses or for biological effects; the effect of radiation is not the same in different bodies. The unit of dose in physical measurements is the röntgen, a quantity of X or gamma rays which induces ionisation of 1000 billion atoms when passing through 1 cm of dry air under normal conditions. For other radiations, such as alpha, beta, etc, the strength of a röntgen is that which induces the same number of ionisations under similar conditions. However, radiation does not only yield its energy by ionisation, but also by excitation, interaction, etc. In many applications it would be of more use to measure radiation by the amount of energy lost when passing through 1 g of matter. In this case the unit is the *rad*, a strength of radiation which releases 100 ergs by passing through 1 g of matter. Finally, for biological effects, a dose should be defined that would be valid whatever the nature of the tissues through which it passed. Here the question is complicated by the fact that various radiations have different effects on tissues. One unit of dose used is the *rep* (röntgen equivalent physical), which corresponds to the energy yielded by radiation of 1 röntgen in 1 g of water. To approach in a more precise fashion the biological effect on man, the rem (röntgen equivalent man) is generally used; this is a radiation dose which induces the same biological effects as 1 röntgen. (See **effectiveness, relative biological**.) Definition of this unit should be treated cautiously, as localised biological effects depend on the tissues (skin, muscles, etc), whereas the total biological effect depends very much on the parts of the body affected. Eyes, glands, bone marrow and liver are for instance more sensitive to radiation than other parts of the body. To sum up, the unit of the dose must be selected with due regard to the effect under consideration. A dose received as the result of cosmic radiation and of natural radioactivity is about three milliröntgens per week. For personnel working in atomic power plants the dose received is usually restricted to 300 milliröntgens per working week.

● **cumulative dose,** the dose accumulated in a single body through repeated exposure to radiation. For man, spaced-out exposure is less dangerous than exposure at close intervals. Biological reactions tend to destroy the effects of radiation after a certain time.

● **depth dose,** a dose of radiation absorbed at a certain depth by biological tissues. It may be defined as a percentage of the skin dose or of the air dose.

● **exit dose,** a radiation dose at the surface of a body facing away from the incident radiation.

● **integral dose,** the total dose absorbed by an object or a human being during exposure to radiation. For instance, the integral dose to be given to a patient undergoing X-ray treatment would be limited.

● **maximum permissible dose,** established according to circumstances, with authority either directly by legislation or by an accepted code of practice, departure from which may incur criminal or civil sanctions. Most codes are now based on the dosage recommended by the **ICRP** (qv). The ICRP issued recommendations in 1950. These were revised in 1958 and further revised in 1962. The commonly quoted permissible dose of 0.3 rem/week for occupational exposure stems from the early recommendations and is *not* in general valid. No dose larger than the minimum possible is permissible in any circumstances. Occupational exposure of research workers, workers in radiation processing or atomic energy plants, medical radiologists and radiographers, etc must be limited to 5 rems per year to the gonads and blood-forming organs. Women of reproductive age must have exposure of the abdomen limited to 1.3 rems in any quarter, to reduce risk of over-exposure of an early foetus. The dose limit for the population at large is to be one tenth of the corresponding occupational dose limit. These limits do not include exposure to natural radiation or exposure *as a patient* for medical purposes. Limitation of the medical dose rate is left to the growing good sense of the medical profession.

● **median lethal dose,** a dose which is capable of producing the death of 50 per cent of the animals or individuals of a group in a given time.

● **skin dose,** the dose received by the surface of a body. In evaluating it, the fact is taken into consideration that some of the radiation is diffused by the body and reaches the skin from inside.

●**tolerance dose,** see **dose,** a radiation dose which an individual may receive without detriment. There is no evidence that such a dose exists, particularly as regards genetic risks. *Permitted doses* are established by convention and regularly revised, eg by the International Commission on Radiation Protection. (See **ICRP** and **dose.**)

dosimeter, an instrument which measures radiation doses.—In practice, these instruments detect only one kind of radiation. Measurement of gamma ray doses is usually effected through the materialisation of a certain proportion of radiation in a thin lead plate, the ionisation measured being that of the materialisation electrons. Measurements of neutron doses are effected through the medium of charged particles produced in the nuclear interactions of these neutrons. To measure ionising radiations, small portable **electroscopes** (qv), having the shape of a fountain-pen, called pocketmeters, are frequently used. Some perfected dosimeters contain a mixture similar to the composition of human tissues, which is placed in an ionisation chamber so as to measure biological effects directly.

dosimetry, technique of the utilisation and instrumentation of measurements of radiation dosage.

DRAGON, an internationally sponsored (DECD) high temperature gas reactor on an experimental scale (20 MW), using Th and U^{235} fuel, running up to fuel surface temperatures of 1100° C, with graphite moderator and helium coolant. Situated at Winfrith, England.

DYSON, Freeman J. (1923–) English mathematician and physicist. He has clarified the foundations of quantum electrodynamics and worked on the spectra of random systems.

E

e, symbol of the *elementary electric charge.*—The proton possesses a positive elementary charge (+e), the electron a negative elementary charge (−e).

ENEA, European Nuclear Energy Agency. The aim of this agency is the peaceful use of nuclear energy. Member states include United Kingdom, German Federal Republic, France, Italy, Belgium, Spain, Sweden, Netherlands, Switzerland, Turkey, Denmark, Austria, Norway, Greece, Portugal, Ireland, Luxembourg and Iceland.

effectiveness, relative biological (RBE). Radiations produce different biological effects according to their nature. To find these effects, calculations are made of the amount of energy dispersed throughout a biological tissue by different radiations all giving the same dose by a standard physical measurement. The proportions of these amounts of energy represent the *relative biological effectiveness* of the different radiations. If the effectiveness of X-rays and gamma rays is taken as a unit, the relative biological effectiveness of electrons is also 1, that of high-speed neutrons and protons is of the order of 5, and that of slow neutrons and alpha particles is of the order of 10. It is not always the case that a given biological effect (eg induction of cataract) depends only on the energy dissipated in the tissue. For such specific effects the above figures may be misleading. See the latest available edition of **ICRP** recommendations (qv).

effects of radiation, see **radiation effects.**

efficiency of a counter, see **counter.**

effluent, radioactive, a liquid, or more often a radioactive gas released in some kind of process.—Special precautions have to be taken to prevent any radioactive effluent from mixing with the air, for its assimilation by the respiratory tract would be dangerous. For instance, the plant for separating uranium in the form of a gas compound has to be absolutely gas-tight, uranium being an alpha radioactive body in a natural state.

EINSTEIN, Albert (1875–1955) German physicist, naturalised Swiss, then American. His work on the theory of relativity caused him to be considered the greatest modern scientist. In 1905 he produced a quantum interpretation of the photo-electric effect and at the same time he built up the special theory of relativity which included the celebrated equivalence of mass with energy. He then conceived generalised relativity, a theory of gravitation in four-dimensional non-Euclidean space, and a series of attempts to obtain a unified theory of gravitation and of electromagnetism. He received the Nobel Prize for Physics in 1921 for his work on the photo-electric effect.

Albert Einstein (Photo Keystone)

● **Einstein's law.** A name usually given to one of the numerous physical laws established by Einstein. It is also known as the *law of the equivalence of mass with energy*. This law, deduced from the principle of relativity, expresses the theory that matter and energy are equivalent. A system which radiates energy sees its mass decrease, a system which absorbs it, sees its mass increase. The variation of energy is proportional to the variation of mass. Generally speaking, energy and mass are equivalent apart from a fixed constant of proportionality. This constant is the square of the speed of light. It is very high, because the speed of light is high, which explains that the variations of mass are very small for the energies usually observed. Let us consider for example, a large quantity of water, 1 tonne (or 1 m^3) and heat it up from 0° C to 100° C. If we proceed by means of electric heating, it will be necessary to consume 120kWh, or 12 kW for ten hours. Since the water has received energy, the mass has increased according to Einstein's law, by 5 millionths of a gramme. This is not a measurable difference. On the other hand, when the energy coming into play is considerable, as in the case of nuclear and thermonuclear reactions, the mass variation is no longer negligible, but is perfectly capable of being measured in these nuclear reactions. Let us take another example, that of the Sun, which emits energy whose source is in nuclear and thermonuclear reactions; an energy of which the Earth receives only a small fraction. One finds that the Sun's mass decreases by about 10 million tons per second. This mass, which is only an infinitesimal part of the total mass of the Sun, is none the less quite appreciable at our level.

einsteinium, an artificial element whose atomic number, protons in the nucleus, is 99. It was discovered in 1954 by bombarding uranium with nitrogen ions according to the reaction:

uranium 238 (92 protons, 146 neutrons)
+nitrogen 14 (7 protons, 7 neutrons)
gives einsteinium 246 (99 protons, 147 neutrons)+6 neutrons.

Other isotopes of this element have also been discovered. All are unstable, and show radioactive decay.

elastic, descriptive term used of an interaction (collision, scattering) between two microscopic systems, atoms or particles, when their respective energy is unchanged. The fraction of energy transmitted from one system to the other appears only in the shape of variations in speed. The respective rest masses of the two systems in interaction remain unaltered and no other mass is formed in the interaction.

electric dipole, configuration of two equal and opposite electric charges (see **dipole**).

electrodynamics, a part of physics which refers to the study of electric charges in motion. Used as a synonym for **electromagnetism** (qv). The work of **Maxwell** (qv) made optics a part of electrodynamics.

electromagnetism, the science of electric and magnetic phenomena.—Maxwell's equations enable these two kinds of phenomena to be described in a theory which synthesises them. The latest theory of electromagnetism, since developed, is a quantum theory. The actions which take place between two systems subjected to electromagnetic effects can only be whole multiples of the elementary quantum of action due to Planck. In this theory, which is called *quantum electrodynamics*, it is supposed that electromagnetism may be described by means of an exchange of photons between the two systems in interaction. The photon is called a particle of the *electromagnetic field*. Because of the various electromagnetic manifestations which have been successively discovered, several names have been given to the photon according to the energy which it possesses, although its nature remains always the same. Thus, radio-electric waves, infra-red rays, ultra-violet rays, light, X-rays and gamma rays are all of the same nature and are also different manifestations of electromagnetism.

● **electromagnetic,** that which refers to electric and magnetic phenomena. —The electric field and the magnetic field are closely related. Maxwell-Lorentz's theory of electromagnetism, which synthesises the two aspects, demonstrates for example that if there is an electric field present for a first observer, there exists for a second observer, moving with respect to the first, a magnetic field joined to the electric field. Therefore, the fundamental reality of the phenomena is described by an electromagnetic field.

It is said that two particles possess electromagnetic interactions when the actions which they produce one upon the other may be described by an electromagnetic field. It is the electromagnetic forces which bind the electrons of an atom to the nucleus of the atom. Chemical forces are due to electromagnetic interactions between atoms of two bodies.

electrometer, an instrument for measuring electric charge.—Electric charges are collected in this appliance on a metallic electrode. When this electrode is placed in an electric field, it is subject to a force proportional to the electric charge it carries. This electrostatic force is also proportional to the electric field; it possesses the same direction if the charge is positive, and an opposite one if the charge is negative. In practice the necessary electric field is established between two metallic conductors by raising them to different electric voltages. The force exerted on the charge to be measured may be deduced, for instance, from the flattening of a spring holding up the charged electrode.

A Kelvin electrometer with multicellular quadrants (Photo Ecole supérieur d'Electricité)

electron, a fundamental particle whose mass is a little less than a billionth of a billionth of a billionth of a gramme. The electron always carries either a positive or a negative charge. The negative electron enters into the composition of atoms in the shape of electronic shells surrounding the nucleus. The atom is electrically neutral. The nucleus contains the same number of protons as there are electrons in the atom. The negative charge of the electrons compensates for the positive charge of the protons. The negative electron, a universal component of matter, is frequently merely called *electron*, sometimes *negatron* or *negaton*. The electric charge of the electron cannot be divided. It is called *elementary charge* and its existence was demonstrated by the work of Jean Perrin. The positive electron, also called *positron* or *positon* or *anti-electron*, is produced at the same time as the phenomena of radioactivity, or as the materialisation of radiation. Electrons are stable whether positive or negative; they do not disintegrate. However, the positive electron has only a limited mean life, because it reacts on negative electrons of matter by annihilating them:

e positive+e negative *gives* gamma rays.

The positive electron was demonstrated in cosmic radiation by Anderson in 1933. Although it is not possible to imagine the electron as an electrically charged ball, in theoretical work use is made of a length known as the *classical radius* of the electron, with a value of approximately 0.3 millionths of a millionth of a centimetre. However, in wave mechanics it is demonstrated that there exists a non-zero probability of finding an electron at distant points in space. The **de Broglie wavelength** (qv) associated with an electron, which to some degree defines its localisation, is shorter the more energetic the electron. The electron possesses a spin connected with the intrinsic angular momentum of the electron. This spin is 1/2, and the electron obeys Fermi-Dirac statistics; it is then said that the electron is a **fermion** (qv).

● **Auger electron,** an electron ejected from an atom by absorption of excitation energy which is stored in that atom. (See **Auger effect.**)

● **Compton electron,** an electron ejected from an atom by photon scattering. (See **Compton effect.**)

● **conversion electron,** an electron ejected from an atom by absorption of the energy stored in the excited nucleus. (See **conversion, internal.**) Internal conversion is a different phenomenon from the *Auger effect*, because the latter effect in no way involves the nucleus.

● **electron cloud,** an assembly of electrons which surround the nucleus in an atom.—This term derives from the fact that only the mean position of an electron may be determined; the presence of an electron may be imagined as a kind of cloud, the concentration of which is at its maximum around the mean position.

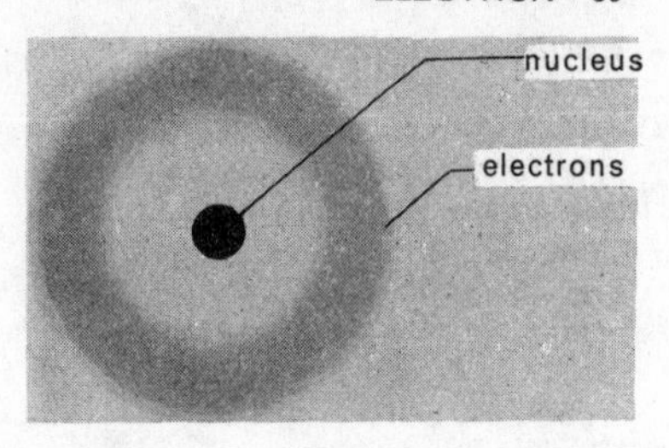

Electron cloud

● **electron conduction,** in metals, an electron which can pass from one atom to the next, thus providing a vehicle for electric current. Since an electron carries a negative charge, its displacement inside metal takes place in a direction contrary to the conventional direction of electric current in metal.

● **heavy electron,** the name given to the *muon* or **mu** lepton (qv). The muon does not seem, in fact, to have any properties which are different from those of the electron, except for its mass. Recent experiments appear, however, to demonstrate that the neutrino associated with the muon in *weak interactions* is not the same as the one associated with the electron.

● **knock-on electron,** an electron torn from an atom by an energetic incident electron, either positive or negative.

● **lone electron,** an electron belonging to an electronic shell of the atom when it is alone on this shell (see **atom**). This is especially the case with an electron of the outer shell of certain metallic atoms, such as sodium, potassium, etc. The greater part of the properties of these metals are due to the lone electron.

● **orbital** or **planetary electron,** an electron belonging to an orbit in an atom. The orbit of an electron is the trajectory followed by the electron in its rotation round the nucleus of the atom as in Bohr's theory (see **atom**). The electron is sometimes called planetary, because of the analogy of its motion with that of the planets around the Sun.

● **outer electron,** an electron belonging to the outer shell of the atom.—Metals have their outer shell filled with a small number of electrons. For instance, the outer shell of sodium contains a single outer electron; that of zinc has two. On the other hand, oxidising elements have their outer shell almost complete. That of oxygen, for instance, contains six outer electrons on a shell capable of receiving eight. Bodies with a complete outer shell are chemically inert. Neon, for example, contains eight outer electrons on its outer shell which is complete. Outer electrons decide the chemical properties of an element and generally speaking its physical properties as well, where these do not involve the internal structure of the atom, eg conductivity, colour, crystalline structure, etc.

● **valency electron.** In a molecule which consists of several atoms, atomic electrons are shared. For example, the methane molecule consists of four hydrogen atoms and one carbon atom. (*See diagram, p. 158.*) Each hydrogen atom has its own electron. The four electrons of the hydrogen atoms are shared with the four outer electrons of the carbon atom so as to constitute approximately one complete electronic shell with eight electrons. This shared electron is called a *valency electron*.

electronvolt, a unit of energy used in atomic and nuclear physics whose symbol is eV. It is equal to the energy acquired by an elementary electric charge subjected to a voltage of 1 V in a vacuum. Also used are the KeV, which has a value of 1000 eV, the MeV which has a value of 1 million electronvolts, and the GeV which has a value of 1 billion electronvolts.

electrophoresis, movement of colloidal particles suspended in a liquid medium under the influence of an applied electric field.

electroscope, an apparatus for measuring electric charge, used in **radioactivity** (qv) to detect a flux of charged particles.—It is mainly composed of two electrodes electrically charged and surrounded by air. The passage of charged particles through the air induces ionisation of the atoms of the air. The ions and electrons thus released are electrically charged and they are attracted to the electrodes of the electroscope. When they arrive on these, they lower the electric charge of the electroscope, causing a deviation of the reading given by the electroscope. One electrode consists of a conductor to which a thin, flexible piece of gold-leaf has been attached. When the conductor is electrically charged, this leaf is repelled by the conductor to a position in which the electric forces compensate for its weight. By measuring this position it is possible to measure the electric charge. When a flux of charged particles passes through the electroscope, the charge decreases and the thin piece of gold-leaf approaches the conductor. The electroscope, which is a delicate and imprecise instrument, is no longer much used. The only current use of it is in the pocketmeter, a small portable instrument used for measuring the strength of radiations received by an individual. Periodically recharged, it is used by the health services attached to nuclear establishments.

electrostatic, that which concerns the properties of stationary electric charges.—Electrostatic forces acting between the charges are given by Coulomb's law. These are repulsive forces between two positive or two negative charges, and forces of attraction between a positive and a negative charge. The electrostatic force is proportional to the strength of each of the two charges and varies in inverse ratio to the square of their distance. At a double or triple distance, etc, it is divided by 4, 9, etc. The laws of electrostatics may be deduced from Maxwell's theory, which expresses all the properties of electricity, either stationary or in motion.

electrostatic deflector, see **deflector.**

electrostatic generator, see **generator, electrostatic.**

electrostatic lens, see **lens, electrostatic.**

element, a substance composed of atoms all with the same atomic number. Each atom of an element contains the same number of electrons around its nucleus and the same number of protons in its nucleus. The number of neutrons in the nucleus may vary slightly and, in consequence, the ●**mass number** (qv). The sum of the number of protons and the number of neutrons may also show slight variations. Atoms of the same element having different mass numbers are called **isotopes** (qv). Their chemical properties are practically identical, which explains that elements found in nature are usually a mixture of isotopes. Their physical properties are very similar. An element is called *natural* if it is found in nature. It is called *artificial* if it exists solely as a laboratory product, eg *transuranians*, which are elements of a mass superior to that of uranium, are artificial elements. They are unstable and disintegrate by radioactivity, which explains their absence in nature. (*See table p. 93.*)

elementary charge, see **charge.**

elementary particle, see **particle.**

eliminator of electrostatic charge, see **charge eliminator.**

emanation, a radioactive product escaping in gaseous form from the substance in which it was produced either through disintegration or by fission. (Example: xenon gas may be produced in uranium fission.) ‖ The term is also sometimes used to describe **emanon** (qv).

emanon, an element with atomic number 86.—Each of its nuclei contains 86 protons. The natural isotopes, actinon, thoron and radon have an atomic mass respectively of 219, 220 and 222 which corresponds respectively to 133, 134 and 136 neutrons. Its name derives from the fact that it appears in a gaseous form in radioactive disintegrations. Its three isotopes are produced respectively in the radioactive chains of actinium, thorium and radium.

emission, induced. Atoms can emit photons in proportion to the number of photons passing through the atom. This is called *induced emission*.

emission, spontaneous. Atoms can emit radiation (ie photons) even

CLASSIFICATION OF THE CHEMICAL ELEMENTS

Each box in this table corresponds to one element, giving its name and symbol, atomic number (number of electrons of the atom) at top left and atomic mass, below to the right. The atomic electrons are placed in successive shells; the elements which appear on the same line, or period contain the same number of shells. A single one for hydrogen and helium. Two for the following period which goes from lithium to neon and so on. Elements placed in the same vertical column contain the same number of electrons in the outer shell, starting with 1 for the hydrogen column up to 8 for that below helium. (Helium itself is an exception in number, but its properties belong to this column.) They show great analogies. A single box has been reserved for metals from rare earths (lanthanides), very close elements, details of which are given below. The same applies to the elements which follow radium (Actinides).

1 1 H HYDROGEN																	2 4 He HELIUM
3 6·9 Li LITHIUM	4 9 Be BERYLLIUM											5 10·8 B BORON	6 12 C CARBON	7 14 N NITROGEN	8 16 O OXYGEN	9 19 F FLUORINE	10 20·2 Ne NEON
11 23 Na SODIUM	12 24·3 Mg MAGNESIUM											13 27 Al ALUMINIUM	14 28·1 Si SILICIUM	15 31 P PHOSPHORUS	16 32·1 S SULPHUR	17 35·5 Cl CHLORINE	18 39·9 A ARGON
19 39·1 K POTASSIUM	20 40·1 Ca CALCIUM	21 45 Sc SCANDIUM	22 47·9 Ti TITANIUM	23 51 V VANADIUM	24 52 Cr CHROMIUM	25 54·9 Mn MANGANESE	26 55·8 Fe IRON	27 58·9 Co COBALT	28 58·7 Ni NICKEL	29 63·5 Cu COPPER	30 65·4 Zn ZINC	31 69·7 Ga GALLIUM	32 72·6 Ge GERMANIUM	33 74·9 As ARSENIC	34 79 Se SELENIUM	35 79·9 Br BROMINE	36 83·8 Kr KRYPTON
37 85·5 Rb RUBIDIUM	38 87·6 Sr STRONTIUM	39 88·9 Y YTTRIUM	40 91·2 Zr ZIRCONIUM	41 92·9 Nb NIOBIUM	42 96 Mo MOLYBDENUM	43 99 Tc TECHNETIUM	44 101·1 Ru RUTHENIUM	45 102·9 Rh RHODIUM	46 106·4 Pd PALLADIUM	47 107·9 Ag SILVER	48 112·4 Cd CADMIUM	49 114·8 In INDIUM	50 118·7 Sn TIN	51 121·8 Sb ANTIMONY	52 127·6 Te TELLURIUM	53 126·9 I IODINE	54 131·3 Xe XENON
55 132·9 Cs CÆSIUM	56 137·4 Ba BARIUM	57 to 71 LANTHANIDE SERIES OF RARE EARTHS	72 178·6 Hf HAFNIUM	73 180·9 Ta TANTALUM	74 183·9 W TUNGSTEN	75 186·3 Re RHENIUM	76 190·2 Os OSMIUM	77 192·2 Ir IRIDIUM	78 195·1 Pt PLATINUM	79 197 Au GOLD	80 200·6 Hg MERCURY	81 204·4 Tl THALLIUM	82 207·2 Pb LEAD	83 209 Bi BISMUTH	84 209 Po POLONIUM	85 210 At ASTATINE	86 222 Rn RADON
87 223 Fr FRANCIUM	88 226 Ra RADIUM	89 to 104 ACTINIDE SERIES OF RARE ELEMENTS															

LANTHANIDES	57 138·9 La LANTHANUM	58 140·1 Ce CERIUM	59 140·9 Pr PRASEODYMIUM	60 144·3 Nd NEODYMIUM	61 145 Pm PROMETHEUM	62 150·4 Sm SAMARIUM	63 152 Eu EUROPIUM	64 156·9 Gd GADOLINIUM	65 158·9 Tb TERBIUM	66 162·5 Dy DYSPROSIUM	67 164·9 Ho HOLMIUM	68 167·2 Er ERBIUM	69 168·9 Tm THULIUM	70 173 Yb YTTERBIUM	71 175 Lu LUTETIUM	
ACTINIDES	89 227 Ac ACTINIUM	90 232·1 Th THORIUM	91 231 Pa PROTACTINIUM	92 238·1 U URANIUM	93 237 Np NEPTUNIUM	94 244 Pu PLUTONIUM	95 243 Am AMERICIUM	96 247 Cm CURIUM	97 249 Bk BERKELIUM	98 251 Cf CALIFORNIUM	99 254 Es EINSTEINIUM	100 253 Fm FERMIUM	101 256 Mv MENDELEVIUM	102 254 — —	103 257 Lw LAWRENCIUM	104 — — KURCHATOVIUM

when there is no electromagnetic field. This is called *spontaneous emission*.

emitter, a nucleus or an assembly of nuclei, with a definite atomic number and atomic mass which disintegrates when emitting a certain type of particle. Uranium 233, atomic number 92 and mass number 233 is an alpha emitter with a 267,000 year half-life. Iodine 128, atomic number 53 and mass number 128, used as a tracer, is a beta emitter with a twenty-five minute half-life. Tantalum 181, atomic number 73 and mass number 181, is a gamma emitter with a half-life of 0.022 thousandths of a second.

emulsion, nuclear photographic, a photographic plate invented for the detection of charged particles.—The photographic plate is marked along the trajectory of the particle which leaves a track in it. It is to the photographic plate that we owe the discovery of radioactivity, since in 1896 Becquerel discovered that a uranium ore had marked photographic plates. This accidental marking led to the development of a technique for the specific purpose of detecting particles. The pion, which is responsible for nuclear forces, was detected in 1947 in nuclear plates. The disintegrations of the mu, pi and K mesons have also been studied in the plates. Techniques employed with the plates to identify particles are various. They principally enable functions of the velocity and mass of the particle to be determined. The main ones are: measurement of the range of a particle until it is stopped in the emulsion; measurement of ionisation, achieved by counting the number of grains developed on the track per centimetre; measurement of scattering, achieved by observing the small deviations of the trajectory in the emulsion. Observation of tracks in nuclear plates requires the use of microscopes, the size of the grains developed being of the order of some ten thousandths of a millimetre. The delicate measurements and analysis of the plates demand great care. Their field of use is restricted since other, more flexible and more complete detection devices have been discovered, such as the bubble-chamber, spark chamber, etc.

endoenergetic, synonym for **endothermic** (qv).—The adjective *endothermic* which is less well adapted but more usual, derives from an expression used for chemical reactions in which energy appears in the form of heat.

endothermic, refers to a nuclear reaction which cannot occur unless a certain amount of energy is provided. —This energy is transformed into mass during the reaction, so that the final total of the masses produced is superior to the initial total of the particles entering reaction. An endothermic reaction can only take place starting with a certain energy possessed by the incident particle, which is called the *threshold*.

energy, a physical quantity which generalises the idea of work. The mechanical work of a force acting in the direction of displacement is equal to the product of the force by the distance of displacement. The energy may assume different forms. It is called *potential* when it is stored in a physical system and may be released by any kind of process (eg a tight spring possesses a potential energy which may be liberated by releasing the spring). *Kinetic* energy is the energy possessed by a body in motion. It is greater the higher the mass and speed of the body in motion. The *thermal* energy of a system is greater the higher its temperature. Different forms of energy may be changed one into the other. For instance, it is possible, by consuming electric energy, to produce mechanical work (electric motor), to produce thermal energy (heating a resistance) and to store potential energy (charging a condenser). Thermal energy is due, furthermore, to the movement of molecules or atoms and may be regarded as kinetic energy. The fundamental *law of the conservation of energy* is as follows: in an isolated system, total energy remains constant; if the energy disappears in one aspect it reappears completely in other aspects. Einstein's law of the equivalence of mass with energy establishes in addition that matter is a form of energy. If matter is formed, energy disappears and vice versa. The law of the conservation of energy, including *mass energy* is always assumed in every field of physics. For instance, in reactions in which particles are formed, the equivalence may be measured between the mass of the particle formed and the loss of kinetic energy by the initial system. In this case, the mass of the particles formed is precisely equivalent to the difference between the kinetic energy of the initial system and the kinetic energy of the final system.

● **atomic energy,** a form of energy produced by the fission of heavy atomic nuclei into lighter nuclei, or by the fusion of light atomic nuclei into heavier nuclei.—The escape of energy is due to modification of the nuclei; atomic structure does not play an essential part in it. The term *nuclear energy* is better for this type of energy.

● **binding energy,** an energy released when two or more particles assemble together to form a stable assembly.—The mass of the hydrogen atom is slightly lower than the masses of the proton and electron combined, the difference being exactly equivalent to the energy released by the formation of the hydrogen atom. This variation is low, of the order of 15 billionths of the total mass. In the case of nuclear forces, on the contrary, the difference is considerable. When a proton and a neutron assemble to form a deuterium nucleus, the mass of the system decreases by about one thousandth. If one wishes to separate two particles which form a stable assembly, an energy at least equal to the binding energy must be supplied to the system. If, for instance, one wishes to separate the proton from the neutron when they have formed a deuterium nucleus, and release them, an energy at least equivalent to a thousandth part of its mass must be returned to the nucleus. The proton and electron are bound in the hydrogen atom by electromagnetic forces with an energy of 13.5 electronvolts. To dissociate a hydrogen atom into a proton and an electron, an energy at least equal to this value must be provided. The proton and neutron are bound in the deuterium nucleus by nuclear forces with an energy of 2.2 million electronvolts. The deuterium nucleus has to be provided with an energy at least equal to 2.2 million electronvolts to dissociate it into a proton and a neutron. The mass of an assembly of bound particles is smaller than the mass of its components by a quantity equivalent to the binding energy. (See **Einstein's law.**)

• **energy of thermal motion,** a form of energy which all bodies possess, and which increases with temperature. It is due to the various motions (translation, rotation, vibration) by which the atoms and molecules which constitute matter are agitated. (See **agitation, thermal.**)

• **radiative energy,** an energy carried by electromagnetic radiation (radio waves, light, X-rays, gamma rays). The energy carried by the electromagnetic radiation particle (the photon) is the greater the higher its frequency. To simplify, it may be said that the energy of a photon is greater the faster the vibrations of the electric and magnetic fields associated with it. An example of radiative energy: infra-red radiations emitted by a heating appliance are quickly absorbed into matter; the infra-red radiative energy is in this case converted into thermal energy.

enrichment, an increase, in an isotopic mixture, of the percentage of one of the isotopes. (See **separation of isotopes.**) (Example: a mixture of natural water and heavy water may be enriched by electrolysis.) ‖ An *enrichment factor*, the ratio of the percentages of a given isotope after and before an operation of isotopic separation.

epithermal, used to describe neutrons having an energy rather above thermal energy.—Neutrons which possess an energy which corresponds to the ordinary temperature of 15° C, are called thermal neutrons. They have an energy of 0.025 electronvolts. *Epithermal neutrons* are those whose energy is between 0.5 and 15 electronvolts.

equilibrium, radioactive. Some radioactive nuclei possess the property of giving products which are radioactive. (See **series, radioactive.**) These secondary radioactive products may disintegrate again into tertiary radioactive products, etc. The radioactive series whose first member is uranium 238 thus traverses 14 consecutive disintegrations before arriving at a stable nucleus: lead 206. When disintegration of the first member is very slow, its radioactivity may be considered to be constant: during an equal interval of time, the number of nuclei which disintegrate is always the same in a given sample. If the disintegration of the second member is distinctly faster than that of the first member, it appears that the radioactivity of the second member is also constant: during an equal interval of time the number of nuclei of the second member which disintegrates is always the same in the sample, and so on throughout the radioactive series. It is then said that there is *radioactive equilibrium*, sometimes called *secular equilibrium* because it deals with nuclei with long periods. Radioactive equilibrium is also referred to when a radioactive body is produced by nuclear reaction, such as bombarding a target with a beam of particles having a constant intensity. After a certain time, the body formed in the nuclear reaction also acquires a constant radioactivity through the balance of its rates of formation and decay. In a fairly old uranium ore, the number of atoms of each member of a radioactive series appears to be proportional to the period of this member. Since the consecutive disintegrations are in equilibrium, each member except the first is produced at the same speed as that at which it disintegrates.

● **thermodynamic equilibrium.** A system is in thermodynamic equilibrium when all the thermodynamic variables (pressure, temperature, thermodynamic potentials) are constant everywhere. In thermodynamic equilibrium atoms may absorb photons but they will also emit the same number of photons with exactly the same energy. The usual distribution laws refer to a system in thermodynamic equilibrium.

equivalence of mass with energy, a law which establishes the equivalence of matter and energy. (See **Einstein's law.**)

erythema, a reddening of the skin which may be induced, among other things, by exposure to ionising radiations and ultra-violet rays.

EURATOM, European Community for Atomic Energy.—For the promotion of the peaceful uses of atomic energy and protection against hazards. Member States: German Federal Republic, France, Italy, Belgium, Netherlands and Luxembourg.

euxenite, an ore containing uranium. It is found in the USA, Madagascar and Norway.

eV, symbol of **electronvolt** (qv).

evaporation, a phenomenon by which protons, neutrons or alpha particles are ejected with low speeds from a nucleus in a nuclear reaction.

excess, neutron, A–2Z, see **neutron excess.**

exchange force, the interaction invoked to explain **saturation of nuclear forces** (qv) in the nucleus. It has no equivalent in the macroscopic physical field. It causes the exchange operations of co-ordinates or spin of two particles to appear in the expression for their energy.

exchange of charge, or **charge exchange.** In reactions which set in motion two particles of different charges, a fairly large proportion of cases may be observed in which the electric charge appears to be transferred from one particle to the other. This is especially the case with the reactions of neutron on proton above about 10 million electronvolts. A certain proportion of the neutrons is reflected back, a phenomenon which may be explained by assuming that the incident neutron in fact carries on towards the front, but that in passing it has captured the charge of the target proton and become a proton itself, whereas, on the contrary, the target proton has yielded its charge and is reflected towards the back in the form of a neutron. The phenomenon of charge exchange is again produced in a reaction such as:

negative pion+positive proton
gives neutral pion
+neutral neutron.

This reaction, in which the negative pion and proton cancel their charges, forms a large proportion of the reactions observed; for very high-energy pions its strength decreases.

excitation, supply of energy to a particle system (molecule, atom, nucleus, particle), the system passing from the ground to the excited state. The transfer of energy may be effected by the absorption of a gamma ray, or by reaction on any kind of particle, the incident particle yielding some of its energy in the reaction.

excitation function, see **function, excitation.**

exclusion, see ● **Pauli's exclusion principle.**

exothermal, said of a nuclear reaction in which a certain quantity of energy is released. A disintegration is an exothermal reaction, when part of the mass of the initial particles is transformed into kinetic energy.

explosion, nuclear, an explosion in which nuclear energy is released. Apart from military uses (see **A-bomb**) it is proposed to use it for large-scale civilian projects such as the piercing of tunnels. Various plans are based on the possible use of a subterranean nuclear explosion as a heat source. In certain types of soil it can be estimated that the heat released remains concentrated in a local area surrounded by a solid gangue formed during the explosion from neighbouring rocks. There is, however, a serious drawback to nuclear explosions, that of the radioactivity released at the moment of explosion, some of which persists for a long time afterwards (see **bomb**). However, in the case of a subterranean explosion, the radioactivity would be relatively well contained within the gangue.

F

family, radioactive, see **series, radioactive.**

ferghanite, a uranium ore found in Turkestan.

A subterranean nuclear explosion at Nevada (USA) in 1957. The cloud of dust which is merely the result of the shock-wave is not radioactive. (Photo USIS) *See also illustration p. 98.*

A subterranean nuclear explosion has caused an actual hill on the Nevada testing ground. This is visible in the foreground of the photograph. In a very short space of time, by the end of the third explosion, it reached the not inconsiderable height of 90 m. On its summit may be seen the projection of sand used for tamping what may be compared to a wide and deep mine-shaft. (Photo USIS)

FERMI, Enrico (1901–54) Italian physicist. His main work deals with atomic and nuclear physics. With Dirac he constructed a statistical theory, and with Pauli he prophesied the existence of the neutrino. He also achieved the first uranium fission with the help of slow neutrons. After receiving the Nobel Prize for Physics in 1938, he directed the construction of the first uranium reactor at Chicago in 1942. *See illustration opposite.*

● **fermi,** a very small unit of length used in nuclear physics, because its size is of the order of the dimensions of the proton and neutron. (It is worth a millionth of a millionth of a millimetre, eg the radius of the proton is of the order of 1.2 fermi.)

● **Fermi constant,** the theory of weak interactions first established by Fermi, gives an account of various phenomena, among which are:

beta disintegration:
neutron *gives* proton + negative electron + neutrino

pion disintegration:
pion *gives* mu lepton + neutrino

mu lepton disintegration:
mu lepton *gives* electron + neutrino + antineutrino

the capture of an electron of the atom by the nucleus, as well as numerous other disintegrations.

In this theory, the interacting force is the same for all these different phenomena, and is expressed by the **coupling constant** (qv) denoted by g, in this case called the *Fermi constant*.

●**Fermi degeneracy,** see **degeneracy.**

●**Fermi-Dirac statistics,** a theory which expresses the manner in which particles called *fermions* are distributed when quantisation is taken into account. In this case energy can only assume a certain number of distinct values. The *Fermi-Dirac statistics* are only concerned with a certain type of particle; *fermions.* All known particles are either fermions or bosons. *Spin*, a quantity that may be represented as bound to the angular momentum of rotation of the particle on itself, is a half-integer for fermions in atomic units, eg 1/2, 3/2, 5/2, etc whereas it is an integer for bosons. When the number of possible energy states for particles is very great compared with the number of particles, Fermi-Dirac statistics become identical with Boltzmann's classical statistics which do not take quantisation into account. Two fermions cannot occupy the same quantum state in Fermi-Dirac statistics, contrary to the two bosons in Bose's statistics. A wave function is associated with each particle. This is a mathematical quantity from which the probability of finding a particle in a given state may be deduced. The wave function of a fermion system is anti-symmetrical: ie it changes sign when all the co-ordinates, including the spin, of two fermions are interchanged; whereas for a boson system it is symmetrical.

Enrico Fermi

●**Fermi energy.** Energy of the highest occupied state of fermions in a degenerate gas (gas in which all fermions occupy all the lowest levels).

●**Fermi selection rules,** rules permitting one to select possible final states in beta decay. Known also as Fermi-Gamow-Teller selection rules.

fermion, a particle which obeys the **Fermi-Dirac statistics** (qv) (eg the proton, neutron, electron are all fermions, all three of them have 1/2 spin.

fermium, an artificial element with the atomic number 100, discovered in the form of the isotope with mass number 254.

fertile, term used of a material capable of being transformed into a fissile material and used in a reactor.—The transformation is usually effected by neutron bombardment, eg non-fissile uranium 238 may be transformed by neutron bombardment into uranium 239. The latter also disintegrates by beta radioactivity and leads to plutonium 239 which may undergo fission. Uranium 238 is said to be fertile.

FEYNMAN, Richard P. (1918–) American physicist. A specialist in quantum electrodynamics, he introduced the use of graphs to study complex processes and has made original contributions to most branches of theoretical physics.

field, a physical quantity used to express action at a distance.—Two elements of matter are attracted to each other with a force which depends on their mass and distance. The force of attraction is directed in the straight line connecting the two elements. At each point in space it is said that the gravitational field vector due to one element of matter, is a vector characterised by its length, its direction in space and its sense. If a second element of matter is placed at any point, it will be subjected to a gravitational force. This force will be the product of the field vector and the mass of the second element. Electric actions may also be expressed through the medium of a field. Two positive charges repel each other in the same way as two negative ones. A positive charge and a negative charge are attracted to each other. The electric force depends on the charges and on their distance. The idea of *field* may be extended to include the nuclear forces which bind the components of the nucleus, neutrons and protons. In the present state of our knowledge, it is impossible to give a simple form to this field. In modern quantum mechanics the term also designates any function (scalar field), or set of functions (vectorial, tensorial or spinorial field) used to describe elementary particles.

● **guiding field,** the name given to the magnetic field in accelerators.—In effect, it guides the particles on to a path which is approximately circular; without it, the path would only be rectilinear.

● **particle of the field,** a particle in terms of which the existence of a field is discussed. The forces between two particles may be explained by an exchange of *field particles*. The photon called according to its energy, *gamma ray*, *X-ray*, *light* or *radio-electric wave*, represents the electromagnetic field; the pion and possibility other mesons represent the nuclear field. To represent the gravitational field the existence of a graviton has to be assumed, although it has never been observed in the form of a particle. Some theories on weak interactions also postulate the existence of an intermediate boson.

film, a photographic film used for detecting radiation in the protection of personnel.—Several kinds of film may be fixed on to the same small plate, each one for a given type of radiation. (See **emulsion, nuclear photographic.**)

filter, a term of wide meaning which describes any device which enables radiations to be selected according to their nature or according to their energy.

fine structure, see **structure, fine.**

fissile, said of a substance whose nuclei may undergo **fission** (qv) through the absorption of an incident neutron. (This is the case for uranium 235 or plutonium 239.)—The nucleus which absorbs the neutron is divided into lighter nuclei, and neutrons are released in the fission. All these products are emitted at different speeds. The released neutrons may in turn induce the fission of other nuclei, etc. The adjective *fissile* is frequently applied to nuclei which undergo fission due to the action of low-energy neutrons called *thermal neutrons*. Sometimes it is also applied to nuclei undergoing fissions due to the action of energetic neutrons: eg uranium 238 is fissile under the action of high-speed neutrons.

fission, a phenomenon which constitutes the source of energy in reactors and nuclear bombs, by means of which a heavy atomic nucleus containing a great many protons and neutrons is split into two or more light nuclei, each one containing a less high number of protons and neutrons.—Fission was discovered in 1939 by Hahn and Strassmann. Some nuclei, like those of uranium 233, uranium 235 and plutonium 239 have a property which enables them to be broken by the action of not very high-speed neutrons. The uranium nucleus 235 is a heavy nucleus, because it contains many protons (92) and neutrons (143). When a slow neutron arrives within a fairly close distance of the nucleus, the nuclear forces act and the equilibrium of the nucleus is broken; the nucleus splits into two or more *fission fragments*. Each of these fragments contains a certain number of protons and neutrons, so that of itself it constitutes a new and lighter nucleus. Furthermore, a certain number of neutrons which do not belong to any nucleus (they are called *free*) are emitted in the fission and there is also, almost always, an emission of gamma rays. The number of protons and neutrons remains the same in the fission reaction, only their manner of grouping alters; light nuclei are formed, starting with a heavy nucleus. The simultaneous emission of free neutrons may easily be understood when one considers that light nuclei contain fewer neutrons than heavier nuclei. (See **neutron excess**) Thus fission releases a certain surplus of neutrons. One possible reaction is, for instance:

uranium 235 (92 protons, 143 neutrons)+neutron
gives strontium 94 (38 protons, 56 neutrons)
+xenon 140 (54 protons, 86 neutrons+2 neutrons+gamma ray.

Other fissions would give different fragments and a different number of free neutrons. Can the phenomenon of fission be explained simply? The theory established by Bohr and Wheeler is based on a simple analogy: the *drop of water model*. Let it be assumed that a drop of water is subjected to forces which deform it; the drop of water will, up to a certain point, retain its primary unity. Beginning with fairly strong stress, it divides into two or three smaller drops according to the kind of stress which it undergoes. It so happens that it takes little energy to split the nuclei of uranium 235, 233 and plutonium 239 by a similar process. It is established that the nucleus divides into two fragments of unequal mass rather than into two equal fragments. It may also divide into three fragments, so that the fission fragments possess masses which vary between 50 and 170, though mainly in the region of 94 and 140. The situation is the same for the nuclei of uranium 233 and plutonium 239. On the other hand, fission due to high-speed neutrons gives the highest proportion of equal fragments. Research on fission has concentrated mainly on slow neutrons, since these produce a greater proportion of fission reactions than

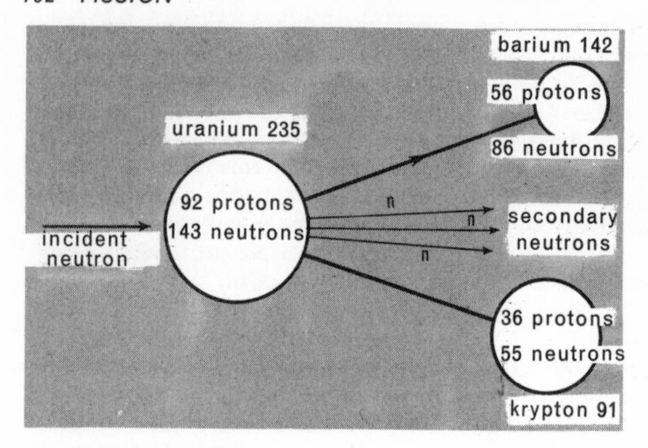

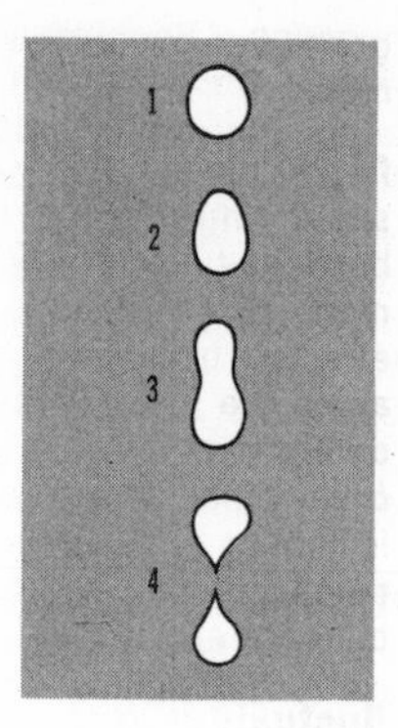

On the left, diagram of the fission of uranium 235. On the right, water-drop model.

fast neutrons. However, neutrons released in fission possess a certain energy; they must therefore be slowed down for them to reach the energy at which they become effective. Their energy is, on average, some millions of electronvolts, whereas the energy at which they become effective is reduced by a factor of the order of a million; to this end, a slowing agent is used so that the neutrons lose their energy through successive impacts on its nuclei. A large number of the fission fragments are radioactive, emitting an alpha, beta or gamma radiation. During these successive radioactivities neutrons are also emitted, called *delayed* by contrast with the *prompt* neutrons emitted during fusion. These two groups of neutrons may contribute to the working of a reactor, the assembly of delayed neutrons emitted during the few seconds following fission permitting a more stable control of them. There is about one delayed neutron for 100 prompt neutrons. The delayed neutrons consist of five main groups whose lifetimes are 0.43, 1.52, 4.51, 22 and 56 seconds. During fission a large amount of energy is released. In an ideal nuclear power plant, several hundred thousand kilowatt hours could be extracted from 1 g of uranium, but technical considerations cause this figure to fall much lower. This energy is due to the fact that neutrons and protons are more bound in the light nucleus than in the heavy nucleus, so that at the moment of fission the difference between the binding energies appears in the form of gamma radiation, of the velocity of the free neutrons and fission fragments. Disintegrations following on fission also release energy. Some of this energy would be usable in the form of heat inside the reactors, while certain radiations would pass through the sides of the reactor, and would have to be stopped in a shield for the protection of personnel. In nuclear bombs only a fraction of uranium or plutonium undergoes fission, so that the usable amount of energy is also not maximal in this case. The heat given off is, however, much greater than in standard explosive appliances. *Fission yield* is the proportion of nuclei having undergone fission inside a bomb or a reactor.

flight time, an interval of time separating the passage of a particle between two given points.—Measurement of flight time, which may be effected by means of counters, enables the speed of the particle to be determined, when the distance or *base*, which separates the two points is known. Modern techniques enable measurements down to a tenth of a billionth of a second to be made.

fluctuation of range or **straggling,** a variation in the distance travelled by particles of a given type, when they are slowed down in matter, from identical energies to the stopping point. These fluctuations have their origin in the statistical nature of the slowing down process. A particle loses energy in numerous consecutive reactions with electrons and nuclei of the matter through which it passes. From this it results that each particle has its own history throughout the length of the slowing down process, whereas only average effects may be calculated or measured. Fluctuations in the range are greater the lighter the particles. (See **path length.**)

fluid, a gas or a liquid.

fluorescence, an emission of light or, in a more general sense, of electromagnetic radiation resulting from the absorption of other radiations.—The incident radiation which induces fluorescence may be composed of ions, particles or photons. In contrast to phosphorescence, fluorescence only lasts for the time during which the incident radiation excites the fluorescent body. (See **luminescence.**)

fluorography, photography of an image reproduced on a fluorescent screen.

fluoroscope, an apparatus consisting of an X-ray valve and a fluorescent screen, used for observing the internal parts of the human body or of metallic objects. X-rays pass through matter more or less easily according to its nature and thickness, and excite the fluorescent screen more or less strongly.

fluoroscopy, a fluoroscope examination.

flux, the amount of radiation passing through a surface.—A flux of particles is usually expressed by the number of particles which pass per second through a surface of 1 cm^2. For electromagnetic radiation (light, X-rays, etc) it is frequently expressed by the amount of energy which passes per second through a surface of 1 cm^2. In this case it is called a *flux of radiation*: eg a *neutron flux* (flux of neutrons).

FOCK, Vladimir A. (1898–) Russian physicist who has worked particularly on atomic and quantum radiation research and recently on the general theory of gravitation.

focusing, an action carried out on the charged particles of a beam so as to make them all pass a given point. This term is derived from optics.—Its application has been extended from luminous to particle beams on account of the analogies which exist between them. Acts of focalisation are carried out as much inside accelerators, so that the particles remain grouped in time and space, as in handling the secondary beams supplied by the accelerators,

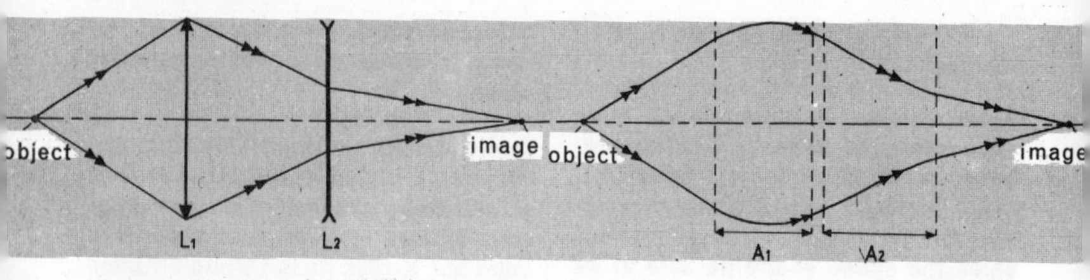

On the left, the path of light rays in an optical system composed of a thin converging lens L_1 *followed by a thin diverging lens* L_2. *On the right, paths of particles in a system composed of quadrupoles; quadrupole* A_1 *being convergent, quadrupole* A_2 *divergent. The paths of luminous rays and the particle trajectories are indicated by double arrows. (It should be observed that the properties of a quadrupole depend on the plane on which the trajectories are considered, which is contrary to the behaviour of the optical lens.)*

so as to bring particles of a given type in to detection apparatus of reduced size.

● **electrostatic focusing,** the focusing action exercised by an electric field acting on a beam.—In the case of a Van de Graaff accelerator for instance, a bent tube is placed along the path of the particles and an electric field is produced in it by applying a high voltage between two electrodes. The particles pass through a thin slot at the entrance and continue on their way between the two electrodes. What happens to those which possess a definite velocity? If they make small angles at the entrance to the ideal path, they will be brought together at the exit, the electric field deflecting mainly the outer particles. Those particles which possess a different velocity from the selected velocity would also be reassembled at the exit, though at different points. To select particles according to their velocity, it is sufficient to arrange a slot at the exit, which will allow those particles which possess a certain speed to pass; the others would be stopped by the edges of the slot.

● **magnetic focusing,** see **magnetic focusing.**

● **radial focusing** or **radial stability,** using of particles in an accelerator at a defined radius in the accelerator.—In a circular accelerator, particles should on average follow a path the radius of which is determined by their velocity. Radial stability implies that the particles oscillate around this radial position without departing too much from it. Radial stability is achieved by imposing certain conditions on the guiding magnetic field; this should vary with radius in the accelerator. One says that it has a certain *gradient*.

● **strong focusing,** a focusing process for an accelerator beam using an alternating succession of magnetic fields, the one increasing and the following one decreasing with increasing radius in the accelerator. It is also called *focusing by alternating gradient*.—This enables the size of a beam of particles to be greatly reduced by reducing the deviation of the trajectories from the ideal orbit. It is mainly used in very large accelerators. The dimensions of the beam being reduced, it is possible to decrease the volume in which the magnetic field must be maintained to guide the beam and in consequence to reduce considerably the size, weight and power demand of the electromagnets which produce the magnetic field.

force, central, a force which is directed towards a centre (centre of force) and which does not vary according to its direction from the centre. On the other hand, force usually depends on the distance to the centre of force. Gravitational forces (to which weight is due), or the electrostatic forces between two charges, are central forces. Nuclear forces may be divided into *central* and *non-central* forces. The latter depend on the relative direction of the spins of two nuclear particles in interaction.

fractional distillation, see **distillation, fractional.**

fragment, a particle produced by the division of a heavier particle. (See **fission.**)

● **fast fragment,** a fission fragment emitted with great momentum.

● **fission fragment,** a nucleus undergoing **fission** (qv) forms two or more lighter nuclei which are called *fission fragments.*

● **heavy fragment,** a fission fragment consisting of a great many neutrons and protons, constituting a heavy nucleus.

francium, an element with the atomic number 87, discovered by Marguerite Perey in 1938.—It was given this name in honour of the physicist's country. It is the heaviest of the metals. Originally isolated in the form of francium 223 (87 protons, 136 neutrons) and produced in a small proportion in the alpha disintegration of actinium 227, it belongs to the actinium series. Since then, other francium isotopes have been discovered.

FRANCK, James (1882–) German physicist. With G. Hertz he received the Nobel Prize for Physics in 1925.

FRANK, Ilya Mihailovitch (1903–) Soviet physicist. With Tamm and Cerenkov, he received the Nobel Prize for Physics in 1958 for his work on the theory of the Cerenkov effect.

fuel, a fissile material used in nuclear reactors. ‖ A mixture containing a

Fuel elements of natural and enriched uranium (Photo P. Jahan)

fissile material, such as natural uranium. The principal fuels which may be used in a reactor are:
a) *natural uranium* which is a mixture of uranium 238, non-fissile, in a 99.3 per cent proportion, and of uranium 235 fissile, in 0.7 per cent proportion, or *enriched uranium*, with more uranium 235, or else pure uranium 235;
b) *plutonium 239*: artificially produced in reactors from uranium 238;
c) *uranium 233* which is also artificially produced from thorium.

function, excitation, the correspondence between the value of the *cross-section* of a reaction between two particles and the energy of the incident particle. The excitation function is expressed by tracing an excitation curve which gives the function value for each value of the energy. This term is especially used for reactions induced by photons. It originates from the fact that gamma rays, which are photons, may excite a nucleus by placing it on a higher level of energy called the excited level. Delimitation of the excitation curves of nuclei has enabled the values of the energies of different excited levels of the same nucleus to be determined. In fact, to each of these levels corresponds a large **cross-section** (qv) which is shown by a peak in the excitation curve. Information on the structure of the nucleus may be obtained from the study of excitation curves.

furnace, atomic, a furnace which uses the heat released by fission reactions or by the action of an intense beam of particles.

fusion, with fission, one of the two possible sources of nuclear energy.—The phenomenon of fusion is, on the whole, the opposite of fission. In the latter, heavy nuclei decompose so as to produce lighter nuclei, giving off energy. In fusion, on the contrary, light nuclei assemble together to produce heavier nuclei. In very light elements, protons and neutrons are not closely bound; they are more closely bound in heavier elements. The energy which corresponds to these binding differences is given off in the fusion reaction. For fusion to take place, the two light nuclei involved must approach each other at very short distances, of the order of their dimensions. But, since these nuclei contain protons and have positive electric charges, they repel each other. So as to overcome this repulsion, high velocities have to be communicated to them. The temperature which corresponds to the speeds of thermal motion at which fusion has a reasonable chance of being produced attains millions of degrees centigrade. This is the reason why the detonator of a thermonuclear bomb consists of a nuclear bomb, which alone can provide such a temperature. It is also why control of fusion with a view to commercial use still meets with great difficulties. The lightest element—hydrogen, whose nucleus contains only one proton—gives few fusion reactions, so that other elements would be preferred to it, such as deuterium or heavy hydrogen whose nucleus contains 1 proton and 1 neutron; or again, tritium or extra-heavy hydrogen, which contains 1 proton and 2 neutrons. The following are the most interesting reactions:

deuterium (1 proton, 1 neutron)+ deuterium (1 proton, 1 neutron)
gives helium 3 (2 protons, 1 neutron) +1 neutron;

deuterium (1 proton, 1 neutron)+

deuterium (1 proton, 1 neutron) *gives* tritium (1 proton, 2 neutrons+ 1 proton).

Both of these reactions are produced at equal rates, the first generating 3.2 million electronvolts, the second 4 million. They have the advantage of requiring deuterium only, which could be extracted from ordinary water. (See **heavy water.**)

The reaction which gives the most energy (ie 17.6 million electronvolts) is the following:

deuterium (1 proton, 1 neutron)+ tritium (1 proton, 2 neutrons) *gives* helium 4 (2 protons, 2 neutrons) +1 neutron.

The energy released in fusion reactions appears in the form of the speed of the nuclei which have been produced; the greater part of the energy being taken by the lightest nucleus; ie by the neutron or proton in the preceding reactions. For commercial use the extraction of deuterium from water would be a more economical operation than the extraction of uranium ores, and water resources are practically unlimited. Fusion phenomena would probably produce less radioactivity than fission phenomena, although the neutrons produced in the reaction would require considerable shielding. Finally, it would no doubt be possible to use the energy released for the production of electricity directly, without passing through the medium of a thermal plant, which is always difficult to handle and of poor efficiency. Fusion energy has not yet been used practically on account of difficulties presented by control of the reaction. To reach the temperatures required for fusion, the usual materials cannot be employed. The **plasma** (qv), which is a group of particles in very rapid motion, must be contained inside a magnetic bottle by setting up a magnetic field strong enough to deflect the particles and prevent them from hitting the walls. Between the plasma and these walls there will be

A stellarator used in research into ways of controlling fusion to enable it to be used in industry

a vacuum. Particles nevertheless escape from this bottle and although they run no risk of causing the sides to melt through, because they are found in too small quantities, they may lower the rate of fusion since, on making contact with the sides, they cool off. Research has demonstrated that the product of the density of the particles is limited in value by the time during which they are confined so that one is directed towards an apparatus operating in bursts. For the fusion reaction to be maintained, it is necessary to work at a temperature higher than that known as ignition temperature, which is about 45 million degrees for the deuterium-deuterium reaction, and 400 million degrees for the deuterium-tritium reaction. Below this temperature, the reaction would burn out because energy radiated by the plasma is higher than the energy produced inside it. Finally, the plasma has to be of very great purity, because the presence of heavy nuclei would induce loss of energy through **bremsstrahlung** (qv). Thus, if fusion reactions in theory place an inexhaustible source of energy at man's disposal, the problems met with in using it have not been solved as yet. The vast amount of research already carried out has not yet provided any obvious result.

G

gadolinium, an element, atomic number 64, which undergoes beta disintegration when subjected to neutron bombardment.—It is used in neutronography or radiography by neutrons. The neutrons are intercepted more or less according to the nature and thickness of the object to be radiographed, and induce variable radioactivity in a gadolinium shell. Once the neutron source has activated the shell, this is left for a fairly long time against a photographic plate so that the majority of the radioactive nuclei have time to disintegrate.

gamma, a name given to the photon, a particle of the electromagnetic field, when it is of sufficient energy (higher than 10 kilo-electronvolts). Photons are called gammas when they undergo interactions with nuclei or elementary particles. Of identical nature, though usually with a less high energy, a photon due to the de-excitation of an atom is called an X-ray; photons (of decreasing energies) are called *ultraviolet, visible light, infra-red* and *radio waves.* The idea of a particle associated with a luminous wave or, more generally, with an electromagnetic wave, was introduced by Einstein in 1905 to explain the phenomena of radiation and the photo-electric effect. Gamma radiation was distinctly identified by Villard in 1900 at the beginning of research into radioactivity. Unstable nuclei may sometimes decay by gamma emission as well as by alpha or beta emission. Fairly frequently, a gamma ray emission may be observed following an alpha or beta disintegration. An excited nucleus is formed in this first disintegration, which leaves an excess of energy. In a relatively short time, corresponding to periods of less than a second or a minute, the excited nucleus loses its excess of energy by emitting a gamma ray. The final residual nucleus has the same number of protons and neutrons as the original excited nucleus. The mass of the final nucleus is slightly lower than that of the initial nucleus, with a quantity equivalent to the energy of a gamma ray. (See **Einstein's law.**) This phenomenon is called an isomeric transition. Conversely, a nucleus bombarded by a gamma ray may be raised to an excited state by absorption. This phenomenon appears with great frequency when the gamma rays possess an energy which corresponds exactly to the supplementary mass of an excited state of the nucleus. Another frequent method of producing gamma rays is based on *bremsstrahlung* (or radiation). Electrically charged particles are slowed down in matter by means of electromagnetic actions with electrons and nuclei of the atoms (braking by the nuclei is the more important). Energy lost in the slowing down of charged particles is recovered in the form of gamma rays, from which a beam may be formed through suitable selection of their directions and energies. Radiation production is greater the faster and lighter the charged particles. This explains why a high energy electron accelerator is generally used to produce beams of gamma rays. Finally, certain nuclear reactions induced by the action of protons or neutrons produce excited nuclei, which are de-excited by gamma ray emission. Gamma rays passing through matter are absorbed progressively, giving rise to the following principal phenomena:

the photo-electric effect: an electron is ejected from an atom, and the gamma ray disappears

the Compton effect: an electron is set in motion, the gamma ray losing part of its energy

materialisation: a gamma ray passing close to a nucleus forms a pair of electrons, one positive, the other negative. Matter is formed and the energy of the gamma ray disappears. The Compton effect is preponderant for low-energy gamma rays, while materialisation is dominant for high-energy gammas. The distance travelled by gamma rays in matter does not have a unique value when the rays are of definite energy. There is a progressive reduction of a beam of gamma rays; half of them will have disappeared by the end of a certain thickness of matter. By the end of double the thickness only half of the previous gamma rays remain, ie one quarter. By the end of three times the thickness of matter, there remains only one eighth, etc. It is the shielding from reactors and accelerators of gamma rays, which, like shielding from neutrons, demands most care. The physical characteristics of the gamma ray are those of the photon. It does not possess a *rest mass.* It travels through space at the speed of light. Its spin, a quantity proportional to its intrinsic angular momentum, equals 1. It carries no electric charge.

gammatherapy, a medical treatment which consists of irradiation by means of a gamma ray source.

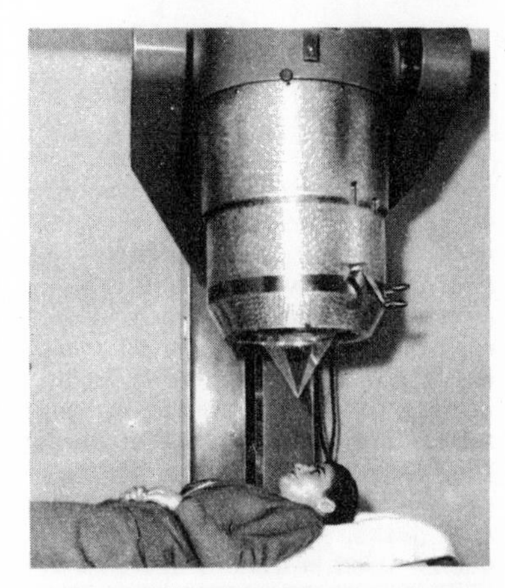

A cobalt bomb, source of the gamma rays used in the treatment of some types of cancer (Photo Keystone)

GAMOW, George Anthony (1904–) a physicist of Russian extraction, naturalised American, 1939. His research has been on the structure of the atom, the laws of radioactivity, relativistic cosmology, thermonuclear reactions in the stars and the possible existence, since then confirmed, of the antiproton.

gas, rare, a gas found in small quantities in the Earth's atmosphere.—Rare gases are classified in the following table, which gives the distribution of the electrons of the atom on the subshells of shells K, L and M, as well as their abundance in the air in millionths. Argon is the most used and the most abundant. All the rare gases possess the characteristic of being chemically inert. The electrons of a rare gas are distributed on electronically saturated shells or subshells, so that there is no room for the electrons of another atom on these shells and chemical binding is impossible. Helium and radon possess the same property. Recent research has, however, arrived at the discovery of several chemical compounds of rare gases. Rare gases are frequently used in devices operated by an electric discharge (Geiger counter, spark detectors, flashlights, discharge tubes). Neon provides two lines, one orange-red the other green; krypton a yellow-green line and xenon a blue line.

	K	*L*	*M*	*N*	*O*	*proportion in millionths*
Neon	2	2+6				18
Argon	2	2+6	2+6+10			9,400
Krypton	2	2+6	2+6+10	2+6		1
Xenon	2	2+6	2+6	2+6+10	2+6	0.05

GAUSS, Johann (1777–1855) German mathematician who made outstanding contributions to the development of mathematics and mathematical physics. His name is used for the unit of magnetic field.

GEIGER, Hans (1882–1945) German physicist. An assistant to Rutherford, while under his supervision he determined the charge of the alpha particle. He demonstrated that the atomic number of a chemical element represents the number of charges of the nucleus. With Müller, he invented a particle counter, the *Geiger-Müller counter.*

Geiger-Müller counter, see **counter.**

GELL-MANN, Murray (1929–) American physicist who has contributed to fundamental particle theory, particularly as regards the use of symmetry principles.

generator, electrostatic, a generator of current based on electrostatic effects. It provides very high voltages, up to several million volts, although of low strength, of the order of a millionth or a thousandth of an ampere. It is mainly used in **accelerators** (qv) of low energy particles, such as the Van de Graaff. It is also used in deflectors of beams of charged particles (see **separator**). Ordinary generators, dynamo and alternator, employ the properties of conductors immersed in a variable magnetic field. In electrostatic generators electric charges are accumulated which are deposited on to an insulating substance, for instance by friction. The electric charges are carried by an insulating belt, on to a large conducting electrode. The belt transfers its charge to the electrode by means of a charge comb which consists of sharp points. The electric field, locally very high on the points of the comb, carries the charges on to the electrode. The voltage which an electrostatic generator can provide is limited by the corona effect which leads to spark breakdown. This restricted voltage may be increased by submerging the generator in an atmosphere of gas under pressure and by using certain gases for which the breakdown voltage is particularly high. The corona effect may be used to stabilise the voltage provided by the generator. The Van de Graaff at Wisconsin, for instance, is submerged in a mixture of air and freon under 7 atmosphere pressure.

neutron generator, see **neutron.**

geomagnetic effect, the effect of the terrestrial magnetic field on cosmic radiation. The magnetic field is weak, of the order of the gauss only, whereas it is known how to produce with ease a field of several tens of thousand of gauss in particle accelerators. The Earth's field, however, extends over hundreds of thousands of kilometres, which explains why its action on cosmic radiation is by no means negligible. Study of the deviation which electrically charged particles undergo in the terrestrial magnetic field, shows that the strength of radiation reaching the Earth's surface vertically is stronger at the poles than at the equator. Particles which arrive vertically at the pole, travel parallel to the magnetic field and the action of this on the particles is zero. Particles arriving vertically at the equator are perpendicular to the magnetic field, and undergo maximal deviation. It may also be observed that at the poles, not all particles can enter the Earth's atmosphere vertically, whereas at the equator particles may only enter the Earth's atmosphere vertically provided they have sufficient energy, ie about 15 GeV. The other particles are deflected by the magnetic field.

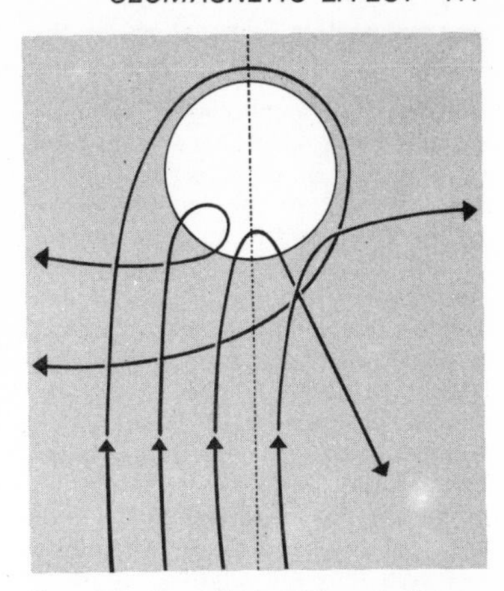

Geomagnetic effect. The circle represents the Earth's equator: the trajectories are those of high energy protons travelling in the equatorial plane of the terrestrial magnetic field

geomagnetism, magnetism of the Earth.

geometry, a technological term indicating the geometrical arrangement of a group of detectors around a phenomenon to be studied.—The geometry is said to be *good* when it is peculiarly well adapted to measuring the quantity sought (mass, mean lifetime, etc); and when it gives a good degree of precision. When one wishes to detect all the nuclear reactions produced on a target by an incident beam, it is necessary to place detectors around the target in all directions, so as to detect the products of the reaction in whichever direction they are emitted; there is then *good geometry*.

GERMER, Lester Halbert (1896–) American physicist. With Davisson, he discovered the phenomenon of interference in crystals irradiated by electrons, thereby giving experimental grounds to the theory of wave mechanics of de Broglie.

GeV, symbol of **gigaelectronvolt** (qv).

ghost or **phantom,** a sample used in measurements of radioactivity which has the same behaviour as a biological tissue.—It may be used to study the effects of radiation on man; detection devices (ionisation chambers, for instance) being placed at different points of the ghost. From them information may be deduced about the dose received at different levels (skin, bones, etc). Water, or occasionally beeswax, is frequently used in experiments for the sake of convenience, as biological tissues consist largely of water.

gigaelectronvolt, a unit worth one billion electronvolts.

GLASER, Donald Arthur (1926–) American physicist. In 1960 he received the Nobel Prize for Physics for his invention of the liquid hydrogen or helium bubble-chamber.

glass, lead, when control or handling of radioactive products demands visual supervision, ordinary glass is not always an adequate solution. On the one hand, glass becomes opaque when subjected to strong radiation, it has therefore been necessary to invent special glass capable of withstanding a radiation dose five times greater than ordinary glass. On the other hand, ordinary glass is not always a sufficient shield against radiation for the protection of the operator. Glass made with lead, which has been studied for use with X-rays and other radiations, provides more effective shielding. However, it stands up less well to the action of the radiations which render it opaque. Furthermore, lead glass needs to be protected against corrosion.

glove-box, an appliance which enables radioactive products to be handled. It consists of a sealed container, one of the sides of which is provided with mobile rubber gloves. These prevent the hands of the operator from coming into direct contact with radioactive products. *See illustration on p. 113.*

GOEPPERT-MAYER, Maria (1906–) American physicist. Professor at California University. She has worked especially on the structure of the atomic nucleus. Her discoveries relating to the shell model of the nucleus earned her the Nobel Prize for Physics in 1963; she shared it with Hans Jensen who had also worked on the same problem, as well as with Eugene Wigner.

GOLDSTEIN, Eugen (1850–1930) German physicist. Through his research on discharges in rarefied gases he discovered positive or canal rays.

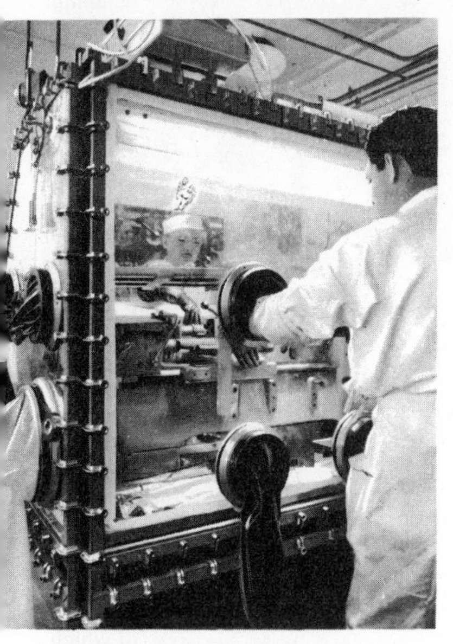

Glove-box containing a lathe for machining combustible elements with a plutonium base (Photo CEA)

gram-molecule or **mole,** a mass of a given compound, proportional for each compound to the mass of its molecule.—The standard unit is established by taking the gram-molecule of isotopically normal oxygen to be 32 grams. (See atomic **mass.**)

graphite, one of the two crystalline forms of carbon, the other being the diamond.—Carbon atoms in graphite are to be found at the corners of hexagons set at regular intervals in a plane lattice, the planes being in some way piled on each other yet without being strongly bound. Graphite is the most usual form of carbon; the formation of diamonds in the Earth's crust may be explained by the high temperatures and high pressures which existed in the past. Because carbon absorbs few neutrons, whereas they lose an appreciable amount of their energy in collisions with carbon nuclei, graphite is frequently used as a moderator in nuclear reactors. Although heavy water is superior to carbon as a moderator—neutrons lose more energy in it, at each impact, than in carbon—graphite remains much more economic. It can be prepared in large quantities and obtained in a very pure state, the burden of impurities capable of absorbing neutrons being therefore considerably reduced. *See illustration on p. 114.*

gravitation, an act of attraction taking place between two objects possessing mass, from which is derived the weight of objects on earth as well as the movement of planets of the Solar System.

graviton, a particle whose existence has been theoretically assumed, but which cannot be identified with present methods of detection. (It may be said that it is the particle of the gravitational field, in the same way as the photon is the particle of the electromagnetic field.)—According to theoretical considerations, it is thought that its mass is zero and that it travels at the speed of light. Its spin, intrinsic angular momentum, would be 2. Due to the fact that gravitational interactions are extremely weak, it is not possible to detect a reaction induced by a graviton passing through a thickness of matter

Placing graphite blocks in the core of the G1 reactor at the Marcoule (France) Nuclear Power Plant. The men are working inside the reinforced concrete shield. At the back is the rear of the exit plate, with a tube for each active rod. (Photo CEA)

such as exists in normal detection apparatus, whereas it is possible to detect those induced by photons whose interactions are much more frequent.

group of neutrons, an idea introduced by Fermi into reactor calculations. Since neutron reactions vary according to their velocities, it is possible to decompose their effects by classifying them into groups, the numbers of which are increased as and when one desires to increase the precision of the results obtained.

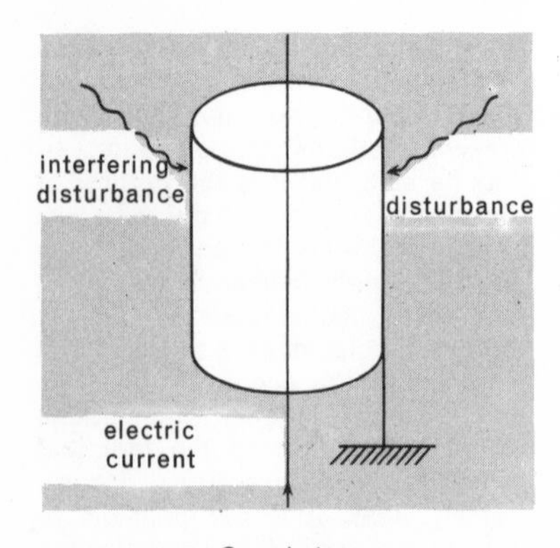

Guard-ring

guard-ring, a cylindrical metal envelope sheathing a conductor to protect it from random atmospheric electromagnetic radiation. Counters, which are highly sensitive, are surrounded by a similar guard ring to cancel the effects of atmospheric or industrial interference which might be in danger of falsifying the index of the counter.

guiding field, see **field.**

gun, an apparatus which produces a strong, narrow beam of particles. It may be used in various ways, such as irradiation, production of induced radioactivity, sterilisation, heating. The particles which constitute the beam are usually electrons or ions.

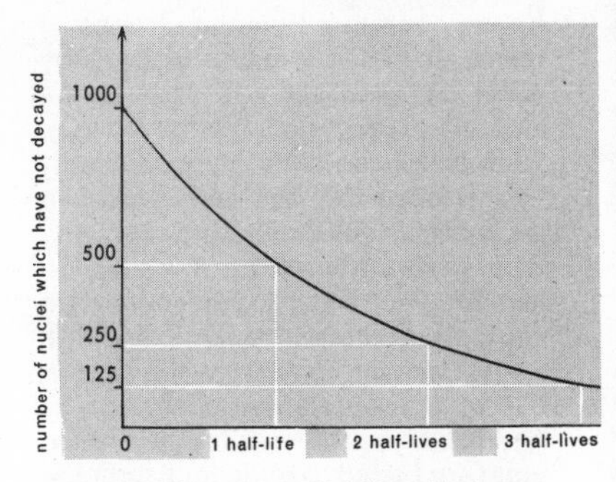

Half-life: if at the initial time there are 1000 radioactive nuclei, by the end of one period only 500 remain, by the end of two periods, 250, etc

H

H, symbol for **hydrogen** (qv).

h, symbol for **Planck's constant** (qv). The size of atoms, the colour of thermal radiation and the uncertainty relations all depend directly on the value of h.

HAHN, Otto (1879–) German physicist. He isolated mesothorium and discovered protoactinium (with L. Meitner), radiothorium and uranium 11. He received the Nobel Prize for Chemistry in 1945 for having demonstrated uranium fission with Strassmann.

half-life, in radioactivity, the length of time in which half the radioactive nuclei of a sample have disintegrated. By the end of a period of time equal to two half-lives, half the remaining nuclei have in turn disintegrated, in all:

$$1/2+1/2\times1/2=3/4.$$

By the end of a period of time equal to three half-lives, $3/4+1/2\times1/2\times1/2=7/8$ of the nuclei have disintegrated, etc. The radioactivity of a sample which contains enough nuclei is therefore theoretically of unlimited duration. However, it decreases rapidly with the number of periods. Radioactive substances produced in nuclear reactors are frequently stored for some months before being handled. Radioactive elements of short half-lives, of less than some tens of days, possess in this case a radioactivity which has been reduced to an insignificant value. In European scientific literature the word *period* is often used in place of the illogical term half-life.

HAMILTON, William Rowan (1805–65), Irish mathematician. Physicists owe to him the formulation of classical mechanics in a way that transforms readily to quantum mechanics. This was the technique employed by **Schrödinger** (qv).

●**Hamilton function,** an operator function of position and momentum corresponding to the total energy of a mechanical system. The equations of motion in quantum mechanics are constructed from this function.

heavy water, a compound used in reactors. The molecule of ordinary water contains two hydrogen atoms and one oxygen atom (symbol: H_2O). Each of the two hydrogen atoms may be replaced by a heavy hydrogen atom, also called **deuterium** (qv). The hydrogen atom consists of one proton and one electron. The *deuterium* atom contains a neutron, a particle with a weight similar to that of the proton but without an electric charge. The neutron and proton of the deuterium atom are bound together and form the nucleus. One heavy water molecule contains two deuterium atoms and one oxygen atom (symbol D_2O). Heavy water is used in reactors as a moderator. The neutrons of a reactor have to be slowed down from the energy at which they are produced to the energy at which they become effective. Hydrogen is the best slowing agent, a neutron losing on average 50 per cent of its energy on impact with a proton. However, the protons absorb a great many of the neutrons. The deuterium nucleus is a good slowing agent, giving a loss of energy of 44 per cent per impact. As it absorbs some 30 times fewer neutrons than the protons, heavy water is greatly superior to ordinary water as a moderating agent. It is also present in a very small proportion (one 6000th) in ordinary water. It may be separated by distillation (see **separation of isotopes**), or by electrolysis, a method used in its preparation during World War II. Heavy water was then a strategic material of the highest importance, since it enabled the first reactor to operate, from which all the information relating to military uses of nuclear energy for perfecting the first atomic bomb was obtained.

A factory at Rjukan (Norway) for the manufacture of heavy water (Photo Kit Robbins-Rapho)

HEISENBERG, Werner (1901–) German physicist. He is considered to be one of the most important theoreticians of the present day. He constructed quantum mechanics. As an application, he discovered the allotropic forms of hydrogen. He is the creator of the matrix theory of quantum mechanics; of the uncertainty principle, and of a theory of nuclear forces. For these works he was awarded the Nobel Prize for Physics in 1932. *Illustration p. 117.*

● **Heisenberg's principle** or **uncertainty principle,** see **uncertainty relations.**

Werner Heisenberg (Photo Agence intercontinentale)

helium, the second element, after hydrogen.—The helium atom contains two electrons and a nucleus consisting of two protons and two neutrons. Both the electrons are to be found on the **K-shell** (qv), which is complete; helium is chemically inert. It may be used as a coolant in nuclear reactors, since it absorbs very few neutrons. However, being light, it carries little heat and has to circulate very rapidly. On the other hand its cost price is high. A liquid coolant is generally preferred to it; helium is the gas which liquefies at the lowest temperature, at 269° C below zero. In the liquid state it has a special property, that of superfluidity, which has been studied in relation to quantum theories of many-body systems.

HERTZ, Gustav (1887–) German physicist, a nephew of Heinrich Hertz, the physicist, well known for his work on the propagation of electromagnetic waves (*Hertzian Waves*). He studied the phenomena of fluorescence. In 1913 he introduced the concept of energy level of electrons in the atom and received the Nobel Prize for Physics in 1925, with James Franck.

heterogeneous, said of a **reactor** (qv) composed of separate elements (fuel, moderator, reflector, coolant).

heterokinetic, said of an assembly consisting of elements with different velocities (ie in a *heterokinetic beam,* not all the particles possess the same speed).

HEVESY, Georg Karl von (1885–) Swedish chemist of Hungarian origin. For his work on the separation of isotopes (he obtained the isotope of mass 41 from radioactive potassium) and on radioactive nuclei he was awarded the Nobel Prize for Chemistry in 1943.

hexafluoride of uranium, a gaseous uranium compound, the molecule of which consists of 1 uranium atom and 6 fluoride atoms. At present it is exclusively used in the *separation of isotopes* of uranium.

homogeneous, this is said of a reactor in which two or more of the elements are closely intermingled in the shape of a liquid or a powder (eg suspension of oxide of uranium in water may be used, the uranium being the fuel, the water the moderator).

homokinetic, said of an assembly consisting of particles all with identical or allied velocities (ie in a *homokinetic beam* the particles all have approximately the same velocity).

hot, generally used when referring to material with high radioactivity which requires to be handled with care.

• **hot laboratory,** a place in which strong radioactive sources are used; those above 100 millicuries, for instance. Special manipulation systems, ventilation and shielding devices must be installed in it.

hydrogen, the first and lightest of the elements. Its nucleus consists of only one proton. The hydrogen atom consists of one proton and one electron. Hydrogen together with oxygen enters into the composition of water, H_2O, each molecule of water consisting of one oxygen atom and two hydrogen atoms. Water may be used in a reactor as a coolant and as a moderator, since the hydrogen nuclei are those on which neutrons lose the most energy. Heavy water D_2O which contains deuterium in place of hydrogen is, however, preferred since it slows down the neutrons almost as well and absorbs far less of them than hydrogen. Ordinary water contains a weak proportion of **heavy water** (qv): 1/6000. Deuterium is a hydrogen isotope. As its nucleus contains one proton and one neutron, it is therefore twice as heavy as hydrogen. It is sometimes called *heavy hydrogen*. Its chemical and atomic properties are similar to those of light hydrogen. There is a third isotope of hydrogen, tritium, sometimes called *extra-heavy hydrogen*. Its nucleus contains one proton and two neutrons. This isotope is unstable and decays by beta radioactivity with a half-life of 12.5 years. A fourth hydrogen isotope has recently been successfully manufactured whose nucleus contains one proton and three neutrons; it is very unstable. The

Liquid hydrogen reservoir (Photo Aluminium Review)

hydrogen atom being the simplest, primary research into atomic structure has concentrated on it. Its spectrum, which may be derived within the framework of quantum theory, provides a detailed check of the theory. Hydrogen is frequently used in nuclear physics as a target in experiments with counters or bubble-chambers. Its simple nucleus produces reactions whose interpretation is obvious. It is used in liquid form so that the beam of incident particles encounters a sufficient number of protons. This liquid state implies that it is necessary to maintain a temperature of approximately 250° C below zero. Hydrogen is a powerful explosive; mixed with oxygen a spark is sufficient to provoke its combustion. It needs, therefore, to be used with extreme caution.

hydrogenoid, an atomic system formed by a nucleus with a positive electric charge around which gravitates only one electron with a negative electric charge. The hydrogen atom is the simplest of the hydrogenoids. It consists of a proton around which gravitates an electron. The subsequent hydrogenoids are ions, ie atoms from which electrons have been torn until only one remains round the nucleus. Thus, the helium atom is composed of two electrons; the helium ion He^{+}, from which one electron has been torn, is a hydrogenoid. The lithium atom consists of three electrons; the lithium ion Li^{++} from which two electrons have been torn is a hydrogenoid, etc. Study of hydrogenoid spectra has been very useful in research on atomic structure within the framework of quantum theory.

hyperfragment, a nucleus in which a hyperon replaces a proton or a neutron. (Eg helium is one of the most common *hyperfragments*.) The ordinary helium nucleus consists of two neutrons and two protons. The lambda hyperon, an unstable particle slightly heavier than the neutron, may enter the nucleus in place of a neutron; thus a hyperfragment is obtained which consists of two protons, one neutron and one lambda hyperon. Since the hyperon is bound by the nuclear forces inside the hyperfragment, the latter does not disintegrate as rapidly as a free hyperon. However, the hyperfragment is not a stable system, so that it ends by disintegrating with emission of a pion. For the helium hyperfragment, for instance, the products are a helium 3 nucleus (2 protons, 1 neutron), a proton and a negative pion. Hyperfragments may be produced by bombarding nuclei with fairly high-energy particles. As the fragment includes a hyperon of non-zero **strangeness number** (qv), its production is particularly abundant when particles, such as K mesons, with a similar strangeness number, are used as incident particles. Study of hyperfragments provides information on the comparative nuclear forces to which nucleons (protons and neutrons) and hyperons are subjected. *Double hyperfragments* have recently been observed; they each contained 2 strange particles.

hyperon, a heavier particle than the neutron.—Hyperons are unstable and disintegrate rapidly usually giving a nucleon (neutron or proton) and a pion. The first hyperons were called V^0, because their disintegration was observed in the form of:

V^0 *gives* proton+negative pion.

The two charged secondary traces may be detected in a Wilson chamber, whereas the V^0, which is electrically neutral, leaves no trace. The V^0s consisted of both lambda hyperons and K mesons, which were subsequently differentiated. Charged hyperons, slightly heavier than the V^0

hyperons	*strangeness*		*anti-hyperons*
neutral lambda	−1	+1	neutral anti-lambda
negative sigma	−1	+1	negative anti-sigma (which is positive)
neutral sigma	−1	+1	neutral anti-sigma
positive sigma	−1	+1	positive anti-sigma (which is negative)
negative xi	−2	+2	negative anti-xi (which is positive)
neutral xi	−2	+2	neutral anti-xi

were also discovered and finally the antihyperon (see **antiparticle**). Hyperons are *strange particles.* They group together in multiplets, a group of hyperons with the same strangeness number and allied masses, but whose electric charges are different. Twelve are actually known (see table above). Hyperon disintegration is rapid. The lifetimes are of some tenths of a billionth of a second. That of the neutral sigma, which gives a lambda and a gamma ray, is even more rapid. Charged lambdas and sigmas disintegrate on giving a nucleon and a pion. The xis disintegrate on giving a nucleon and a pion. Research carried out on hyperons enables progress to be made in understanding nuclear interactions as well as weak interactions.

I

IAEA, International Atomic Energy Agency. The aim of this agency of the United Nations is the peaceful use of atomic energy. It consists of 95 member States. The most important, according to their financial contributions, are: the United States, the USSR, Great Britain, France and Germany.

ICRP, International Commission on Radiological Protection, charged with the collection of information on radiation hazards and the establishment and regular review of maximum permissible **dose** (qv) rates for various occupations. National codes of practice are normally based on these ICRP recommendations.

independence, charge, see **•charge independence.**

inelastic, this is said of an interaction (collision, scattering, etc) in which there is an absorption of energy.— The kinetic energy of the secondary particles is in this case less than that of the primary particles, the difference appearing in the reaction in the form of created particles, an increase in the mass of the initial particles or of radiation. For example, the reaction

proton+proton *gives*
proton+proton+neutral pion

is inelastic. Some of the kinetic energy possessed by the incident proton before the reaction is used to form the mass of the pion (another part being also used to communicate a certain kinetic energy to it). The remainder of the incident proton's energy is distributed between the two outgoing protons.

injection, this is a delicate operation which consists in leading the beam of particles of a primary accelerator to the main accelerator.—In high-energy accelerators, particles to be accelerated are injected when they already possess a certain velocity. This initial velocity has been communicated to them by a low-energy accelerator, such as a Van de Graaff or a linear accelerator. *See also illustration p. 122.*

interaction, actions which take place between two or more physical systems. All elements of matter or of radiation in the universe are in a

Injection of protons into the CERN (Geneva) synchrotron. The protons, from the Linac primary accelerator, come from the left and are tangentially injected (in the centre of the picture) into the circular trajectory of the synchrotron. On the right can be seen the circular construction of the synchrotron. (Photo Ecole Polytechnique, Paris)

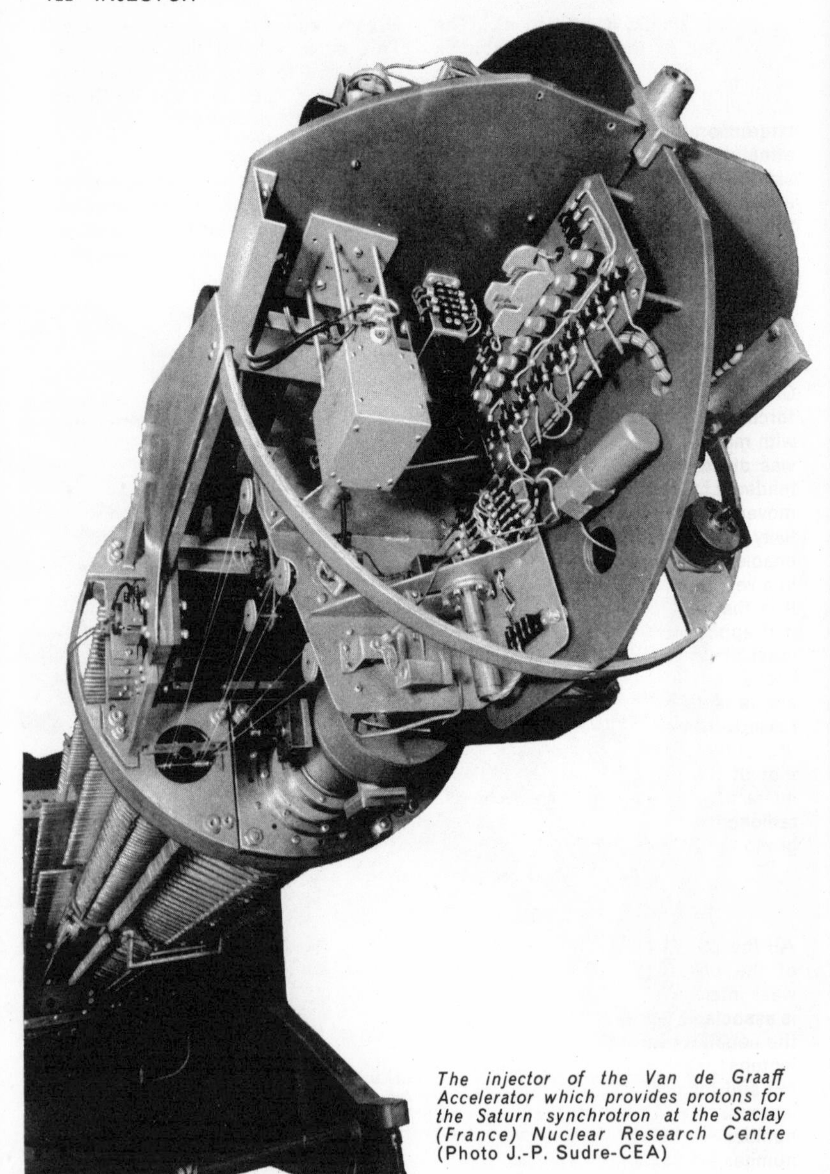

The injector of the Van de Graaff Accelerator which provides protons for the Saturn synchrotron at the Saclay (France) Nuclear Research Centre (Photo J.-P. Sudre-CEA)

permanent state of interaction. When a particular interaction between two systems is studied, they are considered as if free from their other interactions, which are hoped not to affect the phenomenon under consideration. When a nuclear interaction between two protons is studied, their weight, ie their gravitational interaction, is considered negligible. Up to the present, four types of interaction have been isolated in nature: *gravitation, weak interactions, electromagnetic interactions* and *strong* or *nuclear interactions.*

Gravitation is the result of attractive forces between systems endowed with mass or energy. Its universality was discovered by Newton, who extended it from the fall of bodies to the movement of the planets. The relativity concept introduced by Einstein enabled the theory to be established in a very complete and exact fashion. It is the weakest of the interactions. If it appears to be the one with the most obvious manifestations, that is because *electromagnetic interactions* are rarely brought into play, atoms having a zero electric charge, because that of the negative electrons cancels that of the positive nucleus. *Weak interactions* are responsible for beta radioactivity. For example, disintegration of the neutron:

neutron *gives* proton
+electron+neutrino.

All the particles, with the exception of the photon, appear to undergo weak interactions. The idea of *lepton* is associated with them: the electron, the negative mu and the neutrino are leptons; the electron, the positive mu and the antineutrino are all antileptons. By attributing the leptonic number +1 to the leptons and the number −1 to the antileptons, it will be seen that the number of leptons remains constant in the interaction. In the neutron example, the leptonic numbers are as follows:

neutron *gives* proton
0 — 0
+negative electron+antineutrino
+1 −1

The total number of leptons is zero, before and after the weak interaction. Disintegrations of the pion, mu lepton, K meson, etc are also weak interactions:

pion *gives* mu lepton+neutrino;
mu lepton *gives* electron+neutrino
+antineutrino
K meson *gives* mu lepton+neutrino.

Finally, certain disintegrations of *strange particles* do not produce any leptons, for example:

K meson *gives* pion+pion.

They nevertheless possess some characteristics of weak interactions. *Electromagnetic interactions* give rise to electric, magnetic and luminous phenomena. (See **electromagnetism.**) They concern all systems which have an electric charge or a magnetic moment (a characteristic similar to that of a small magnet). The proton possesses a positive electric charge and a magnetic moment. The neutron has a zero electric charge, but may undergo electromagnetic interactions through the medium of its magnetic moment; they are generally weak. An atom also has a zero total electric charge, but its magnetic moment is not usually zero. Photons (gamma rays, X-rays, ultra-violet rays, light, infra-red rays, radio-electric waves) are vehicles for electromagnetic interactions.

Strong or nuclear interactions. Only some particles are subject to them;

on the one hand, baryons, which include nucleons (neutron and proton) and hyperons (lambda, sigma, xi), all the baryons being at least as heavy as the protons. On the other hand, the vehicles for strong interactions, called mesons, sub-divide into two groups: the pions and the K mesons. Research into strong interaction is at present being directed along two lines. The one aims to explain the structure of the nuclei of atoms, whereas the other aims to define the characteristics of fundamental particles which undergo these interactions. Nuclear interactions play a great part in the Sun and stars, and on Earth they have already led to stable systems, the nuclei. (See **nuclear force.**)

Of the four preceding forms of interaction, the best known are gravitation and electromagnetic interactions. The theories of these interactions have reached a degree of perfection which makes it possible to predict very precisely the results of measurement to the millionth or billionth. Despite continuing progress, knowledge of weak and strong interactions has not yet found a definitive form.

internal conversion, see **conversion, internal.**

ion, an atom (or molecule) which has gained or lost electrons (of a negative electric charge). An atom which has gained an electron has a negative electric charge; an atom which has lost an electron has a positive electric charge. Solutions which are called *electrolytic* contain molecules or atoms in the shape of ions. A solution of copper sulphate $CuSO_4$ in water contains a certain proportion of dissociated molecules; the ion SO_4, which consists of one sulphur atom and 4 oxygen atoms, contains two supplementary electrons; it has a negative charge. The ion Cu^{++} has lost two of its electrons; it has a positive charge. If a body is raised to a very high temperature, all its atoms are fully ionised, ie decomposed into positive ions, the nuclei, and into negative ions, the electrons. Other phenomena may induce **ionisation** (qv) of the atom.

ion exchanger, a chemical product which enables certain elements to be fixed. These exchangers are of current use in nuclear chemistry, mainly to extract from among the radioactive elements produced in a reactor, those which are the most active, so as to eliminate the greater part of radioactivity. The same technique is used to extract the plutonium formed from a uranium rod after it has functioned inside a reactor. Plutonium is a fissile material which may be used in a fresh reactor, after the uranium rod has been exhausted in a first reactor. The principal ion exchangers are synthetic resins. How is the fixation on an electron exchanger carried out? The exchanger is in solid form, whereas the element to be isolated is in an electrolytic liquid solution. In this solution molecules are dissociated into ions. The property of the ion exchanger is precisely to possess loosely bound ions inside its structure which may be exchanged with those of the solution. Thus the ions of the liquid settle on the solid while the ions of the solid are handed over to the liquid.

ionisation, a phenomenon in which an ion is produced.—Ionisation may be induced by the passage of charged particles into matter. The ionising particle loses some of its momentum, which is used to extract electrons bound to the atom. This loss of energy is the greater the more bound the electron. 13.5 electronvolts are required to remove the electron from a hydrogen atom; 5 to 8 electronvolts to extract an outer electron from a metal atom; 15 to 20 electronvolts to extract the first electron of rare gases such as neon, argon, etc. Extraction of the subsequent electrons demands more and more energy (up to several thousand electronvolts). Thus the electrons of the outer shell of the atom are the easiest to tear off and atoms which contain few electrons on the outer shells, such as the metal ones, for instance, are the easiest to ionise. Ionisation may also be produced by X or gamma rays or collisions (see **photo-electric effect, ●Compton effect**). This is the phenomenon most frequently used in detection appliances such as **●Wilson chambers,** nuclear photographic **emulsions,** Geiger-Müller **counters, ●spark chambers,** etc (qqv).

●ionisation potential, energy necessary to remove one electron from an atom.

ionising, said of a corpuscle or a beam of particles which induce ionisation.

ionium, a name sometimes given to thorium 230, an alpha radioactive element belonging to the uranium series.—Its mean lifetime is 80,000 years.

irradiation, exposure of people or material to radiation.—Irradiation suffered by a human being is said to be *external* when the radiation source is situated outside the body, and *internal* when it lies inside the body as the result of contamination by way of the digestive or respiratory tracts. (See **dose.**) It may be deliberately performed in medicine, chemistry or in metallurgy. *See illustration p. 126.*

isobar, term used for nuclei having the same mass number.—Thus chromium 50, vanadium 50 and titanium 50 are isobars, all three of them stable. Their nuclei are composed as follows:

chromium 50: 24 protons, 26 neutrons;
vanadium 50: 23 protons, 27 neutrons;
titanium 50: 22 protons, 28 neutrons.

Isobars of a stable nucleus are frequently unstable and disintegrate by alpha, beta or gamma radioactivity.

isodose line or **curve,** a line which connects points irradiated in identical fashion in a system subjected to radiation.—Isodose lines have been traced for the human body subjected to radiation used for medical treatment, eg radiography, X-rays, etc.

isomer, term for two or several nuclei with the same composition, yet able to exist in different energy states.—Isomeric nuclei contain the same number of protons and neutrons. In consequence, they have the same atomic number and mass number. An isomeric nucleus in the lowest energy state is called a *fundamental nucleus,* it is the one with the lowest mass. The other isomers are in unstable states, ie they disintegrate giving a gamma ray and the fundamental nucleus (disintegrations may also take place through intermediate isomeric nuclei). The name of *isomer* is generally reserved for the nuclei which disintegrate slowly, with periods of from several millionths of a second to several years. The name of *excited nucleus* describes more especially nuclei which return more

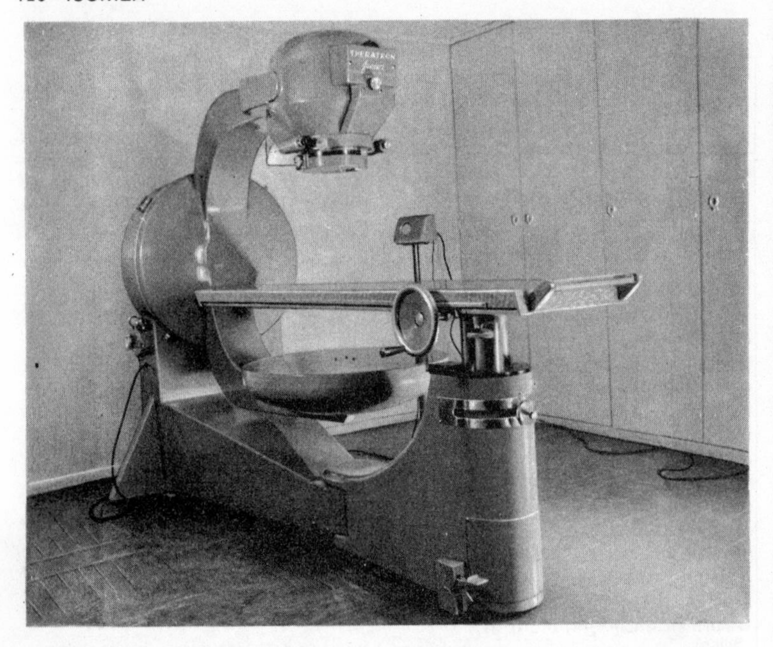

A cobalt therapy appliance which allows an irradiation field to be obtained with better definition than can be had by X-ray therapy (Photo Compagnie générale de radiologie)

rapidly to the fundamental state. The distinction between these two kinds of nuclei is not strict. Bromine 80, for example, possesses two isomeric states and one excited state.

● **isomerism** or **isomery,** character of **isomers.**

isospin, synonym of isotopic **spin** (qv).

isotone, said of nuclei which contain the same number of neutrons. They differ by the number of protons. For example nuclei of neon 20 and of oxygen 18 are isotones. They are made up as follows:

neon 20: 10 protons, 10 neutrons;
oxygen 18: 8 protons, 10 neutrons.
The isotone nuclei of a stable nucleus may be either stable or unstable.

isotope, said of nuclei containing the same number of protons.—The isotopic nuclei therefore belong to the same element: their chemical and atomic characteristics are practically identical. They differ by the number of neutrons. Uranium 235 (92 protons, 143 neutrons) and uranium 238 (92 protons, 146 neutrons) are isotopes. Uranium 238 is slightly heavier than uranium 235 because of the three supplementary neutrons. (See *Table.*)

TABLE OF NATURAL ISOTOPES

element	atomic number	isotope	abundance
Hydrogen H	1	H^{1}	99.984
		H^{2}	0.016
Helium He	2	He^{3}	1.3×10^{-4}
		He^{4}	100
Lithium Li	3	Li^{6}	7.42
		Li^{7}	92.58
Beryllium Be	4	Be^{9}	100
Boron B	5	B^{10}	19.6
		B^{11}	80.4
Carbon C	6	C^{12}	98.89
		C^{13}	1.11
Nitrogen N	7	N^{14}	99.63
		N^{15}	0.37
Oxygen O	8	O^{16}	99.76
		O^{17}	0.04
		O^{18}	0.20
Fluorine F	9	F^{19}	100
Neon N	10	Ne^{20}	90.92
		Ne^{21}	0.26
		Ne^{22}	8.82
Sodium Na	11	Na^{23}	100
Magnesium Mg	12	Mg^{24}	78.70
		Mg^{25}	10.13
		Mg^{26}	11.17
Aluminium Al	13	Al^{27}	100
Silicon Si	14	Si^{28}	92.21
		Si^{29}	4.70
		Si^{30}	3.09
Phosphorus	15	P^{31}	100
Sulphur S	16	S^{32}	95.0
		S^{33}	0.76
		S^{34}	4.22
		S^{36}	0.01
Chlorine Cl	17	Cl^{35}	75.53
		Cl^{37}	24.47
Argon A	18	A^{36}	0.34
		A^{38}	0.06
		A^{40}	99.60
Potassium K	19	K^{39}	93.10
		K^{40}	0.0118(RN)
		K^{41}	6.88
Calcium Ca	20	Ca^{40}	96.97
		Ca^{42}	0.64
		Ca^{43}	0.15
		Ca^{44}	2.06
		Ca^{46}	0.003
		Ca^{48}	0.18
Scandium Sc	21	Sc^{45}	100
Titanium Ti	22	Ti^{46}	7.93
		Ti^{47}	7.28

element	atomic number	isotope	abundance
Titanium Ti	22	Ti^{48}	73.94
		Ti^{49}	5.51
		Ti^{50}	5.34
Vanadium V	23	V^{50}	0.24
		V^{51}	99.76
Chromium Cr	24	Cr^{50}	4.31
		Cr^{52}	83.76
		Cr^{53}	9.55
		Cr^{54}	2.38
Manganese Mn	25	Mn^{55}	100
Iron Fe	26	Fe^{54}	5.82
		Fe^{56}	91.66
		Fe^{57}	2.19
		Fe^{58}	0.33
Cobalt Co	27	Co^{59}	100
Nickel Ni	28	Ni^{58}	67.88
		Ni^{60}	26.23
		Ni^{61}	1.19
		Ni^{62}	3.66
		Ni^{64}	1.08
Copper Cu	29	Cu^{63}	69.09
		Cu^{65}	30.91
Zinc Zn	30	Zn^{64}	48.89
		Zn^{66}	27.81
		Zn^{67}	4.11
		Zn^{68}	18.57
		Zn^{70}	0.62
Gallium Ga	31	Ga^{69}	60.4
		Ga^{71}	39.6
Germanium Ge	32	Ge^{70}	20.52
		Ge^{72}	27.43
		Ge^{73}	7.76
		Ge^{74}	36.54
		Ge^{76}	7.76
Arsenic As	33	As^{75}	100
Selenium Se	34	Se^{74}	0.87
		Se^{76}	9.02
		Se^{77}	7.58
		Se^{78}	23.52
		Se^{80}	49.82
		Se^{82}	9.19
Bromine Br	35	Br^{79}	50.54
		Br^{81}	49.46
Krypton Kr	36	Kr^{78}	0.354
		Kr^{80}	2.27
		Kr^{82}	11.56
		Kr^{83}	11.55
		Kr^{84}	56.90
		Kr^{86}	17.37
Rubidium Rb	37	Rb^{85}	72.15

RN: natural radioactivity

TABLE OF NATURAL ISOTOPES

element	*atomic number*	*isotope*	*abundance*
Rubidium Rb	37	Rb^{87}	27.85 (RN)
Strontium Sr	38	Sr^{84}	0.56
		Sr^{86}	9.86
		Sr^{87}	7.02
		Sr^{88}	82.56
Yttrium Y	39	Y^{89}	100
Zirconium Zr	40	Zr^{90}	51.46
		Zr^{91}	11.23
		Zr^{92}	17.11
		Zr^{94}	17.40
		Zr^{96}	2.80
Niobium Nb	41	Nb^{93}	100
Molybdenum Mo	42	Mo^{92}	15.84
		Mo^{94}	9.04
		Mo^{95}	15.72
		Mo^{96}	16.53
		Mo^{97}	9.46
		Mo^{98}	23.78
		Mo^{100}	9.63
Ruthenium Ru	44	Ru^{96}	5.51
		Ru^{98}	1.87
		Ru^{99}	12.72
		Ru^{100}	12.62
		Ru^{101}	17.07
		Ru^{102}	31.61
		Ru^{104}	18.58
Rhodium Rh	45	Rh^{103}	100
Palladium Pd	46	Pd^{102}	0.96
		Pd^{104}	10.97
		Pd^{105}	22.23
		Pd^{106}	27.33
		Pd^{108}	26.71
		Pd^{110}	11.81
Silver Ag	47	Ag^{107}	51.35
		Ag^{109}	48.65
Cadmium Cd	48	Cd^{106}	1.22
		Cd^{108}	0.88
		Cd^{110}	12.39
		Cd^{111}	12.75
		Cd^{112}	24.07
		Cd^{113}	12.26
		Cd^{114}	28.86
		Cd^{116}	7.58
Indium In	49	In^{113}	4.28
		In^{115}	95.72 (RN)
Tin Sn	50	Sn^{112}	0.96
		Sn^{114}	0.66
		Sn^{115}	0.35
		Sn^{116}	14.30
		Sn^{117}	7.61
Tin Sn	50	Sn^{118}	24.03
		Sn^{119}	8.58
		Sn^{120}	32.85
		Sn^{122}	4.72
		Sn^{124}	5.94 (RN)
Antimony Sb	51	Sb^{121}	57.25
		Sb^{123}	42.75
Tellurium Te	52	Te^{120}	0.09
		Te^{122}	2.46
		Te^{123}	0.87
		Te^{124}	4.61
		Te^{125}	6.99
		Te^{126}	18.71
		Te^{128}	31.79
		Te^{130}	34.48
Iodine I	53	I^{127}	100
Xenon Xe	54	Xe^{124}	0.10
		Xe^{126}	0.09
		Xe^{128}	1.92
		Xe^{129}	26.44
		Xe^{130}	4.08
		Xe^{131}	21.18
		Xe^{132}	26.89
		Xe^{134}	10.44
		Xe^{136}	8.87
Caesium Cs	55	Cs^{133}	100
Barium Ba	56	Ba^{130}	0.10
		Ba^{132}	0.10
		Ba^{134}	2.42
		Ba^{135}	6.59
		Ba^{136}	7.81
		Ba^{137}	11.32
		Ba^{138}	71.66
Lanthanum La	57	La^{138}	0.089 (RN)
		La^{139}	99.91
Cerium Ce	58	Ce^{136}	0.19
		Ce^{138}	0.25
		Ce^{140}	88.48
		Ce^{142}	11.07
Praseodymium Pr	59	Pr^{141}	100
Neodymium Nd	60	Nd^{142}	27.11
		Nd^{143}	12.17
		Nd^{144}	23.85
		Nd^{145}	8.30
		Nd^{146}	17.22
		Nd^{148}	5.73
		Nd^{150}	5.62 (RN)
Samarium Sm	62	Sm^{144}	3.09
		Sm^{147}	14.97 (RN)
		Sm^{148}	11.24

RN: natural radioactivity

TABLE OF NATURAL ISOTOPES

element	*atomic number*	*isotope*	*abundance*
Samarium Sm	62	Sm^{149}	13.83
		Sm^{150}	7.44
		Sm^{152}	26.72
		Sm^{154}	22.71
Europium Eu	63	Eu^{151}	47.82
		Eu^{153}	52.18
Gadolinium Gd	64	Gd^{152}	0.20
		Gd^{154}	2.15
		Gd^{155}	14.73
		Gd^{156}	20.47
		Gd^{157}	15.68
		Gd^{158}	24.87
		Gd^{160}	21.90
Terbium Tb	65	Tb^{159}	100
Dysprosium Dy	66	Dy^{156}	0.052
		Dy^{158}	0.090
		Dy^{160}	2.29
		Dy^{161}	18.88
		Dy^{162}	25.53
		Dy^{163}	24.97
		Dy^{164}	28.18
Holmium Ho	67	Ho^{165}	100
Erbium Er	68	Er^{162}	0.14
		Er^{164}	1.56
		Er^{166}	33.41
		Er^{167}	22.94
		Er^{168}	27.07
		Er^{170}	14.88
Thulium Tm	69	Tm^{169}	100
Ytterbium Yb	70	Yb^{168}	0.14
		Yb^{170}	3.03
		Yb^{171}	14.31
		Yb^{172}	21.82
		Yb^{173}	16.13
		Yb^{174}	31.84
		Yb^{176}	12.73
Lutetium Lu	71	Lu^{175}	97.41
		Lu^{176}	2.59
Hafnium	72	Hf^{174}	0.18
		Hf^{176}	5.20
		Hf^{177}	18.50
		Hf^{178}	27.14
		Hf^{179}	13.75
		Hf^{180}	35.24
Tantalum Ta	73	Ta^{180}	0.012
		Ta^{181}	99.99
Tungsten W	74	W^{180}	0.14
		W^{182}	26.41
		W^{183}	14.40
		W^{184}	30.64
		W^{186}	28.41
Rhenium Re	75	Re^{185}	37.07
		Re^{187}	62.93 (RN)
Osmium Os	76	Os^{184}	0.018
		Os^{186}	1.59
		Os^{187}	1.64
		Os^{188}	13.3
		Os^{189}	16.1
		Os^{190}	26.4
		Os^{192}	41.0
Iridium Ir	77	Ir^{191}	37.3
		Ir^{193}	62.7
Platinum Pt	78	Pt^{190}	0.013
		Pt^{192}	0.78
		Pt^{194}	32.9
		Pt^{195}	33.8
		Pt^{196}	25.3
		Pt^{198}	7.21
Gold Au	79	Au^{197}	100
Mercury Hg	80	Hg^{196}	0.15
		Hg^{198}	10.02
		Hg^{199}	16.84
		Hg^{200}	23.13
		Hg^{201}	13.22
		Hg^{202}	29.80
		Hg^{204}	6.85
Thallium Tl	81	Tl^{203}	29.50
		Tl^{205}	70.50
Lead Pb*	82	Pb^{204}	1.48
		Pb^{206}	23.6
		Pb^{207}	22.6
		Pb^{208}	52.3
Bismuth Bi	83	Bi^{209}	100
Thorium Th	90	Th^{232}	100 (RN)
Uranium U	92	U^{234}	0.006 (RN)
		U^{235}	0.72 (RN)
		U^{238}	99.27 (RN)

* From Great Bear Lake galena.

RN: natural radioactivity.

● **isotopic,** that which concerns isotopes.

● **isotopic spin,** see **spin.**

isotopy, character of the isotope.

isotron, an apparatus intended for the separation of isotopes.—Its principle, originated by R. P. Wilson, consists in grouping separately the ions of the two isotopes which are to be separated, by the action of electric fields. The ions are then caught on collectors. This apparatus has worked in the U.S. with uranium 235 and 238.

J

JENSEN, Hans (1906–) German physicist, professor at Heidelberg University.—In 1963 he shared the Nobel Prize for Physics with Mrs. M. Goeppert-Mayer and Eugene Wigner, for their work on the shell structure of atomic nuclei. (See **models of the nucleus.**)

JOLIOT-CURIE, Frédéric (1900–58) French physicist. In 1953 he shared the Nobel Prize for Chemistry with his wife Irène Joliot-Curie. With her he undertook numerous researches into the structure of the atom. By obtaining isotope 13 of nitrogen, isotope 30 of phosphorus, isotope 27 of silicon and isotope 28 of aluminium, they discovered the first artificial radioactive elements. For his nuclear chemistry laboratory at the Collège de France, Paris, he built the first cyclo-

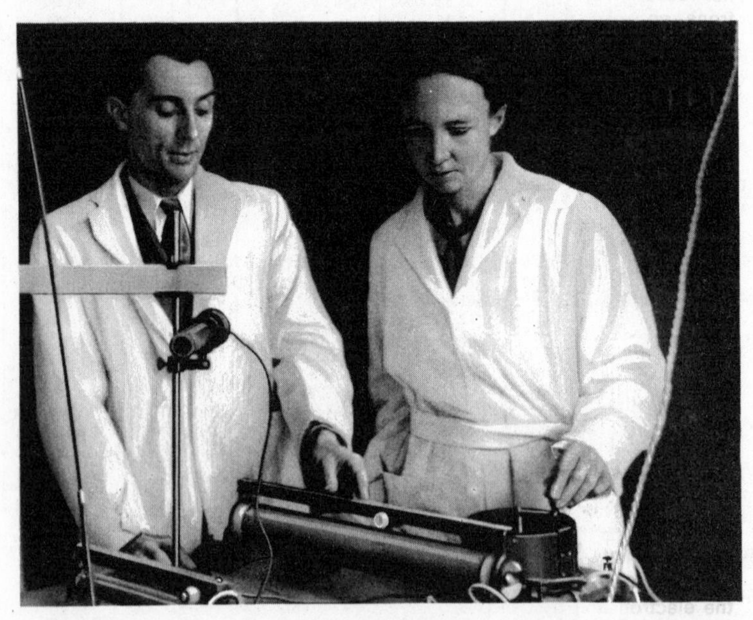

Frédéric and Irène Joliot-Curie in their laboratory, in 1932 (Photo Keystone)

tron in Western Europe. He also studied uranium fission, chain reaction and its applications, and directed the construction of the first French atomic pile. After being director of the National Centre for Scientific Research, he was appointed the first High-Commissioner to the Atomic Energy Commission. He founded the Nuclear Physics Centre at Orsay.

JOLIOT-CURIE, Irène, (1897–1956) French physicist, daughter of Pierre and Marie Curie and wife of Frédéric Joliot. She shared the Nobel Prize for Chemistry with him in 1935, for the discovery of artificial radioactivity. Her work, frequently carried out with her husband, dealt with radioactivity, artificial transmutation of elements and nuclear physics. In particular, her researches on the action of neutrons on uranium nuclei, were an important step towards the discovery of fission. She took part in the foundation of the Atomic Energy Commission, of which she was a commissioner for six months, and in the construction of the first French atomic pile.

JORDAN, Pascual (1902–), German physicist. With Heisenberg and Born, he contributed to the development of quantum mechanics.

K

K-shell, the first of the electron shells surrounding the atomic nucleus (see **shell**). There can only be two electrons on this shell.

K meson or **kaon,** fundamental particle about 965 times heavier than the electron.—It is a meson because its mass is intermediate between that of the electron and that of the proton, which is 1836 times heavier than the electron. K mesons are sometimes called *heavy mesons*, in contrast to *pions*, which are about 270 times heavier than the electron. They are considered to be particles of the nuclear field, as are the pions. Their nuclear interactions seem to be slightly weaker than those of the pion. K mesons are particles said to be *strange*, in the sense that they cannot be produced except in pairs, or in association with a hyperon, also a *strange* particle, heavier than the proton. (See **strangeness number**.) The production reactions may, for example, be the following (symbols indicate the electric charges):

pion (−)+proton (+) *gives*
sigma hyperon (−)+ K meson (+);
pion (−)+proton (+) *gives*
K meson (+)+K meson (−)
+neutron.

The manner in which the K mesons are produced leads to the hypothesis that a quantity called *strangeness number* is preserved in the reaction. To the positive K meson a strangeness number +1 may be ascribed, to the negative K meson a strangeness number −1, to the sigma hyperon a strangeness number −1. The foregoing reactions, taking the strangeness number into consideration, may be written:

pion+proton *gives*
0 + 0 =
K meson+K meson+neutron
+1 −1 + 0
pion+proton *gives*
0 + 0=
sigma hyperon+K meson
−1 +1.

K mesons are grouped in two categories:

1) The positive K meson and the neutral K meson, of strangeness number +1

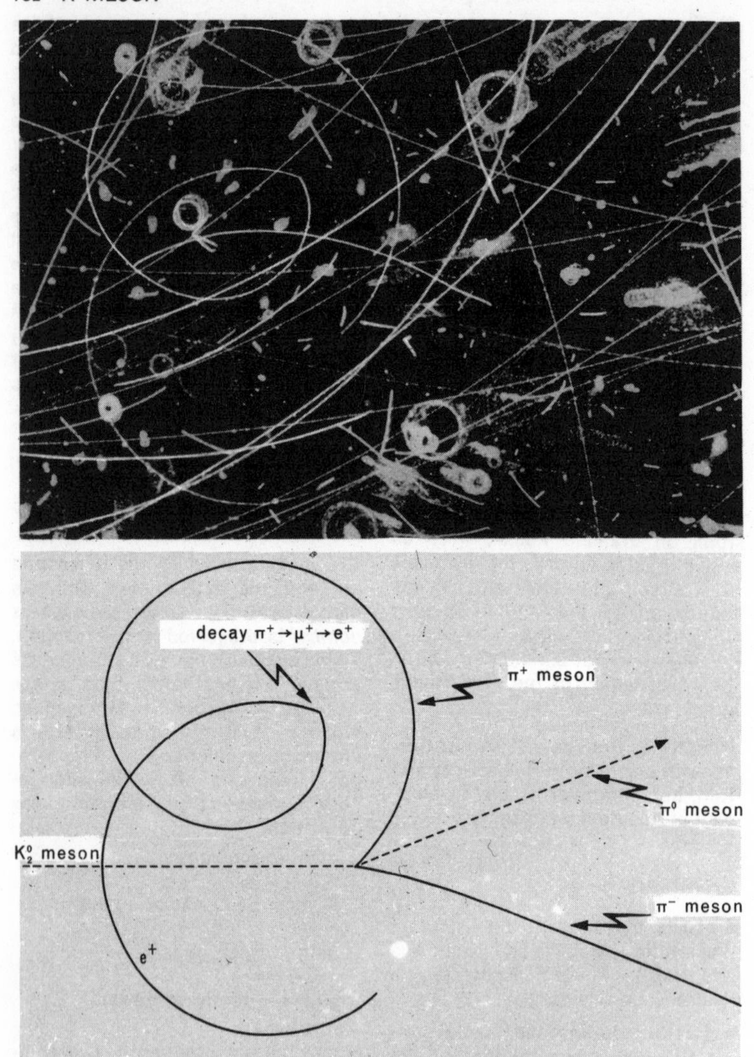

An example of the disintegration of a heavy meson with a long mean life (K_2^0), in the mode π^+, π^-, π^0. It shows an event photographed with the help of the 600 litre Wilson chamber of the Ecole Polytechnique, placed in a neutral beam from the proton synchrotron Saturn at Saclay, France.

2) The negative K meson and the neutral antiK meson, of strangeness number −1.
The second two are the antiparticles of the first two. The behaviour of the neutral K mesons is complicated by the fact that they are only to be seen in the shape of mesons called K_1, K_2, each of which may be imagined as being a different combination of K meson and antiK meson. K mesons are very unstable. The K_1 meson disintegrates into two pions, with a mean lifetime of 0.09 billionths of a second. The K_2 meson disintegrates in different ways, with a mean lifetime of 58 billionths of a second. The positive and negative K mesons also have several modes of disintegration; their mean lifetime is 12 billionths of a second. K mesons were discovered in cosmic radiation, then produced in large quantities in high-energy accelerators. From their study, information on the nature of nuclear forces is obtained.

kasolite, a uranium ore; it is to be found in the Congo.

KeV, symbol for *kilo-electronvolts*, a unit of energy worth 1000 electronvolts.

klystron, an electronic valve which enables very high frequencies to be obtained. *See illustration p. 134.*

krypton, an element with atomic number 36. One of the rare gases (see **gas, rare**).

L

L-shell, second electronic shell of an atom (the first is the K-shell). Only 8 electrons can occupy the L-shell.

label, labelled, see **marked, marker.**

laboratory, hot, see ●**hot laboratory.**

Lamb shift, splitting of some lines of the hydrogen spectrum not predicted by Dirac's theory. Quantum field theory, however, agrees with the experimental splitting as measured by Lamb and Retherford to remarkable accuracy.

LANDAU, Lev Davidovitch (1908–) Soviet physicist, a member of the Soviet Academy of Sciences and professor at Moscow University. His discoveries on the condensed state of matter, especially on liquid helium, and his remarkable work in the field of theoretical nuclear physics earned him a Stalin Prize and, in 1962, the Nobel Prize for Physics.

Lanthanides or **rare earths,** a series of elements whose atomic numbers (number of protons in the nucleus) range from 57 to 70.—These are

Lev Davidovitch Landau (Photo Keystone)

Klystron AX 436 B (Photo CSF)

successively lanthanum, cerium, praseodymium, neodymium, prometheum, samarium, europium, gadolinium, terbium, dysprosium, holmium, erbium, thulium and ytterbium. All these elements have allied physical and chemical properties, as the number of electrons on the external shell of the atom is the same; two on shell P. The number of electrons of the internal shells varies from one element to the other.

lanthanum, the first of the lanthanide series.—Lanthanum is an element with atomic number 57. The most abundant of the isotopes is lanthanum 139, each of whose nuclei contain 57 protons and 82 neutrons. Natural lanthanum also contains a small proportion (less than 1 per 1000) of isotope 138, which is unstable and has a very long mean lifetime of 200 billion years. Some 15 lanthanum isotopes have been discovered.

latitude effect, the effect of the terrestrial magnetic field on cosmic radiation. (See **geomagnetic effect.**) From this effect arises a strength of cosmic radiation higher at the poles than at the equator.

lattice, see **reactor, sub-critical.**

LAUE, Theodor Felix Max von (1879–1960) German physicist. He received the Nobel Prize for Physics in 1914 for his discovery of the diffraction of X-rays.

LAWRENCE, Ernest Orlando (1901–58) American physicist. He was the inventor of the cyclotron, of which he built several models. With the help of this accelerator, he carried out extensive research on nuclear transmutations. He was responsible for the separation of uranium 235 in the preparation of the first American atomic bomb. His work brought him the Nobel Prize for Physics in 1939. (See **cyclotron.**)

lead, an element with atomic number 82. Each of its nuclei contains 82 protons. Natural lead consists of four isotopes, each of which contains a different number of neutrons:

- —lead 204 (122 neutrons) in a 1.5 per cent proportion
- —lead 206 (124 neutrons) in a 23.6 per cent proportion
- —lead 207 (125 neutrons) in a 22.6 per cent proportion
- —lead 208 (126 neutrons) in a 52.3 per cent proportion.

Lead 206 is the end-product of the consecutive disintegrations of the radioactive series of uranium; lead 207, that of the actinium series; lead 208, that of the series of thorium; lead 204 is not produced in a radioactive series. This means that the proportion of lead 204 found in ores containing both lead and elements of the uranium, actinium or thorium series, determines the ordinary lead content in the ore. The study of ores containing elements of the radioactive series of uranium 238, which leads to lead, has enabled some idea of the age of the Earth and of ores to be obtained. A. O. Nier and A. Holmes estimate the time which has passed since the formation of the Earth's crust as being from 3 to 4 billion years. The time that passed between the formation of the Earth as a distinct body and the formation of the Earth's crust is generally considered much less than this. Analysis of lead ores therefore suggests that the Earth is about 4 billion years old. Ordinary lead is regularly used in shielding against radiation. On account of its high density (11.3), it constitutes a very good material for

On top of the reactor EL3 at Saclay, withdrawing radio-elements in lead protective containers (shown in foreground) (Photo J.-P. Sudre-CEA)

shielding against gamma rays, as these materialise in elements of high atomic number. Its use in large quantities is, however, restricted by its high cost. When another material is used, such as concrete, the equivalent lead thickness is used as a measure of its effect. It is the thickness of lead which would reduce the radiation in the same proportion as the thickness of the concrete under consideration. For a given radiation, for example, an equivalent thickness of lead may be 1 cm for a 3 cm thickness of concrete.

● **lead castle,** see **castle, lead.**

lead glass, see **glass, lead.**

leakage of neutrons, see ● **neutron leakage.**

Lead protective partition separating the laboratory (in the photograph), from the apparatus for the production of colloidal gold 198 at the Nuclear Research Centre at Saclay (Photo J.-P. Sudre-CEA)

LEE DAO-TSUNG (1927–) Chinese physicist. With Yang he shared the Nobel Prize for Physics for 1957. These two physicists advanced the hypothesis of the non-conservation of parity in weak interactions, a hypothesis that was experimentally demonstrated.

LENARD, Philipp von (1862–1947) German physicist. He received the Nobel Prize for Physics in 1905 for his work on the ionisation of gases by electrons and on the photo-electric effect.

lens, electrostatic, an appliance employing electric fields to cause a beam of charged particles to diverge or converge.—Its properties present a certain analogy with those of a glass lens which causes a beam of light to diverge or converge. The electrostatic lens is used in nuclear physical studies to provide beams of particles produced in the accelerator with a form appropriate to their use, eg by making them converge on to a target.

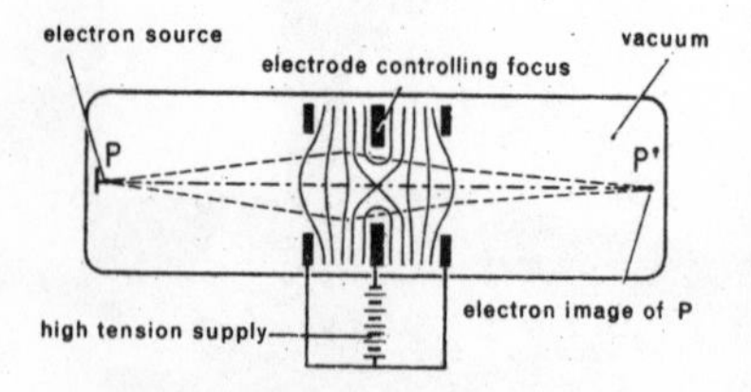

Path of a beam of electrons through an electrostatic lens

LEPRINCE-RINGUET, Louis (1901–) French physicist. Professor at the *Ecole Polytechnique*, Paris, and at the *Collège de France*. Chairman of Scientific Directives at CERN. He has studied cosmic rays with Wilson chambers, especially at the Pic du Midi Research Centre (the mass of various mesons, the properties of strange particles), then fundamental particles with the help of bubble-chambers and the large proton synchrotrons.

lepton, a particle with low mass.—In this category are to be found electrons, mu leptons and neutrinos. The leptons do not take part in nuclear forces; they undergo the three other forms of interaction, ie *electromagnetic, weak, gravitational*. Leptons have a 1/2 spin and Fermi-Dirac statistics. The negative electron, the negative mu lepton and the neutrinos are called *leptons*; the positive electron, the positive mu lepton and the antineutrinos are called *antileptons*. In weak **interactions** (qv), in which the leptons take part, their number remains unchanged, or more precisely, the number of leptons less the number of antileptons is the same before and after the reaction. The intrinsic properties of the electron and of the mu have been closely studied with a view to discovering a difference (other than that of mass), between these two particles, which actually appear to be very similar. Some results suggest that there exists an electronic and a muonic number, both of which are separately conserved in the interactions.

leptonic, that which refers to the lepton (eg the leptonic number of the negative electron is +1, that of the positive electron −1). *Leptonic disintegration* is a disintegration in which leptons are emitted. The pion disintegration:

pion *gives* mu lepton+neutrino

is a leptonic disintegration.

LEUCIPPUS (*c.* 460–370 BC) a Greek philosopher, founder of atomism and of mechanistic materialism.

leukemia, an illness which results from a disequilibrium of the blood. It is due very often to an excessive increase of the white corpuscles in the blood; it may be induced by an exposure to radiation.

level. Corpuscular systems, such as the molecule, atom, nucleus and particle may frequently exist in a number of distinct states of energy. Because of the laws of quantisation the possible energies are separated from one another, each one corresponding to a level of the system. The stable level, that which corresponds to the lowest energy (or, which is the same thing, to the lowest mass), is called *ground state*. Systems at levels other than the ground state tend to revert to this lowest state. Levels above the ground state are called *excited levels*. A nucleus is placed in an excited level by the absorption of a gamma ray. It reverts to the ground state through re-emission of a gamma ray.

● **level width,** the range over which the energy of an excited system varies.—An atom excited by an external contribution of energy returns to its normal state, called ground state, by emitting a gamma ray in the majority of cases. The energy of this gamma ray is equal to the excitation energy which was stored in the excited nucleus. More precisely, the nucleus acquires a small part of the energy, because it recoils in the emission phenomenon. The energy of the gamma rays emitted by identical excited nuclei is clearly defined within limits set by the **uncertainty relations** (qv). The natural width of a level corresponds to the slight variations in energy of the gamma rays emitted by the excited nucleus, variations which are related to the lifetime by the uncertainty relations. They do not correspond to two clearly defined limits of energy, but to an energy range in which the majority of emitted rays are found; gamma rays whose energy is very different from the mean energy are rare. Levels may be broadened by various phenomena, for instance by means of thermal agitation. Atomic nuclei are in fact in motion with speeds which are greater the higher the temperature of the substance. A gamma ray energy measured in a detection apparatus appears lower when it derives from a nucleus retreating from the apparatus and vice versa. In this case there is a spreading of the energy level. This phenomenon also exists for the levels of molecules. It is called *Doppler broadening*.

LIBBY, Willard Frank (1908–) American chemist. A specialist in nuclear physics, he established a method for determining the age of objects based on an assay of carbon 14. He received the Nobel Prize for Chemistry in 1960.

lifetime, Fermi, a quantity used in reactors, linked with the distance which a neutron travels after being emitted in the fission of a uranium or plutonium nucleus, until it is slowed down and has achieved *thermal energy*. On this level of energy, neutrons are especially effective in producing new fission reactions, a condition in which a *thermal reactor* should operate.

line, a radiative emission or absorption of sharply defined energy.—The emission of a radiation with variable energy is, on the contrary, called a **spectrum** (qv). An alpha radioactivity, for example, provides a line, or several lines; a beta radioactivity provides a spectrum.

liquid drop model, see **models of the nucleus.**

loop, a closed cooling circuit in a reactor. A reactor is cooled to maintain it at a constant temperature and to use the heat provided. The coolant (of gas or liquid) is subjected to intense radiation inside the reactor, which generates considerable radioactivity in the fluid. It is therefore dangerous to cool it or to use it in turbines for the production of energy in this form. A secondary loop is usually employed to avoid the radioactivity of the primary coolant.

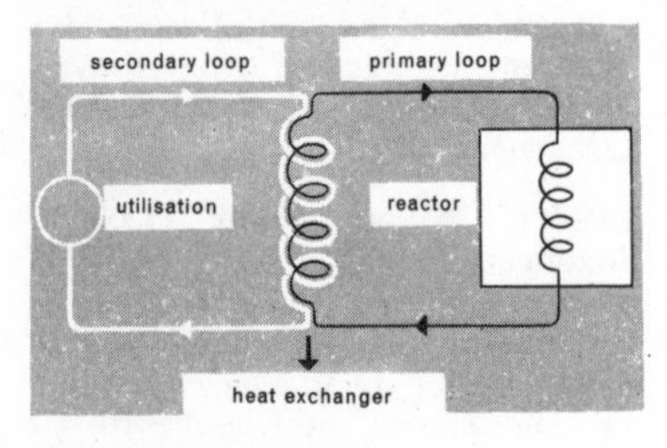

Loop

LORENTZ, Hendrik Antoon (1853–1928) Dutch physicist. A specialist in theoretical physics, he established a theoretical account of electricity by basing his explanations on the presence of electrons in matter. He interpreted the Zeeman effect, and established the equations which bear his name and which describe the ratio of physical quantities measured by two observers in uniform relative motion. These equations enabled Einstein to elaborate the theory of relativity. He shared the Nobel Prize for Physics with Zeeman in 1902.

Hendrik Antoon Lorentz

luminescence, emission of light by a substance receiving external radiation. Certain substances subjected to luminous radiation possess the property of emitting in all directions a radiation of wavelength (or colour) distinct and different from that of the incident radiation. The wavelength of light emitted by luminescence is on average greater than that of the incident light. Two instances may be distinguished: *fluorescence*, which is produced almost instantaneously with the excitation and ceases with it, and *phosphorescence*, which persists for some time after the luminescent substance has ceased to be excited.

Luminescence may, in principle, be excited by all radiations such as light, X-rays, gamma rays, electrically charged particles. In consequence, it is used to detect particles in scintillators.

Fluorescence may be interpreted as an absorption of energy by certain molecules of the fluorescent body. These excited molecules transmit part of their energy to neighbouring molecules by impact; the energised set of molecules is then de-excited by an emission of luminous radiation. *Phosphorescence* may be differently interpreted, by drawing on crystalline structure. According to Lenard's theory an electron would be ejected from the atom of the phosphorescent body by photo-electric effect. The electron ejected in this fashion, occupying a definite place in the crystal lattice, would then be displaced by thermal agitation and recaptured by the atom which at that moment would emit light. This theory enables both characteristics of phosphorescence to be explained: the delay in the light emitted compared with the light absorbed; and the diminishing of phosphorescence with the lowering of the temperature.

M

M-shell, third electronic shell, containing at most 18 electrons.

McMILLAN, Edwin Mattison (1907–) American physicist. The inventor of the synchrotron, he obtained, starting from uranium, a new element: neptunium. With Seaborg he also discovered plutonium and, later, studied the phenomena of spallation. In 1951 he shared the Nobel Prize for Chemistry with Seaborg.

macroscopic, said of a physical system which contains a large number of particles, either molecules or atoms.—A system is generally considered to be macroscopic when its size exceeds the micron (or thousandth of a millimetre). Physical phenomena on the macroscopic level arise in general from actions between microscopic systems. For instance, the magnetic field of an iron crystal originates at the atomic level: it is explained by elementary actions between the iron atoms, whose magnetic moments are oriented along one preferred direction. Macroscopic systems obey classical mechanics, either Newtonian or relativistic.

magic number, see **number.**

magnetic deflector, see **deflector.**

magnetic focusing, a focusing exercised by the action of a magnetic field. An electromagnet is generally used, the pole pieces being shaped like quadrants of a circle. Particles passing between the pole pieces are deflected by the magnetic field. With an appropriate arrangement, particles which pass through an *object slit* all meet again at the exit on an *image line* at which a slit may be attached so as to select particles with a definite mass and velocity. There is a great analogy between this system and an optical system consisting of a prism and a lens. The lens focuses the luminous rays at a certain point, while the prism deviates the luminous rays by causing them to turn at a certain angle depending on their 'colour'. In a magnetic quadrant, the deviation of the particles depends on their velocities.

magnetic moment, characteristic of a particle equivalent to that of a small magnet.—In a magnetic field, a magnet turns in the direction of the field. If one thinks of a magnet as consisting of two magnetic poles, north and south, equal and opposite, separated from each other, the magnetic moment is the product of either pole strength by the distance between them. Study of magnetism demonstrates that in reality magnetic moments are due to elementary circulating electric currents. An atom, a nucleus, a particle all possess, in general, a non-zero magnetic moment. Magnetism of iron, for example, is mainly due to the direction of the magnetic moment related to the spin of the electrons of the iron atoms (the intrinsic angular momentum of the electrically charged electrons).

magnetohydrodynamics, a science whose object is the study of the movement of fluids in interaction with a magnetic field.

Magnetron (Photo CSF)

magnetron, an electronic valve mounted in a magnet, used in the production of high frequency potentials (up to 10 billion cycles per second) in particle accelerators.—The interest of the magnetron lies in the fact that it can provide very high peak power for short periods, its average power output not being very high. For instance, it is possible to obtain 300 kW with a voltage of 15,000 V for one microsecond. If the magnetron functions every millisecond the mean power is only 300 W.

manipulator, remote, an apparatus which enables radioactive products to be moved about from a distance, by reproducing manual motions.—It is sometimes called the *artificial hand*. It consists of controlling metal fingers which are attached to the fingers of the operator. Movement of the controlling fingers is exactly reproduced by means of servo-control mechanisms, by working fingers. The operator merely has to mimic the gestures necessary to the mechanism, these actions being reproduced at a distance by the working fingers. A thick glass porthole enables the operator to supervise the manipulation while remaining protected from radiation. Complicated movements which include turning on a tap, lighting a flame and decanting liquids may thus be performed without any contact with dangerous products. (*See diagrams pp. 143, 144 and 145.*)

marked molecule, a molecule which contains an atom of a recognisable isotope, frequently radioactive.

● **marker,** an isotope so employed.

● **marking,** the marking of elements by means of the addition of radioactive isotopes. (See **tracer.**)

mass. An object's mass is revealed in two distinct aspects of its behaviour. —Its weight is the attractive force acting between the object and the Earth, due to their gravitational masses. Its inertia is measured by the force which must act on the body to produce unit acceleration of it. The observed identity of inertial and

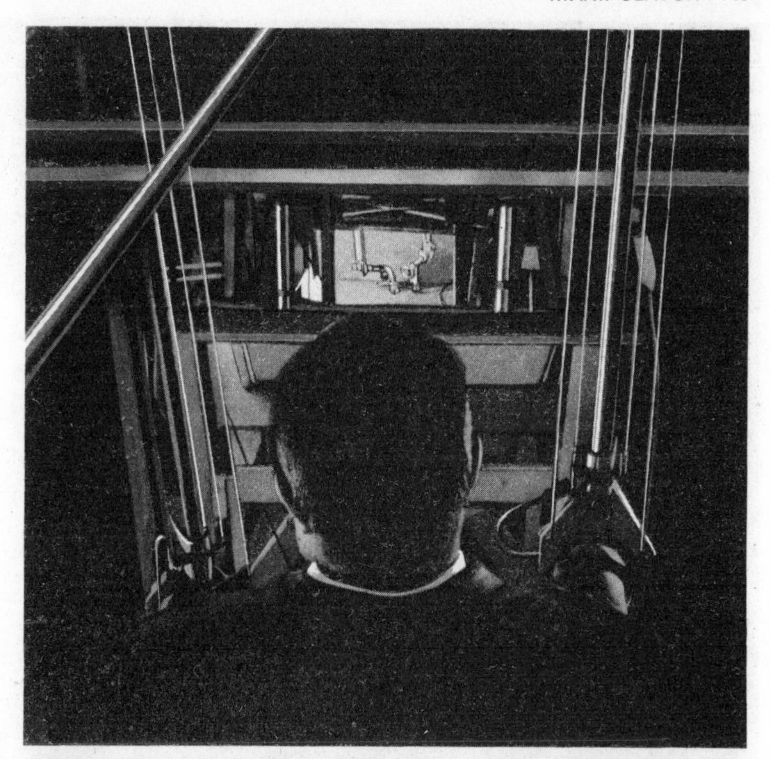

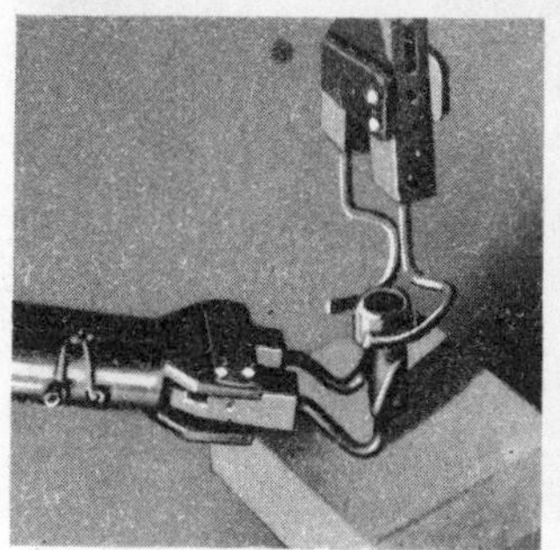

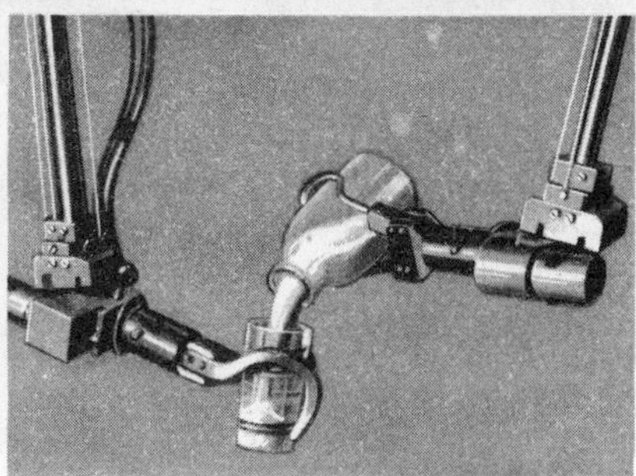

Handling of radioactive substances. The operator is protected against the radiations and follows in a mirror the handling of radioactive test-tubes. Articulated mechanical hands, enable the operator to carry out precise actions from a distance. (Photo Science et Vie)

A manipulator of radioactive objects and substances. This remotely controlled mechanical arm of impressive size, also enables repairs to be carried out on gear inside atomic reactors. It may be seen here picking up a nut with its pincers. The operator directs the appliance from an instrument panel. (Photo USIS)

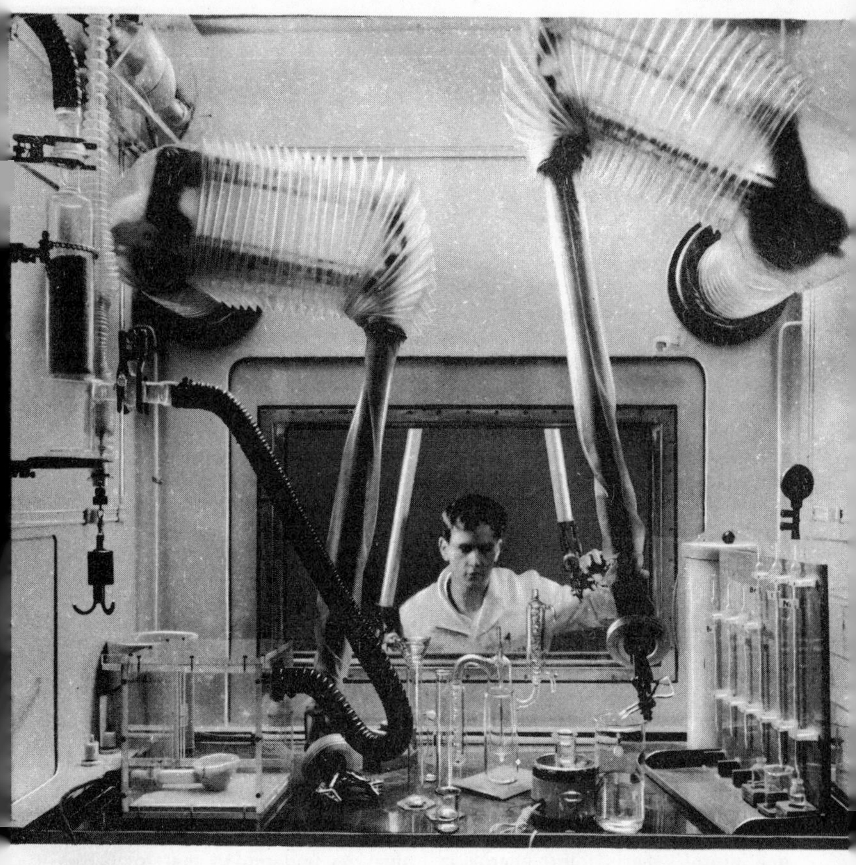

Remote control manipulator at the Saclay Centre for Nuclear Studies (Photo J.-P. Sudre-CEA)

gravitational mass is mysterious in Newtonian mechanics, but fundamental in Einstein's theory of gravitation.

● **critical mass,** the mass of nuclear fuel necessary for chain reaction to develop. (See **critical.**)

● **mass defect,** the difference between the mass of the nucleus and that of the protons and neutrons of which it is composed.—The mass of a nucleus is smaller than the total mass of the protons and neutrons which compose it. Protons and neutrons are energetically bound inside the nuclei. If one wished to obtain protons and neutrons in a free state, it would be necessary to provide the nucleus with an energy equal to the binding energy. According to the principle of the equivalence of mass with energy, the total mass of the nucleus and the mass equivalent to the binding energy is equal to the mass of the free protons and neutrons. Mass defect, being equal to the difference between the mass of the nucleus and that of the protons and neutrons which constitute it, is therefore equal to the binding energy of all the protons and neutrons of the nucleus. This quantity is higher the more stable the nucleus (greater binding energy). Mass defect, therefore, indicates the stability of the nuclei and the possibility of their mutual radioactive transformations. A possible radioactive transformation leads from a less stable nucleus (less bound) to a more stable nucleus (more bound). Mass defect, divided by the number of nucleons (protons and neutrons) gives the binding energy per nucleon. For instance, mass defect is 28 million electronvolts in the helium nucleus, ie the mass of the helium nucleus is inferior by 28 MeV to the total masses of the two protons and two neutrons of which it is composed. The binding energy per nucleon in this case is 28/4= 7 MeV. In hydrogen, which has only one proton, the binding energy is zero. Binding energy is about 7 MeV for heavy elements such as uranium; about 8 MeV for medium elements, and from 2 to 3 MeV for very light elements such as deuterium and tritium. The fission reaction, in which heavy nuclei are split into medium nuclei, provides energy in the order of 8−7=1 MeV per nucleon. Fusion reaction, in which light nuclei assemble to give medium nuclei, gives energy of the order of 8−2=6 MeV per nucleon. These reactions are the two sources of nuclear energy. The second source is sometimes called *thermonuclear reaction*. In both these reactions matter is changed into energy. Fusion reaction provides about six times more energy than fission reaction for the same weight of fuel.

● **rest mass and relativistic mass.** The laws of classical mechanics assumed mass to be constant. The theory of relativity established by Einstein upset these conceptions which were valid on our scale, yet were insufficient either on the microscopic scale or on the macroscopic scale when the speed of the body is comparable to the speed of light. Einstein demonstrated that the mass of a body depends on the relative speed of the measuring system with respect to the body. The quantity which remains constant is the *rest mass,* that which is measured in a system of co-ordinates where the body is at rest. For an observer with respect to whom the body travels, the mass increases with the velocity. This second quantity is called *relativistic mass.* However, the increase of mass is not noticeable until the body has a speed comparable to that of light; ie 300,000 km per sec. It will then be understood that to us the mass appears to be invariable in phenomena normally observed by us. The same principle does not apply to particle phenomena. The electrons of radioactivity, for example, may possess a velocity comparable to the speed of light, yet always below it, because the latter is a maximum speed which cannot be attained by bodies having a non-zero rest mass. Cosmic radiation particles or those produced in large accelerators frequently have a speed almost equal to that of light (0.9 or 0.99 times the speed of light). The mass we measure with fixed apparatus is *relativistic mass*, also sometimes called *total energy*, because it is the sum of the rest-mass energy and the kinetic energy. (See ● **Einstein's law.**) That part of the mass which represents kinetic energy is, in the case of high-speed particles, much higher than the rest mass.

mass number, the number of nucleons in the nucleus, exactly equal (by definition) to the atomic mass in the particular case of the carbon isotope of mass 12. In other nuclei, the atomic mass is slightly different from the mass number, on the one hand because the nuclei may contain different proportions of neutrons and protons, the neutron being slightly heavier than the proton; and on the other hand, on account of the binding energies which vary from one atom to another. The hydrogen atom, whose nucleus contains a single proton, has the mass number 1. However, the proton is without nuclear bond since it alone constitutes the nucleus. The atomic mass of hydrogen is, in consequence, slightly higher than 1, ie 1.008. Chemists often use a unit known as *chemical mass unit* or *atomic weight unit*, which is 0.03 per cent higher than the preceding unit. This is based on the practically convenient choice of the natural isotopic mixture of oxygen atoms as a standard of mass 16. For highest precision, the standard must be a single isotope and, subject to this limitation, carbon is the better standard. The range of mass numbers for elements occurring in nature goes from 1 for hydrogen to 238 for uranium. Mass numbers up to 260 have been obtained artificially by nuclear reactions. (See **atomic mass.**)

matter creation, the transformation of energy into matter (see ● **Einstein's law**).—In nuclear physics the appearance of matter may be observed simultaneously with the disappearance of energy in the reactions:

1) *Formation of mesons.* In a nuclear reaction between an incident particle and a target particle, any number of mesons may be formed on condition that the energy of the incident particle is sufficient. For example:

proton+proton *gives*
new particles
proton+proton+several pions

K mesons may also be formed in the interaction, but with certain restrictions on the parity of the number of Ks emitted. (See **strangeness number.**) For example:

proton+proton *gives*
new particles
proton+proton+positive K meson
+negative K meson.

2) *Formation of particle-antiparticle pairs.* In a nuclear reaction, particles called baryons are emitted in pairs because of the conservation of baryon number. For example:

proton+proton *gives*
new particles
proton+proton+proton+antiproton.

3) *Formation of electron pairs.* In an electron-nuclear reaction, an electron and an antielectron may be formed in pairs. The reaction may be written symbolically:

gamma ray *gives*
new particles
positive electron+negative electron.

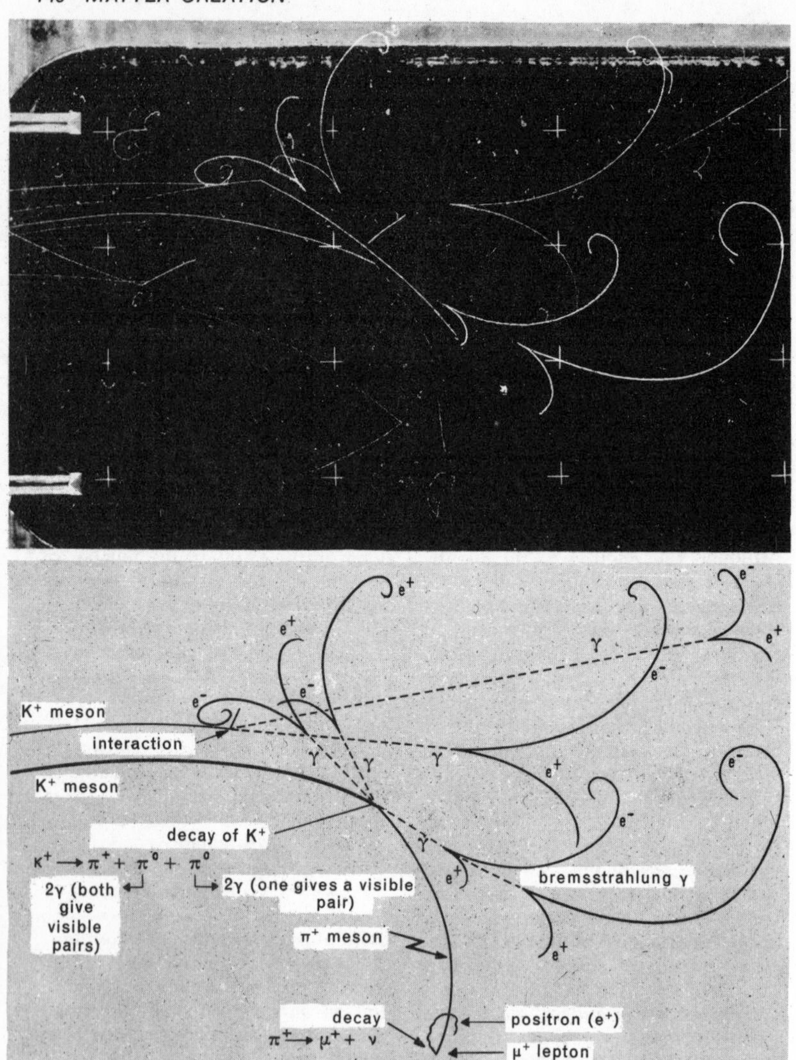

Several examples of the materialisation of photons (γ) into electron pairs in the BP3 Chamber of the Leprince-Ringuet Laboratory at the Ecole Polytechnique, Paris

MAXWELL, J. Clerk (1831–79) British physicist who did outstanding work in electromagnetism (his work in this field resulted in incorporating optics into electromagnetism) and in statistical mechanics (his work in this field resulted in incorporating thermodynamics into mechanics).

● **Maxwell's equations,** a system of equations governing all electric, magnetic and luminous phenomena. (See **electromagnetism.**)

mean life or **lifetime,** the average period of time during which an unstable system of a given type exists.—All the nuclei of a radioactive body do not disintegrate at the same time. Disintegration follows a statistical law. During one and the same interval of time, the proportion of nuclei which disintegrate in a radioactive sample is constant. Thus, during one *mean life*, 63 per cent of the radioactive nuclei disintegrate. During the following mean life 63 per cent of the remaining nuclei disintegrate again, ie

63 per cent × 37 per cent = 23 per cent

so that the total proportion of nuclei which have disintegrated in two mean lifetimes is of

63 + 23 = 86 per cent.

During the next mean life 63 per cent of the remainder disintegrate, ie

63 per cent × 14 per cent = 9 per cent, etc.

The number of radioactive nuclei and, in consequence, the number of nuclei disintegrating per unit time therefore decreases progressively. Thus the radioactivity of a substance decreases more rapidly with time the shorter its mean life. The mean life may be measured in years, days or seconds. The terms period and **half-life** (qv) are also used in place of mean life. The period or half-life is the length of time at the end of which half of the radioactive nuclei have disintegrated. The half-life of a radioactive body is equal to 0.693 times its mean life.

mechanics, quantum, see ● **quantum mechanics.**

MEITNER, Lise (1878–) Austrian physicist. With Hahn, she discovered protoactinium. She has principally studied the properties of uranium and the transmutations of elements.

mendelevium, the name given, in honour of **Mendeleyev,** to an artificial element with atomic number 101, known in the form of isotope 256. Each of its nuclei contain 101 protons and 155 neutrons. It is unstable and disintegrates with a mean lifetime of half an hour.

MENDELEYEV, Dmitri Ivanovich (1834–1907) Russian chemist. Originator of the periodic classification of chemical elements which was the key to the electronic structures of the atom. He was also known for various work in the field of inorganic chemistry.

● **Mendeleyev's classification,** the classification of pure bodies according to their chemical properties.—Drawn up in the last century by the great insight of Mendeleyev, the explanation of it was found in the study of atomic structure. Chemical properties are in fact due to the electrons which surround the nucleus of the atom, mainly to those of the peripheral **shells** (qv). Mendeleyev's classification offers great similarity with the classification of atoms according to the composition of their electronic shells. Pure bodies undiscovered in the last century have come to take their natural place in the gaps left in Mendeleyev's classification. (See **element.**)

meson (from the Greek *mesos*, intermediary), a particle whose mass lies between the mass of the electron and that of the proton.—True mesons divide into two groups: the pions, whose mass is about 270 times that of the electron, and K mesons, whose mass is about 970 times that of the electron. Particular interest was aroused in research on mesons when, in 1935, Yukawa developed the hypothesis of the existence of particles with a mass of between 200 and 300 electronic masses to explain nuclear forces. Particles with a mass equal to 206 electronic masses were indeed found in cosmic radiation. It was thought possible to identify them with the mesons predicted by Yukawa, and they were called *mu mesons.* However, the mu meson behaved in a rather disappointing manner; it should have induced many nuclear reactions if it was the particle of the nuclear field, but it reacted little. It was only towards 1947 that Powell, Occhialini and Lattes showed the existence of another particle with a slightly higher mass, the pion. They observed it in photographic emulsions kept at a high altitude, on top of a mountain. They established that the pion disintegrated, giving a mu meson, and they then measured the ratio between the mass of the pion and that of the mu meson; the pion was really the particle of the nuclear field. (See **pi.**) It was then understood why mu mesons, but not pions, were to be observed at sea-level. The pions of cosmic radiation arriving in the Earth's atmosphere reacted with the atoms of the atmosphere or disintegrated into mu mesons before reaching the ground. The mu meson is in no way a particle of the nuclear field (there is now a tendency to abandon the name *meson* and prefer *muon* for it) since its fundamental characteristic is to be a lepton. The first pions to be observed were in the form of electrically charged particles. Yukawa's theory also predicted the existence of neutral mesons and Robert Oppenheimer suggested that the neutral pion should disintegrate very rapidly in the form:

neutral pion *gives* 2 gamma rays.

It was indeed observed in this form in 1950, and Steinberger, Panofsky and Steller gave a value to its mass by finding the energy distribution of gamma rays produced in a target bombarded by protons of the synchrocyclotron at Berkeley, California. Towards 1950, the study of cosmic radiation with Wilson chambers by groups at Manchester, Rochester and that of Professor Leprince-Ringuet in Paris, demonstrated the presence of unstable particles heavier than the pion, which were called *heavy mesons* or *K mesons* (see **K**). These particles do not come within the framework of Yukawa's theory. Nevertheless, they possess the character of particles of the nuclear field, inducing numerous reactions. These are *strange particles* (see **strangeness number**), as they are only produced in pairs by non-strange particles. The presence of K mesons contributes to increasing the complexity of the nature of nuclear forces, which, up to the present, have not been entirely explained. All mesons are unstable. They also have in common the property of being **bosons** (qv), since their spin is zero.

mesothorium, a name usually given to two elements of the radioactive series of thorium.—*Mesothorium 1* is, in reality, the isotope 228 of radium which decays by beta emission with a mean life of 6.7 years. *Mesothorium 2* is isotope 228 of actinium, which decays by beta emission with a mean life of 6.13 hours.

mesoton or **mesotron,** a name once given to the meson, at the time when the mu lepton appeared to be a **meson** (qv).—Use of it has been abandoned.

metastable, said of a system of particles raised from the normal state, called the ground state, to a state of higher energy (excited state), and able to return to the fundamental state more slowly than excited systems of a similar type.—For instance, an isomer nucleus, an excited nucleus which may return to the fundamental state by the emission of a gamma ray after a perceptible lifetime, is said to be metastable.

MeV, a symbol of *megaelectronvolt*, a unit of energy with a value of 1 million electronvolts.

Michelson, Albert Abraham (1852–1931) American physicist, born in Prussia. He received the Nobel Prize for Physics in 1907 for the optical instruments which he developed. He invented an interferometer with which he measured the speed of light in various media with great precision. With Morley, he carried out the famous experiment demonstrating the non-existence of any measurable displacement of the Earth with respect to the ether, which was at the origin of the theory of relativity.

microcurie, a unit of radioactivity with a value of a millionth of a curie.—In a radioactive source of 1 microcurie 37,000 nuclei disintegrate per second.

microscope, electron and **proton microscope,** microscopes in which a beam of electrons or protons replaces the luminous beam.—The resolving power, the distance between two points which may be separated optically, in a standard microscope depends on the wavelength of the light employed and on the index of refraction of the immersion fluid. These two quantities are subject to limits which may not be exceeded. On the contrary, the wavelength connected with electrons in motion (see ● **de Broglie wavelength**), may be brought to values far below that of visible light, by communicating sufficient velocity to the electrons. The *electron microscope* enables details which cannot be seen by optical methods to be analysed. The *proton microscope*, which uses protons whose mass is 1836 times higher than that of the electrons, makes it possible to obtain even smaller wavelengths. In these devices it is necessary to keep the beam intensity to a sufficiently low value, so that it does not disturb the structure of the object under observation, and so that the heat generated inside the object is not excessive. *See illustrations on pp. 152, 153.*

microscopic, said of a physical system containing a small number of corpuscles (molecules, atoms, nuclei, particles).—Its dimensions are always inferior to that of the micron (a thousandth of a millimetre). Generally said of a phenomenon for which classical mechanics breaks down. (See **macroscopic.**)

microtron, an apparatus for accelerating electrons.—It consists of an electromagnet which establishes a

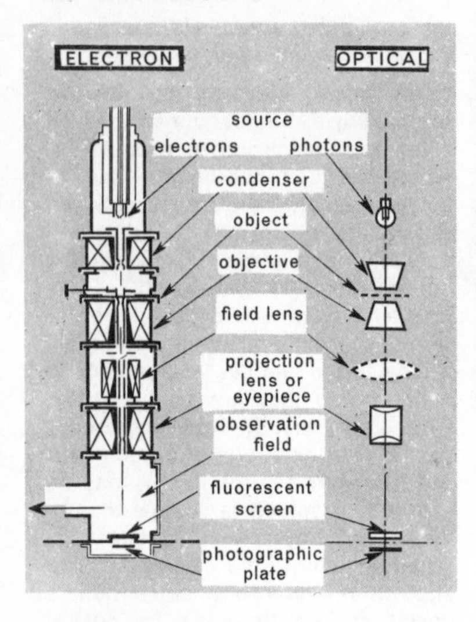

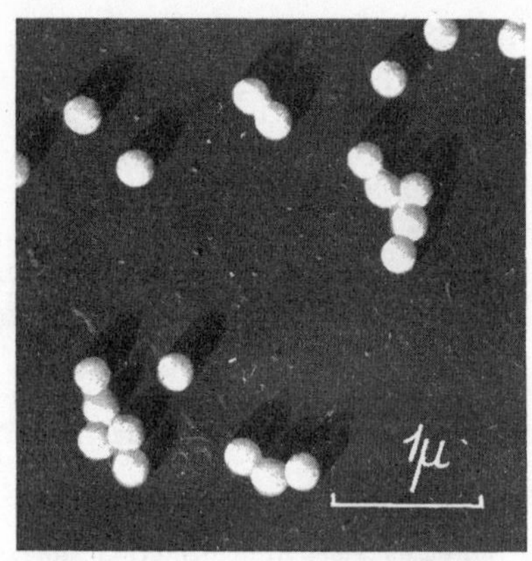

(top right) *Some examinations with an electron microscope. Grains of latex on a carbon film; chromium shading.*

(top left) *Comparative diagrams of an electron microscope and an optical microscope*

(bottom left) *Tobacco mosaic virus (negative)* (Photo Institut-Pasteur, Paris)

(bottom right) *Macromolecular crystal: spiral terraces* (Photo R. W. G. Wyckoff, Lab Phys Biology)

An electron microscope with electrostatic lenses (Photo ONERA)

magnetic field in a cylindrical cavity. The magnetic field holds the particles in circular orbits while a high frequency electric field accelerates the electrons at each revolution. The diameter of the circle traced by an electron increases in the course of the acceleration, as it acquires energy. At the end of the acceleration the electrons are directed on to a target in which they produce the reactions to be studied.

migration, the travel of particles in matter (eg migration of neutrons in a nuclear reactor; migration of ions in an ionised medium).

millicurie, a unit of radioactivity with a value of a thousandth of a curie.—In a radioactive source of 1 millicurie, 37 million nuclei disintegrate per second.

MILLIKAN, Robert Andrews (1868–1953) American physicist. In 1911 he carried out the first measurement of the electron charge. In 1916 he also measured the Planck constant. Later he specialised in cosmic rays and proved experimentally the increase in strength with altitude of this radiation. He received the Nobel Prize for Physics in 1923.

milliröntgen, a radiation unit with a value of a thousandth of a röntgen.

models of the nucleus. The laws governing the structure of nuclei are complex and still imperfectly known. So as to explain the various characteristics of the nuclei, several models have been proposed, each one being constructed with simplified hypotheses, leading to conclusions which give a good account of some of the experimental results, without being able to explain all of them. They may be classified into two groups:

1) Independent particle models in which the nucleons (neutrons and protons) are assumed to interact weakly
2) Models with strong interactions in which all the nucleons are assumed to interact strongly.

●**liquid drop model,** model well adapted to many phenomena which remain obscure in the shell model; the nucleons in it are assimilated to the molecules which constitute a liquid. This explains why the energy with which a nucleon is bound in the nucleus is practically the same for all nucleons; that the density of the nuclei is constant, their bulk increasing regularly with the number of nucleons they contain, these being placed side by side without any range between them. The fission of heavy elements into two or more lighter nuclei is also explained by this model. On the other hand, taking into account the Coulomb forces which tend to separate the electrically charged protons in the nucleus, whereas nuclear forces attract them, the increase in the proportion of neutrons may be calculated (see ●**neutron excess**) according to the increase in the number of nucleons in the nucleus. Other physical phenomena, like the variation in energy of the alpha particles emitted by the radioactive nuclei, may equally well be interpreted within the framework of this model. So as to make further progress in understanding nuclear structure, Bohr and other physicists have proposed a more complex model, taking into account the movements of each nucleon, and the simultaneous movements of assemblies of nucleons. This is the *collective model.* It contains certain improvements with regard to the shell model; in it collective oscillating movements may be assimilated to oscillations of the liquid drop, so that, to a certain extent, it represents a synthesis of the shell model and of the liquid drop model. Nuclear models, although based on approximations, enable a good image of intranuclear phenomena to be obtained, as well as an explanation of the results of a great many experiments. A strict theory of the nuclei which is not, however, possible in the present state of our knowledge, is certain to appear under a much more complex aspect.

● **shell** or **orbital model,** in this model, it is assumed that the nucleons assemble in alternate levels like electrons in the atom. It is known that an atom, all of whose shells are filled, is chemically inactive, creating a closed system, which it is difficult for the electrons of other atoms to penetrate. In the same way, when a nucleus contains either protons or neutrons according to the magic numbers 2, 8, 20, 50, 82 and 126, it is particularly stable; the neutrons and protons in it being strongly bound. Thus the nuclei of helium (2 protons, 2 neutrons), of oxygen 16 (8 protons, 8 neutrons), neon 20 (10 protons, 10 neutrons), etc, are very stable. A large proportion of stable nuclei are also found in nature, having a number of protons or neutrons equal to one of the magic numbers. These nuclei, being stable, compared to other nuclei, undergo fewer reactions when bombarded by particles, their cross section being lower. The expenditure of energy required to extract a neutron or a proton from these nuclei is particularly high. The spin of the nuclei, consisting of an even number of protons and an even number of neutrons, is zero. It would therefore seem that the protons assemble in pairs, their spin being directed in the opposite direction and cancelling each other out, and that the same applies to the neutrons. This behaviour may be explained within the framework of the shell model, as well as within the framework of the *model with the alpha particle*, in which it is assumed that the neutrons assemble by 4s (2 protons, 2 neutrons) to form alpha particles, or helium nuclei. This last model, however, is of restricted scope, and casts little light on understanding of the structure of the nucleus. The shell model, however, accounts for other characteristics of the nuclei, such as magnetic and electrical moments.

moderating power or **slowing down power,** a quantity related to the effectiveness with which the *moderator* of a nuclear reactor slows down the neutrons, from the energy with which they are produced in fission, to that which they should have to procure fission. They lose their energy in the moderator through consecutive impacts with the atoms of the moderator. The number of impacts required to slow down the neutrons is lower the greater the mean loss of energy they undergo. Moderating power is the mean logarithm of the ratio between initial and final energies multiplied by the microscopic collision cross-section. The table on p. 156 shows this, as well as the number of impacts necessary to reduce the neutrons to an energy of 0.025 electronvolts. Characteristics other than the moderating power direct the choice of a moderator. Water is frequently eliminated as it absorbs neutrons considerably. Carbon is frequently used in the form of graphite, on account of its low cost price and its great purity.

moderator	moderating power	number of impacts
Water	1.35	19
Heavy water	0.19	35
Beryllium	0.15	86
Beryllium oxide	0.12	103
Carbon	0.06	115

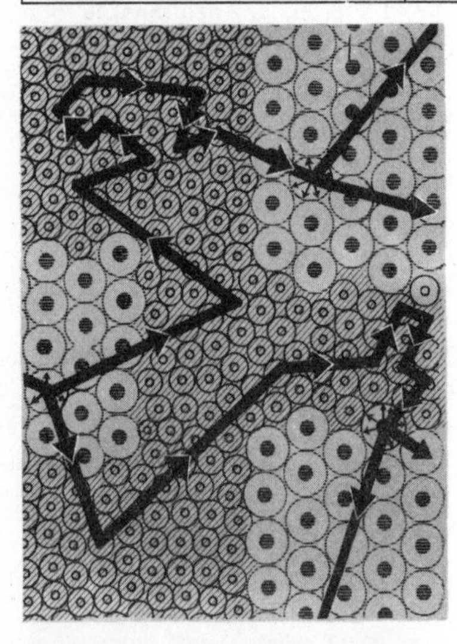

Secondary fission neutrons, shown by black lines, whose mean energy is 1 MeV, are slowed by the atoms of the moderator (carbon, beryllium, heavy water, shown by grey tint), of the reactor. They thus become slow neutrons capable of fissioning the nuclei of uranium 235, black on white ground.

moderator, a substance used in a reactor to slow down neutrons emitted in the fissions of fuel nuclei. Neutrons, when they are produced, possess an energy of several million electronvolts. In thermal reactors, they should have an energy of some hundredths of an electronvolt to be effective and induce further fissions. The slowing down is effected by means of elastic collisions between the neutrons and the nuclei of a moderator, some of the energy of the first being handed on to the second. The energy lost on average by a neutron striking a nucleus being greater the less the mass of the nucleus, the best moderators are light elements, ie, in this order: hydrogen (mass number 1), deuterium (mass number 2), helium (mass number 4), beryllium (mass number 9) and carbon (mass number 12), etc. A moderator should possess a second important property: it should not absorb a large proportion of neutrons, because these would disappear before being slowed down in the event of an absorption. Thus heavy water is preferred to ordinary water, as it absorbs few neutrons. The most frequently used moderators are graphite, heavy water, ordinary water (more economic to start with than heavy water), beryllium, oxygen (when uranium is in the form of oxide in a homogeneous reactor).

modes of disintegration, the alternative disintegration paths of a given particle. Meson K_1^0 may decay in two ways:

K_1^0 *gives* positive pion + negative pion,

or K_1^0 *gives* neutral pion + neutral pion.

The proportion of disintegrations according to these two methods is respectively 68 per cent and 32 per cent.

The radioactive nucleus of actinium 227 may decay in two modes: an alpha disintegration:

actinium 227 (89 proton, 138 neutrons)
gives francium 223 (87 protons, 36 neutrons)
+ alpha (2 protons, 2 neutrons)

and a beta disintegration:

actinium 227 (89 protons, 138 neutrons)
+electron+antineutrino.

The proportions of the disintegrations according to these two methods are respectively, 1.2 per cent and 98.8 per cent.

molar, relating to a gram-molecule of a substance.

mole, gram-molecule (qv).

molecular diffusion, see **diffusion, molecular.**

molecule. The great majority of bodies met with in nature consist of chemical compounds of two or more elements (or pure bodies). The molecule is the smallest quantity of a compound body. It is frequently composed of only a small number of atoms of pure bodies. Two or more identical atoms of the same pure body may, moreover, assemble to form a molecule.—The majority of gases and liquids (such as nitrogen, oxygen, water, etc) are made up of molecules. Only rare **gases** (qv), are monatomic, ie each of their atoms is free, without any bond with its neighbours. In solids, one may distinguish between structures of molecular type (each distinct molecule formed by a limited number of atoms) or of crystal type (formed by a regular lattice of linked atoms which may be extended indefinitely). However, giant molecules frequently connected with living organisms, consist of a great many atoms. Study of the structure and properties of molecules, formerly considered to be a field reserved to chemistry, has, in the past few decades, come to be looked at from the aspect of interactions between the particles of which the molecules are composed. Progress in understanding the structure of the atom has made it possible to apply the methods of quantum mechanics to the structure of the molecule. The following question arises on the subject of the existence of molecules:

Which forces bind the molecules of an atom together?

a) In the nineteenth century, the form in which the formation of a molecule was envisaged, was called the *ionic bond*. The atoms of a pure body may be ionised, some losing an electron and becoming positive ions, others gaining an electron and becoming negative ions. For instance, forces binding chlorine Cl (negative ion Cl^-) and sodium Na (positive ion Na+) in sodium chloride, are due to the attraction of the two electric charges. Reality is somewhat more complex, and other bond types must be recognised.

b) The *covalent bond* takes place between two atoms, both of which possess an incomplete **shell** (qv) of external electrons. The communal sharing (hence the name of this bond) of these electrons ends with the formation of a complete shell, a stable whole, little affected by external actions. Two hydrogen atoms, for example, both of which possess an electron, may assemble to form the

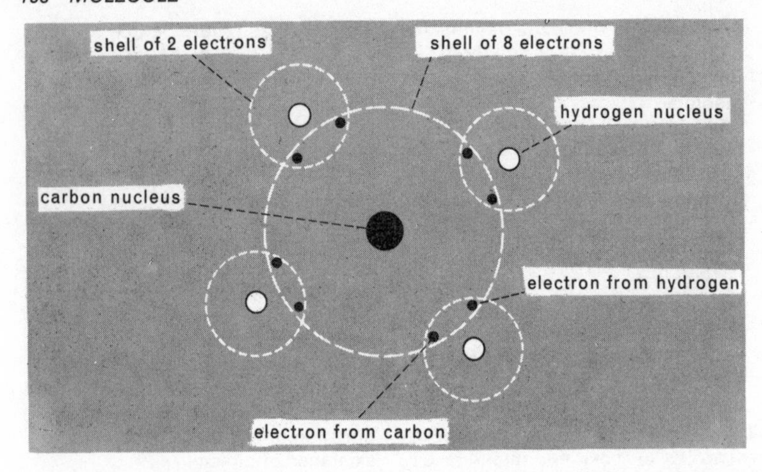

Covalent bond between hydrogen and carbon atoms in a methane molecule

hydrogen molecule, the shell formed, called K shell in an atom, being complete with 2 electrons. The methane molecule contains 1 carbon atom and 4 hydrogen atoms. Each of the hydrogen atoms shares its electron with the carbon atom. The latter possesses 4 electrons to which are added the 4 electrons of the hydrogen atoms. The whole therefore forms a system of 8 electrons, and this system is stable since the number 8 corresponds to a complete electronic shell. Conversely, each of the hydrogen atoms has at its disposal one of the carbon electrons, so the system is stable, since it corresponds to a complete shell with 2 electrons. Chemical stability is assured by the fact that these complete shells are analogous to those of chemically neutral pure bodies. The bonds between the atoms of a molecule frequently have to be interpreted as the intermediate result of these two kinds of valency. Study of the distances between atoms provides an interesting fact in this discussion, since the two electric charges of a molecule with an ionic bond form an electric dipole. Study of band spectra (see **spectrum**) or of diffraction by X-rays enables these distances to be measured indirectly. They are of the order of 0.1 millionths of a millimetre in the hydrogen molecule, and of 0.24 for the molecule of sodium chloride, for example. They are comparable to the dimensions of the atoms: the bulk of an atom is, in effect, determined by the position of the electron shells surrounding the nucleus.

c) Electrons placed around the nucleus of an atom are not necessarily uniformly distributed on an orbit. The probability of finding this electron at a given place, may be very different according to the distance and direction of the nucleus. The molecule of water H_2O, consisting of an oxygen atom and of two hydrogen atoms, is a molecule of the polar type, in which hydrogen electrons and atoms are not distributed in a symmetrical fashion. It is this kind of bond in the molecule which produces the greatest possible overlap between the orbits of the electrons in hydrogen, and the orbits of the electrons in oxygen.

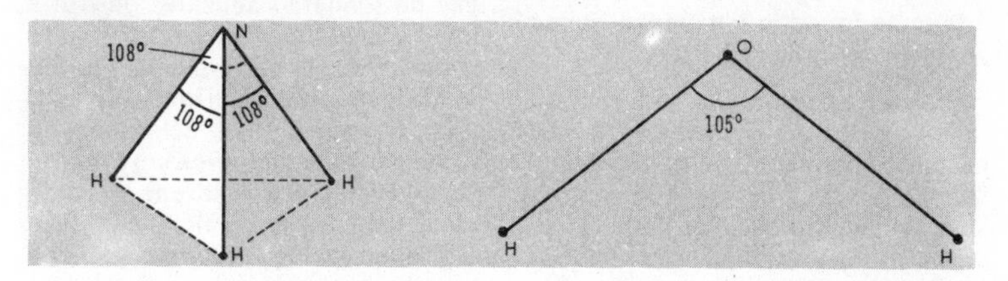

On the left: *a molecule of ammonia.* On the right: *a molecule of water.*

In the case of ammonia, which consists of 1 nitrogen atom and 3 hydrogen atoms, the structure is in the shape of a pyramid, each of the hydrogen atoms occupying a corner of the base.

d) Binding forces between molecules are always weaker than the internal cohesive forces of each of the molecules. They are practically nil in gases, and are higher in solids than in liquids. The molecule is not the only possible state for pure and compound bodies. Metal atoms in the solid state assemble in the form of crystals, in which no molecular structure may be detected. Crystals may also be formed by atoms of different bodies, or again, by molecules. In the latter case, they are called molecular crystals. The diversity and complexity of molecular structures together prevent a simple, universal theory of them being produced. Only general classifications are possible, each body remaining a special case.

●**molecular,** pertaining to the **molecule.**

momentum, a physical quantity defined by the product of the mass of a body by its velocity.—When a particle becomes *relativistic,* that is to say when its speed is no longer very small in proportion to the speed of light, the mass occurring in the expression for the momentum is *relativistic mass.* This mass is that which corresponds to the total energy of the system, an amount of energy equivalent to the mass of the stationary particle and the energy due to the motion.

●**angular momentum,** for a body in circular rotational motion, the product of momentum p by the radius r of the trajectory.—The angular momentum in atomic systems can only

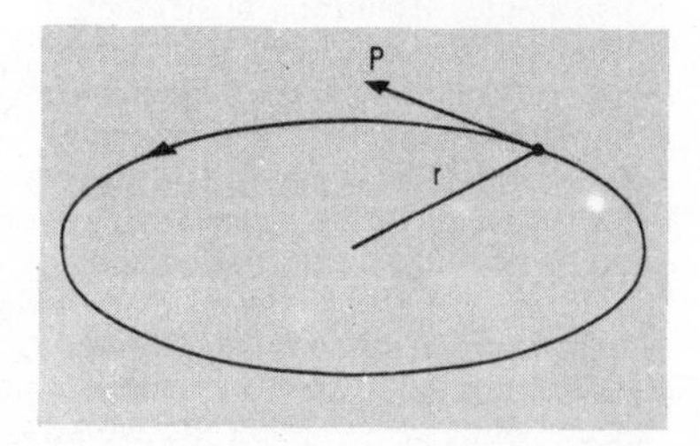

Angular momentum

assume a disconnected series of values, which are whole multiples of the Planck constant divided by 2 π.

monazite, an ore which contains a low quantity of uranium and thorium as well as elements called **rare earths** (qv), in the form of phosphates.—It is mainly used in the production of thorium and of rare earth elements. It is to be found in the United States of America, India and Brazil.

monitor, an apparatus which enables radioactivity in a reactor to be measured continuously, so as to keep it within suitable limits. || An apparatus placed in a beam of particles so as to control its strength in continuous fashion.

monochromatic, said of light when it is composed of radiations of a single colour. || By extension, said of a beam composed of particles with the same momentum or energy. The usage is not well defined.

monochromator, neutron, an apparatus enabling neutrons to be selected according to their speed and direction, and used for the study of the reactions of neutrons on matter according to their velocities. There are three kinds of monochromators: a) *Time of flight selector*—this is only used with sources which provide neutrons in pulses; with accelerators, for example. Neutrons are detected at the source outlet and at a certain distance from the source. Electronic equipment enables the time which the beam of neutrons takes to travel this distance to be measured. It renders the measuring device sensitive for only a short interval of time. Neutrons slower than those selected, would arrive later on the measuring device, while faster neutrons would arrive earlier, at moments when the measuring device has been rendered insensitive.
b) *Mechanical Monochromator* (*chopper*)—used for thermal neutrons.—It consists of a revolving cylinder containing cadmium sections which strongly absorb the thermal neutrons. The measuring device, placed at a definite distance from the cylinder, may be rendered sensitive only at a definite time after the neutrons have passed. A specific velocity corresponds to this interval of time. Velocity selection may also be achieved with the help of a second revolving cylinder, which allows the neutrons to pass some time after the first, and then only those having certain well-defined velocities.
c) *Crystal Monochromator*—it uses the diffraction of neutrons by crystals, the angle of deflection being related to the wavelength of the neutrons and therefore to their velocity (see ● **de Broglie wavelength**). By varying the angle at which the crystal is set, one obtains different neutron velocities.

monoenergetic, said of an assembly of particles having the same energy.—When the assembly is made up of particles of identical nature, the three terms: monochromatic, monokinetic and monoenergetic have the same meaning. In fact, the mass of a particle being given, its momentum decides its velocity and energy.

monokinetic, said of an assembly of particles having the same velocity.

Mössbauer effect, suppression of the Doppler broadening of a low energy gamma ray by the transfer of the recoil momentum not merely to the emitting nucleus but to a massive group of associated atoms.—The suppression is nearly total for a large part of the emission in hard crystalline solids, partial only in liquids. It gives information about atomic association and binding.

mu or **muon,** a fundamental particle which can exist, like the electron, with a positive or negative electric charge.—The mu is 206.8 times heavier than the electron. It is unstable and disintegrates through a weak interaction with a mean lifetime of two millionths of a second:

muon *gives* electron+neutrino +antineutrino.

The intrinsic properties of the muon appear to be very similar to those of the electron and it is sometimes called a *heavy electron*. Its spin is 1/2; the difference of mass between the two particles has not yet received an obvious explanation. The muon was called a *mu meson* when it was discovered in cosmic radiation, in 1937. It was then identified as the meson responsible for nuclear forces, the existence of which had been assumed by Yukawa. However, the interactions of the muon seemed too weak for a particle of the nuclear field. It was only in 1947, with the discovery of the pion, that the nuclear meson was identified. The muon therefore is not a meson, but a lepton, a particle of the same class as the electron. It is one of the main components of low altitude cosmic radiation, as it is produced in the pion disintegration:

pion *gives* mu lepton+neutrino.

Pions originate in the nuclear interactions of primary particles of cosmic radiation. With accelerators, beams of mu leptons were obtained from the disintegration of pions, the latter being produced by the nuclear interactions of the beam in a target. These beams are used for the study of the intrinsic properties of the mu lepton for the study of weak interactions which take place on capture of a mu lepton by a nucleus. Thus,

negative mu lepton+carbon 12 (6 protons, 6 neutrons) *gives* neutrino +boron (5 protons, 7 neutrons).

multiplet, a set of distinct possible states of a particle system, each state being determined by the directions of angular momenta (related to orbital rotational motion) and of the spins (related to intrinsic angular momentum) of the particles of which it is composed. The energy of the radiation emitted by the atoms of excited alkali metals may have two distinct values. It is said that the line forms a doublet; its existence is interpreted by the presence of two possible directions of the spin of the electron of the external shell of the atom, the one along the direction of the angular momentum of the electron in its orbit, the other along the opposite direction. The idea of multiplet has been extended to the state of electric charge of a particle having nuclear interactions. The proton and neutron are considered to be a charge doublet; the proton having a positive charge, the neutron a zero charge. Both having analogous nuclear interactions, the charge is related to the direction of isotopic spin in a fictitious space, ie isotopic space. In the same way the pions form a charge triplet which may possess negative, positive or zero charge values. The masses and interactions of these three mesons are closely allied.

multiplication factor. A neutron induces fission of a uranium or plutonium nucleus in a reactor. Several neutrons are released during fission, so there is a multiplication of the number of neutrons. Between one fission and the next the neutron is slowed down as it travels a certain distance. It may also be absorbed, or may finally induce the next fission. Not all neutrons produced in fission can induce another one. The multiplication factor is the number of neutrons released in a fission which, in practice, may be used to induce other fissions. This is called the *infinite multiplication factor* for a material, when surface effects, such as the escape of neutrons and reflection in the reflector, are not taken into consideration. In the opposite event, it is called *real* or *effective multiplication factor*.

multipole, an assembly of two or more electric or magnetic poles.—An electric dipole is composed of two equal and opposite charges placed a short distance from one another. An assembly of 4 electric charges forms a quadrupole, etc. A magnetic dipole is composed of two equal and opposite magnetic masses, placed a short distance one from the other. It is equivalent to a small loop of electric current. A quantity called *multipolar moment* is connected with each multipole. Study of the quadripolar moments of nuclei for instance, provides information on the internal distribution of the electric charge.

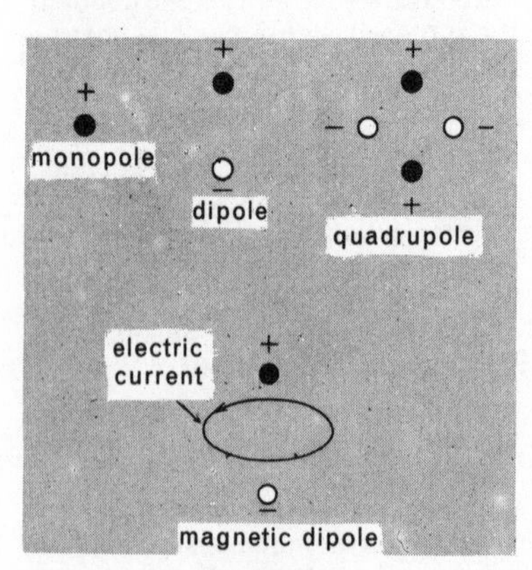

Multipole

multivibrator, an electronic instrument which usually consists of a double valve providing electric pulses of a definite frequency.—It is used, for example, as an impulse generator for the control of apparatus connected with particle detectors.

muon, see **mu.**

muonium, a hydrogen atom in which a mu replaces an electron.—It is composed of a proton and a mu lepton. It has a very short life; the mu lepton disintegrates with a mean life of 2 millionths of a second.

N

N, symbol of the ●**Avogadro number** (qv).

n, symbol of the neutron.

N-shell, fourth atomic shell. 32 electrons can occupy this shell.

natural radioactivity, the radioactivity of substances existing in nature, in contrast to the artificial radioactivity induced by a preliminary bombardment by neutrons, alpha particles, etc. (See **radioactivity.**)

NEDDERMEYER, Seth Henry (1907–) American physicist. A specialist in the field of cosmic rays, he has contributed extensively to demonstrating the existence of mesons.

negaton or **negatron,** the name sometimes given to the negatively charged electron, in contrast to the *position* or **positron** (qv) with a positive electric charge.

neptunium, a transuranian element (heavier than uranium) with atomic number 93; it takes its name from the planet Neptune.—This element was artificially manufactured by E. M. McMillan and P. Abelson in 1940, according to the reaction:

uranium 238 (92 protons, 146 neutrons)
+neutron *gives*
uranium 239 (92 protons, 147 neutrons)
+gamma ray,

followed by the disintegration:

uranium 239 (92 protons, 147 neutrons)
gives
neptunium 239 (93 protons, 146 neutrons)
+negative electron+neutrino.

Neptunium 239 is unstable, its mean life being 2.3 days. One of its isotopes, neptunium 237, is produced in small quantities in nuclear reactors according to the following reaction:

uranium 238 (92 protons, 146 neutrons)
+neutron *gives*
uranium 237 (92 protons, 145 neutrons)
+2 neutrons,

followed by the disintegration:

uranium 237 (92 protons, 145 neutrons)
gives
neptunium 237 (93 protons, 144 neutrons)
+negative electron+neutrino.

Neptunium 237 is unstable, its mean life being 2.200 centuries. Other more unstable isotopes have also been discovered.

neutretto, the name suggested for a hypothetical particle having the same mass as the electron but a zero electric charge.—It has never been discovered.

neutrino, a fundamental particle, electrically neutral, with zero rest mass travelling at the speed of light. Its spin is 1/2.—The hypothesis of the neutrino was advanced to account for the fact that the electrons of a beta disintegration possess different velocities. For instance, in the disintegration:

neutron *gives* proton+negative electron
+neutrino.

Measurements demonstrate that the electron in different events has energy varying between two limiting values. These boundaries are well defined in every known case of beta disintegration. They depend on the mass of the primary particle which disintegrates and on the masses of the secondary particles produced in the disintegration. The laws of mechanics indicate that if only two particles were formed in the disintegration, that is to say, if it were in the following form:

neutron *gives* proton+negative electron,

the electron would always possess the same energy.
In other disintegrations a variable energy may also be observed, for example:

muon *gives* electron+neutrino+ antineutrino.

The neutrino is difficult to detect with the customary detection devices, as it has no electric charge and very seldom reacts on matter. In 1953 Reines and Cowan gave a preliminary experimental indication in favour of the existence of the neutrino by detecting the reaction:

neutrino+proton *gives* neutron +positive electron.

So as to have available a strong source of neutrinos, they set up their equipment beside the reactor at Hanford in the US: a volume of 300 litres of scintillator liquid was to enable them to observe a few reactions. However, certain atmospheric reactions disturbed the experiment, so the results remained tainted with a faint degree of uncertainty. Recent experiments confirm the existence of the neutrino; there would even seem to exist two kinds, one connected with the electron and the other with the mu lepton. Thus the two disintegrations:

pion *gives* mu lepton+neutrino
pion *gives* electron+neutrino

would provide two different neutrinos. In subsequent reactions, the first neutrino would only give mu leptons, the second only electrons. Experiments will have to provide fresh results to strengthen this hypothesis. To each of these neutrinos corresponds its antiparticle: the antineutrino. The name of *neutrino* is usually reserved for neutrinos emitted with a positive mu lepton or a positive electron, that of *antineutrino* being reserved for neutrinos emitted with a negative mu lepton or a negative electron in the above disintegration. This nomenclature corresponds to a conservation of total number of leptons, particles having lepton number +1 and antiparticles lepton number −1.

neutron, a fundamental particle, electrically neutral, 1840 times heavier than the proton.—In an atomic mass unit, the mass of the neutron is 1.0089; its spin is 1/2. Although the neutron has a total zero electric charge, it has a magnetic moment slightly inferior to that of the proton (68 per cent), which possesses a positive electric charge. Neutrons and protons have magnetic moments of opposite directions. This magnetic moment, characteristic of a small magnet magnetically equivalent to the particle, appears to indicate a division of electric charge inside the neutron. With the proton, the neutron is one of the basic components of the nucleus of the atom. It is a relatively recent discovery. In 1930 Irène and Frédéric Joliot-Curie observed that a neutral radiation, the result of induced radioactivity, was able to set in motion protons contained in a paraffin target. They interpreted this phenomenon by assuming it to have been induced by high energy gamma rays. Calculations gave 52 million electronvolts, whereas known gamma rays only possessed a few million electronvolts. It was Chadwick in 1932 who suggested that the incident radiation might be composed of neutral particles with a mass close to that of the proton. In this event, the proton should possess an energy of 5 million

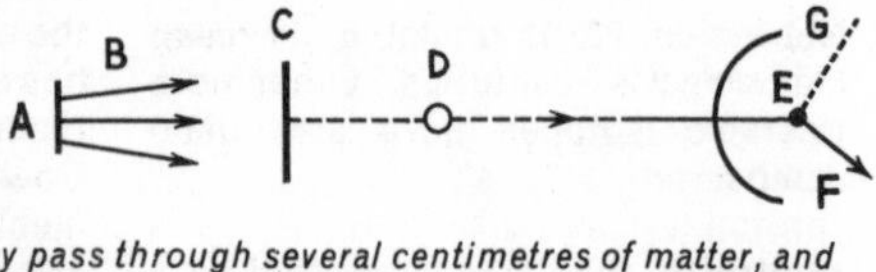

Discovery of the neutron in outline. Radium source A *emitting alpha particles* B*; Beryllium pellet* C *receiving the alphas; from time to time a neutron* D*, is produced by an alpha on a beryllium nucleus. It may pass through several centimetres of matter, and at* E *will collide with a hydrogen nucleus, setting this proton in rapid motion* EF*. It is the track* EF *of the proton that is detected.*

electronvolts, quite comparable to that commonly obtained in processes of induced radioactivity. The reaction of neutron production in this experiment was as follows:

beryllium 9 (4 protons, 5 neutrons) +alpha
(2 protons, 2 neutrons) *gives*
carbon 12 (6 protons, 6 neutrons) +neutron.

The free neutrons are unstable and disintegrate according to the schema:

neutron *gives* proton+electron+ antineutrino

with a mean life of 13 minutes. Neutrons found inside the nuclei are stable. The fact that they are bound causes their mass to appear smaller, inferior to that of the proton. Because of this, the disintegration of bound neutrons in a nucleus becomes impossible.

How are neutrons produced?

They cannot be set in motion in accelerators like electrically charged particles, because an electric field has no effect on them. However, particles from an accelerator can be used as projectiles and be directed on to the nuclei of the target containing the neutrons. Incident particles, protons, deuterons or alpha particles react on the nucleus and may eject the neutrons from it. Reactions of the following type may be used:

lithium 7 (3 protons, 4 neutrons) +proton
gives beryllium 7 (4 protons, 3 neutrons)+neutron.

At a higher energy the phenomenon of *stripping* is used, in which the incident particle is a deuteron, a deuterium nucleus consisting of one proton and one neutron; as the proton possesses an electric charge it is captured by the target nucleus, the neutron not being deflected. In this way beams of neutrons are obtained which possess closely allied speeds and directions. The reaction, by means of which the neutrons were produced at the time of their discovery, is much used, the alpha particles being provided by means of a radioactive radium source. This neutron source is called the *radium-beryllium* source. It is also possible to extract neutrons from nuclei by bombarding them with gamma rays emitted by an artificial radioactive element. Finally, nuclear reactors provide large quantities of very low energy neutrons. The experimental device may be placed right inside the reactor, where the neutrons are present in large quantities. Neutrons are also used outside the reactor, by cutting an aperture in the protective shield.

How are neutrons detected?

Since they possess no electric charge, they have no influence on the usual detection appliances. Products of nuclear reactions induced by neutrons are the means by which they are to be observed. A layer of uranium is placed on the inner partition of a fission chamber. Low energy neutrons induce the fission of uranium nuclei, developing two or three electrically charged fission fragments which may be detected by the ionisation chamber. Boron is frequently used to detect neutrons, as they react with great effectiveness on the nuclei of boron 10, which is present in natural boron in a 20 per cent proportion. Boron trifluoride, BF_3, a gaseous compound, is frequently employed in Geiger-Müller counters and in ionisation chambers. Natural boron may be enriched up to 90 per cent in boron 10, so as to increase the effectiveness of these counters. Finally, high-energy neutrons may convey to hydrogen protons a sufficient speed for them to be detectable by a counter. Protons set in motion in this way are called *recoil protons*. A mechanical chopper may be used to select neutrons according to their velocity. This consists of two gates separated one from the other, which open and close on the path of a beam of neutrons, with a slight time displacement. The speed selected is determined by the distance between the two gates and by the time interval of the displacement. These gates frequently consist of circular revolving discs, with a section removed. Diffraction of thermal neutrons by a crystal is also a means used to select neutrons, the angle according to which they are deflected depending on their velocity.

What are the aims of neutron research? Understanding of neutron reactions on materials is fundamental to the technique of nuclear reactors. Fission reactions have to be studied for combustible materials. Diffusion and absorption reactions have to be studied for moderating materials and coolants, with neutrons of all energies. Since reactor materials are subjected to a high flux of neutrons, it is necessary to place them in similar conditions so as to test them before using them. In the study of nuclear reactions, neutrons are also used as projectiles in the hope of obtaining a better understanding of the structure of the nuclei. Finally, definition of the intrinsic properties of the neutron enables progress to be made in basic research on the structure of matter.

● **fast neutron,** a neutron produced in a fission before it has been slowed down by the action of the moderator.— Its energy is of the order of a million electronvolts, the thermal neutrons having an energy of some hundredths of an electronvolt.

● **instant, immediate or prompt neutron,** a neutron emitted during the **fission** (qv) reaction.

● **neutron excess,** the nuclei of different atoms all contain about the same number of protons, positively charged particles, as of neutrons, electrically neutral particles whose mass is allied to that of the proton. However, there tend to be more neutrons than protons in stable nuclei, with the exception of the hydrogen nucleus, which contains a single proton, and the light helium nucleus which consists of two protons and one neutron. There are also a few stable nuclei, in which protons and neutrons are to be found in equal numbers. Nuclei in which there are more protons than neutrons are not usually stable and disintegrate (with the exception of the two preceding nuclei). The excess E of neutrons is defined by the difference between the number N of neutrons and the number Z of protons. It may be expressed by means of the atomic number Z, which is equal to the number of protons, and by the mass number A, which is equal to the total number of protons and neutrons in the nucleus.

$$E=N-Z=A-2Z.$$

Neutron excess increases with the mass number of the nucleus. In nuclei whose mass is 200, the number Z of protons being 80, the number N of neutrons is 120, so that the excess E of neutrons is 40. For nuclei whose mass is 23, the number of protons being 11, the number of neutrons is 12, so that the excess of neutrons is 1. Even if the relative importance of the masses 200 and 23 in both these examples is allowed for, it is obvious that the neutron excess increases with the mass of the nucleus.

$(\frac{40}{200}=\frac{1}{5}$ is greater than $\frac{1}{23})$.

This fact is explained by Coulombian forces. Electrically charged protons repel each other with more effect the greater their number in the nucleus. Heavy nuclei, of a mass higher than 60, in which the number of protons would be equal to the number of neutrons, would not be stable, they would burst under the mutual repulsion of the protons. That is the reason why no such nuclei are to be found in nature.

● **neutron leakage,** loss of neutrons in a reactor.—Neutrons in motion inside a reactor are deflected (see **scattering**) by the nuclei of the matter present in the reactor: eg fuel, slowing agent, reflector. Some of the neutrons escape through the sides of the reactor. It is precisely the purpose of the reflector to restrict this neutron leakage.

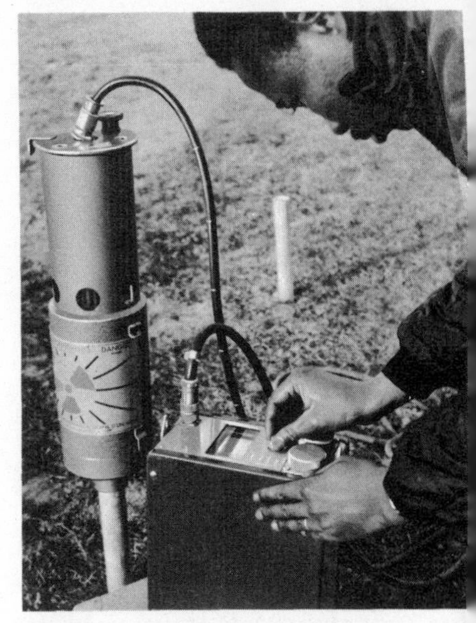

Measuring the humidity of the ground with the help of a neutron probe (Photo library CEM)

● **neutron logging,** a process for radioactive sounding of the subsoil which enables the presence of water or oil to be detected.—The lighter the nuclei of which matter is composed, the more efficient it is for slowing down neutrons. The best element for moderating neutrons is the lightest: hydrogen. Water, and the hydrocarbons of which oil consists, contain an appreciable proportion of hydrogen, whereas the bodies of which the soil is constituted are heavy elements such as calcium and silicon, which have hardly any effect on slowing down neutrons. On the other hand, slow neutron detectors are well known. There are bodies which absorb large quantities of slow neutrons, while they do not, practically speaking, absorb high-speed neutrons. Neutron absorption produces an emission of secondary radiation which is detected with the help of a counter. A neutron source such as radium+beryllium for instance, is placed at the end of the probe casing. The radium emits alpha rays which act on the beryllium to produce high-speed neutrons. At a certain distance above the source, at 50 cm for example, a slow neutron detector is placed. This would possibly be a boron counter. By capture of one neutron, the boron nucleus gives an alpha particle and a lithium nucleus, and the counter is triggered. Operation of the counter would in-

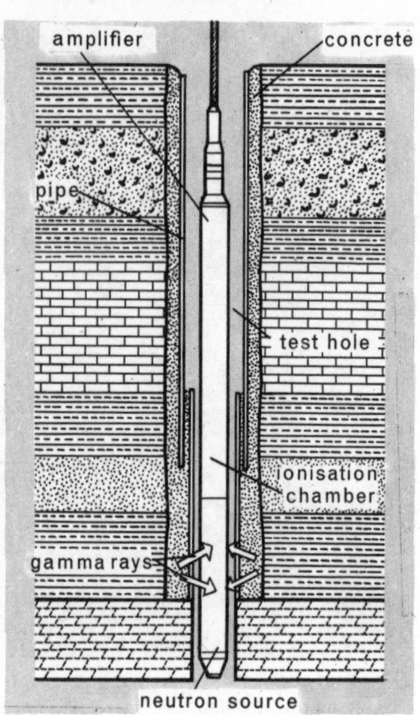

Prospecting of ground by radioactive methods. The neutrons emitted by a source induce radiation which depends on the nature of the ground. Radiation is measured by means of an ionisation chamber.

dicate the presence of hydrogenous compounds in the soil. This process is also used at shallow depths, to measure the degree of humidity of the soil, so as to determine irrigation requirements. Radioactive probes are also used to measure the density of the subsoil. In this case a source of gamma radiation is generally used, the attenuation of which increases with the density of the ground.

neutronography, neutrons used in a way similar to that of X-rays in radiography. Whereas bodies with a low atomic number (light elements) are practically transparent to X-rays, they produce substantial scattering of neutrons. Defects in a piece of metal may be detected by neutrons if care has been taken to allow material containing hydrogen, such as water, petrol or paraffin, to enter the cracks in the metal. As the neutrons possess no electric charge they do not leave direct traces on a photographic plate. Detection of them is achieved by interposing a plate of boron or of cadmium; the neutrons react in this material, emitting charged secondary particles capable of impressing a photographic plate.

neutrontherapy, a medical treatment consisting of an irradiation by neutrons.—Suggested several years ago, little use has been made of it, since its dangers seem in most instances to outweigh its possible advantages.

nuclear, pertaining to the nucleus and nuclei. *Nuclear forces*, forces binding the constituent particles of the nucleus. *Nuclear energy*, an energy given out by the fission of heavy nuclei, or the construction of light ones.

● **nuclear charge,** see **charge.**

● **nuclear density,** density of matter in the nuclei.—This density is very high. In fact, the radius of a proton is about 100,000 times less than the radius of an atom. Therefore, the volume occupied by a proton is:

$$100{,}000 \times 100{,}000 \times 100{,}000 = 1{,}000{,}000{,}000{,}000{,}000$$

(ie a million billion times less than that of the atom). The greater part of the mass is contained in the nucleus. Ordinary measured densities are of the order of a gram per cubic centimetre for solids, which

Neutronography. Pictures of a vacuum gauge, a valve and two phials containing ordinary and heavy water, obtained with X-rays (above) *and with neutrons* (below).

corresponds to the density of the atom or of the molecule. Therefore, the density of matter in the nuclei is about 1,000,000,000,000,000 times greater than the density observed on our scale. If it were possible to stack neutrons and protons with nuclear density, 1 cm^3 would weigh 1 billion tons. In a body such as can be observed on earth, the greater part of the volume of an atom is occupied by the vacuum which exists between the nucleus and the electrons. Astronomical measurements, however, permit the thought that high densities are reached in some stars governed by very high temperatures. There matter is not found in the form of nuclei, but in the form of plasma, in which protons, neutrons and electrons are closely mingled. The density must there reach several tons per cubic centimetre.

● **nuclear force.** The concept of nuclear force has to be advanced to explain the cohesion of nuclei. In a nucleus there are, in fact, protons, particles with a positive electric charge, and neutrons, which are electrically neutral particles. Repellent electric forces tend to separate protons from one another, and the fact that they remain massed inside the nucleus is only to be explained by the action of forces of attraction of a different nature, the nuclear forces. Nuclear forces are therefore stronger than, and opposed to, the electric forces inside the nucleus. The amount of research done on nuclear force does not enable it to be completely understood. Its main characteristics, however, may be determined. The forces between nucleons are strong interactions, much superior to forces of any other kind, such as electrical, weak or gravitational. Their range is limited; their effects do not make themselves felt except at a distance of the order of a millionth of a millionth of a millimetre. Electric forces, on the contrary, although they decrease progressively when the distance increases, have no such sudden cut-off. Nuclear forces saturate. In a nucleus, each proton and neutron only reacts with that or those in its immediate vicinity. On the contrary, the characteristic effect of an electric charge remains uninfluenced by the presence of other neighbouring electric charges. As it is possible to explain electric actions between charged particles in terms of an exchange of photons, so attempts have been made to explain nuclear forces by the exchange of particles between nucleons. Yukawa's theory predicted the existence of the π meson (a particle of the nuclear field whose existence has been experimentally shown) and it enables a certain number of the properties of nuclear forces to be explained while others still remain obscure. The existence of another meson, the K, further encourages one to think that nuclear forces are more complex than Yukawa imagined. Various **models of the nucleus** (qv) serve in turn to explain a particular class of observed nuclear phenomena without any one being able to embrace all the manifestations of nuclear forces.

•nuclear reactor, see **reactor, nuclear.**

nucleon, a constituent particle of the nucleus: either proton or neutron.—These two particles offer great resemblances. Their masses are closely allied, and they appear to have identical nuclear interactions. (See **•charge independence.**) Their essential difference rests in the electric charge which is positive for the proton and zero for the neutron. Since the actions of the electric charge are weak compared to nuclear forces, the neutron and the proton are considered to be two aspects of one and the same particle: the *nucleon*. For instance, in two *mirror nuclei*, a proton occupies the place in one of them which in the other is occupied by a neutron. These two nucleons find themselves in practically identical states, setting aside small differences due to the effect of the electric charge of the proton. The introduction of *isotopic spin* enables the properties of the proton and neutron to be described in a comprehensive fashion, in particular, to predict the frequency of the reactions induced by protons and neutrons. To each of these nucleons, proton and neutron, corresponds an antinucleon (antiproton and antineutron). Nucleon and antinucleon have the same mass, but opposite electric charges. The antiproton has a negative electric charge, the proton a positive electric charge. The antineutron has a zero electric charge, the neutron a zero charge. In nuclear reactions a nucleon and an antinucleon may be simultaneously formed; they cannot be formed separately. For example, the reaction may exist:

proton+proton *gives* proton+proton+neutron+antineutron.

On the contrary, the reaction:

proton+proton *gives* proton+proton+neutron

is impossible.

nucleonium, an assembly formed by a proton with a positive electric charge, and an antiproton with a negative electric charge.—It offers a certain analogy with the hydrogen atom, formed by a proton and a negative electron. The proton and antiproton are, however, much closer together in the nucleonium than the proton and electron in hydrogen, this difference being due to the fact that the mass of the electron is greatly inferior to that of the antiproton. The nucleonium exists only in a transitory state. Proton and antiproton destroy each other by emitting mesons.

nucleus, the central part of the atom, composed of protons and neutrons. Electrons of the atom being about 1836 times lighter than the neutrons and protons, it is mainly from the nucleus that the atom gets its mass. The nucleus has little volume, as in it the protons and neutrons are crowded together almost without any free volume. Its volume therefore increases in proportion to the number of nucleons. It constitutes only a small part of the volume of the atom. In the case of hydrogen, the nucleus of which consists of a single proton, the proton occupies a volume less than a millionth of a millionth of the bulk of the atom. However, the nucleus occupies a larger proportion of the atomic bulk the heavier the element. The radius of the proton is about 1.2 millionths of a millionth of a millimetre. The radius of a nucleus consisting of several nucleons may be calculated from this since they cluster in contact. Although electric forces tend to drive the protons apart, stronger forces bind together both protons and neutrons. These are nuclear forces. The nuclei are characterised by two basic numbers: the *atomic number*, equal to the number of protons, and the *mass number*, equal to the total number of protons and neutrons. Various **models of the nucleus** (qv) attempt to account for the principal properties of nuclei.

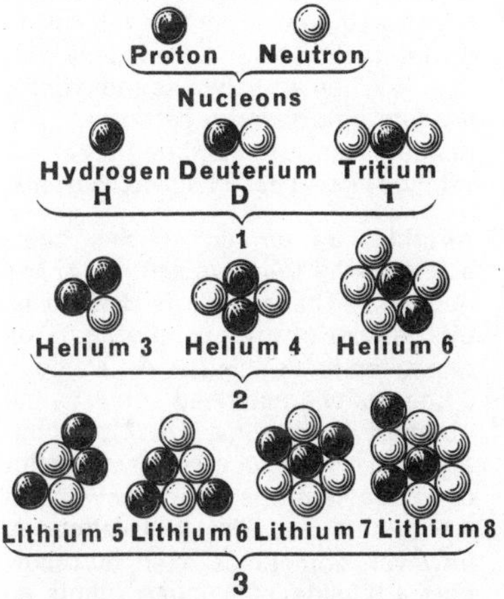

Proton Neutron
Nucleons
Hydrogen H Deuterium D Tritium T
1
Helium 3 Helium 4 Helium 6
2
Lithium 5 Lithium 6 Lithium 7 Lithium 8
3

Composition of some simple nuclei

• compound nucleus, a nucleus formed, in a nuclear reaction, by the coalescence of the target nucleus and the incident particle.—The hypothesis of the compound nucleus, formulated by Bohr, applies to nuclear reactions in which the energy of the incident particles is of the same order of magnitude as the energy with which the neutrons and protons are bound in the nucleus: ie some tens of millions of electronvolts. The incident proton or neutron is in this case acted on by the nuclear forces which govern the interior of the nucleus, and behaves like a proton or neutron of the nucleus, losing its individuality. The same thing applies to the two protons and two neutrons of an alpha particle when it enters the nucleus. The compound nucleus is in an excited state and disintegrates very rapidly. The same compound nucleus may be formed in different nuclear reactions. For example, it is possible to form an excited zinc nucleus by the two following reactions:

copper 63 (29 protons, 34 neutrons) +proton
gives zinc* 64 (30 protons, 34 neutrons);

nickel 60 (28 protons, 32 neutrons) +alpha (2 protons, 2 neutrons)
gives zinc* 64 (30 protons, 34 neutrons).

The same compound nucleus may decay in several ways.

Examples: zinc* 64 *gives*
zinc 63 (30 protons, 33 neutrons)+neutron
or else: zinc 62 (30 protons, 32 neutrons)+2 neutrons
or again: copper 62 (29 protons, 33 neutrons)+proton+neutron.

The model of the compound nucleus is not valid for high-energy reactions: the binding energy then becomes insignificant compared with the energy of the incident particle.

● **even-even nucleus,** a nucleus consisting of an even number of protons and an even number of neutrons.—Stable nuclei of this type are very numerous; there are 162 of them.

● **even-odd nucleus** and **odd-even nucleus,** a nucleus consisting of an odd number of protons and an even number of neutrons (and vice versa for an odd-even nucleus).—Stable nuclei of these two kinds are much more frequent than those of the odd-odd type. There exist respectively 55 and 53 of them; ie 108 altogether.

● **mirror nuclei,** two different nuclei, with the same mass number, possessing the following properties: the first consists of a number of protons higher by one unit than the number of neutrons, the second consists of a number of neutrons higher by one unit than the number of protons. Helium 3 and hydrogen 3 form a pair of mirror nuclei. The first contains two protons and one neutron, the second one proton and two neutrons.—The analysis of the properties of mirror nuclei is particularly useful in the study of *charge symmetry*. The supplementary proton or neutron of each of the two mirror nuclei find themselves subjected to the same nuclear forces if these forces do not depend on the electric charge which is positive for the proton and zero for the neutron. The peculiar effects of the electric charge alone produce a slight difference between the two mirror nuclei. Experiments carried out on these nuclei confirm the hypothesis of charge symmetry.

● **odd-odd nucleus,** a nucleus consisting of an odd number of protons and an odd number of neutrons.—Stable nuclei of this kind are very rare; there are only four of them.

● **recoil nucleus,** a residual nucleus which acquires a certain velocity in its interaction with an incident particle.—When a nucleus is radioactive it emits one or more particles. The residual nucleus, acquiring a certain velocity is also called a *recoil nucleus*.

nuclide, an atomic species characterised by the composition of the nucleus.—The nuclide is defined by the number of protons and neutrons contained in a nucleus. An element, a species characterised solely by the number of protons, therefore embraces several nuclides, the number of whose neutrons is different: these are its isotopes. The word element is, however, sometimes used to designate a nuclide. Obviously this is an abuse of language, but it is fairly common. Whereas the idea of element is sufficient to classify bodies according to their standard properties (chemical properties, physical characteristics, etc) the idea of nuclide is essential in nuclear physics, since the number of neutrons is quite as important as that of protons in the balance of nuclear forces. Sometimes, in speech, nuclei of identical components are divided into different nuclides. They are then classified according to their energy states. (See ● **excited state** and **isomer.**)

number, Avogadro, see **Avogadro number.**

● **atomic number,** a number which characterises a chemical element.—The atomic number is equal to the number of protons in the nucleus of an atom of the element: it is a whole number. In a neutral atom, the number of electrons is equal to the number of protons of the nucleus, and therefore also equal to the atomic number. An element may also be defined by its chemical properties since these, being due to the electrons of the atom, belong solely to the atomic number. The atomic number of elements found in nature ranges from 1 for hydrogen to 92 for uranium. Elements of a higher atomic number, past 101 for mendelevium, have been artificially manufactured by nuclear reactions. But these artificial elements are usually unstable and disintegrate more or less rapidly, which explains why they are not to be found in nature.

● **magic number,** certain particular numbers of protons or of neutrons which confer great stability on the nucleus containing them.—Nuclei which contain a number of protons or a number of neutrons equal to, or just below one of the magic numbers, possess particularly high binding energies; it is necessary to expend more energy to extract a proton or a neutron from them than in the case of other nuclei. The magic numbers are as follows: 2, 8, 20, 50, 82 and 126. The helium nucleus, consisting of 2 protons and 2 neutrons, is a very stable assembly. Nuclei, the number of whose protons or neutrons is slightly higher than one of the magic numbers are on the contrary relatively unstable. The magic numbers may be derived from a model of the nucleus in which neutrons and protons are distributed in shells. (See **models of the nucleus.**)

O

O-shell, fifth atomic shell. At most 50 electrons can occupy this shell.

OCCHIALINI, Giuseppe (1907–) Italian physicist. A specialist in cosmic rays, he contributed to the discovery of the **pion** (qv).

opaque, or **totally absorbing,** barring the passage of radiation by absorption (eg cadmium makes a total absorber with slow neutrons).—An imprecise term which must only be applied to a shell of sufficient thickness. In fact, a certain percentage of absorbed radiation corresponds to a given thickness of any absorber. It is therefore necessary to increase the absorption thickness when it is desired to reduce the strength of the radiation to a very low value.

OPPENHEIMER, Jacob Robert (1904–67) American physicist. Author of numerous works on the quantum theory of the atom. As Director of the Los Alamos Scientific Laboratory at Los Alamos, New Mexico, he took

Jacob Robert Oppenheimer (Photo AFP)

part in the preparation of the first uranium atomic bomb.

orbit, the trajectory followed by a particle in a given (atomic or macroscopic) potential field. In the Bohr model of the atom, electronic orbits are circles centred on the nucleus. In Sommerfeld's more perfected model, the electronic orbits may be ellipses in which the nucleus occupies one of the foci. To each possible orbit corresponds a definite binding energy between the nucleus and the electron. ‖ The trajectory followed by a particle in a circular accelerator. The *equilibrium orbit* is the ideal orbit on which the particle undergoes no oscillations.

orbital, that which refers to an orbit. ‖ *Orbital electron*, an electron belonging to an orbit in an atom. ‖ *Orbital angular momentum*, the angular momentum of a particle relative to a centre of force.

ortho state. Term used of a two-particle system when the spin of each particle has the same orientation.

● **orthohelium,** helium consisting of atoms in which the spins of the two peripheral electrons possess the same direction (see **parahelium**). The helium atom contains only two electrons.

● **orthohydrogen,** hydrogen which consists of molecules in which the spins of the two protons possess the same direction.—The hydrogen molecule contains two hydrogen atoms. The nucleus of the hydrogen atom consists of a single proton. (See **parahydrogen.**)

● **orthopositronium,** positronium in which the spin of the negative electron and that of the positive electron are parallel.

P

packing fraction, the proportion of mass defect to mass number of a nucleus.—Due to the fact that the components of the nucleus, neutrons and protons, are bound together, the total mass of the nucleus is less than that of its components by an amount corresponding to the binding energy. If it is agreed to accept the standard number 16 to measure the atomic mass of oxygen, whose nucleus contains 8 protons and 8 neutrons, the *mass defect* for oxygen is zero. Neutrons and protons are less bound in lighter nuclei, so the atomic mass is relatively greater than the number of neutrons and protons. On the contrary, the nuclei which are heavier than oxygen contain more closely bound neutrons and protons, so the atomic mass is relatively weaker than the number of neutrons and protons. The *mass defect* and, in consequence, the packing fraction is expressed by positive numbers for nuclei lighter than oxygen, and by negative numbers for nuclei heavier than oxygen. However, for very heavy nuclei with a mass higher than 180, repelling electric forces oppose the nuclear binding forces so that the binding energy decreases. The packing fraction is also expressed by a positive number for nuclei with a mass higher than 180.

pair creation, a creation phenomenon in which part of the energy of a photon is transformed into matter in the shape of two electrons, one having a positive, the other a negative charge.—This phenomenon cannot be produced in a vacuum. It requires the presence of a nucleus or, generally speaking, of an electric charge. Thus it may also occur when atomic electrons are present, although in this case the phenomenon is less frequent. That fraction of the energy of the photon which is not used to make electrons is absorbed, for the greater part, in the form of kinetic energy (speed) by the electrons. The remaining energy of the photon is absorbed as kinetic energy of the nucleus which usually recedes at a fairly low speed. When the phenomenon occurs in the presence of an electron, the latter acquires great velocity, so that in the end three electrons may be detected, whose energy is greater the higher that of the original photon. This phenomenon is called a *triplet*. The creation phenomenon is only possible if the photon possesses at least an energy corresponding to the mass of two electrons; ie about 1 million electronvolts.

● **electron pair,** the pair consisting of an electron and of an antielectron formed by annihilation of a gamma ray. Each of the electrons carries an electric charge, negative and positive respectively. The gamma ray carries no electric charge. The materialisation reaction may be written symbolically:

gamma *gives* electron+antielectron.

It is induced by electromagnetic interactions. It appears mainly when a gamma ray passes into the electric field of a nucleus of the atom, the nucleus having a positive electric charge conveyed by the protons contained in it. This phenomenon is called *materialisation* as the electrons possess a *finite rest mass,* whereas the rest mass of the gamma ray is zero. There is formation of matter, in the form of electrons, from radiation. The gamma ray disappears in the reaction. This phenomenon confirms Einstein's law of the equivalence of mass with energy. For a gamma ray to give rise to an electron pair, it must possess an energy at least equivalent to the mass formed: ie about $2\times0.5=$ 1 million electronvolts. Pair formation may also take place, though less frequently, in the electric field formed by one of the electrons of an atom. The gamma ray cannot spontaneously form a pair in the absence of a charged particle, either a nucleus or an electron. The laws of mechanics specify that a third particle must be present in the reaction and that it takes away a fraction of the energy of the gamma ray. In the case of a reaction on the nucleus, the fraction of energy absorbed by the recoil of the nucleus is weak, because its mass is high compared with that of an electron. On the contrary, when the creation is taking place in the presence of an electron, the latter takes away a fraction of energy comparable to that of the electrons formed, so that the initial energy of the gamma ray is distributed between the three electrons, ie the target electron and the two formed electrons. The reaction may be detected in the form of a *triplet* in which two negative and one positive electron may be observed. Formation of pairs by gamma rays increases, above 1 million electron-volts, with the energy of the gamma rays. It tends towards a limit at very high energies. The creation phenomenon is used in the shielding of high-energy gamma rays. Its frequency increases with the atomic number of the nuclei. Therefore a screen consisting of a heavy material constitutes a shield effective against gamma rays, the electrons formed being later absorbed in matter. The phenomenon of pair creation is used to detect high-energy gamma rays. As these possess no electric charge, the usual detection appliances are insensitive to them. On the other hand, tracks of charged electrons may be detected. Measurement of the energy of the electrons makes it possible to argue back to that of the gamma ray, since, generally speaking, the nucleus does not take more than an insignificant fraction of it.

parahelium, helium composed of atoms in which the spins of the two peripheral electrons have opposite directions. (See **orthohelium.**)—The helium atom contains only two electrons around its nucleus. Ortho-

Two gammas deriving from the disintegration of a neutral pion, materialise as electron pairs (Photo Ecole Polytechnique, Paris)

helium and parahelium emit different radiation spectra; the states of the excited atoms correspond to different energies.

parahydrogen, hydrogen consisting of molecules in which the spins of the two protons have opposite directions. —The hydrogen molecule contains two hydrogen atoms; the nucleus of the hydrogen atom consists of a single proton. (See **orthohydrogen.**) Hydrogen contains 75 per cent of orthohydrogen and 25 per cent of parahydrogen at room temperature. At its boiling point at atmospheric pressure, ie 253° C below zero, orthohydrogen tends to change into parahydrogen so as to achieve its equilibrium composition, which at that temperature is practically pure parahydrogen.

parameter, impact, the distance between the centre of the target particle, assumed to be stationary, and the path of the incident particle

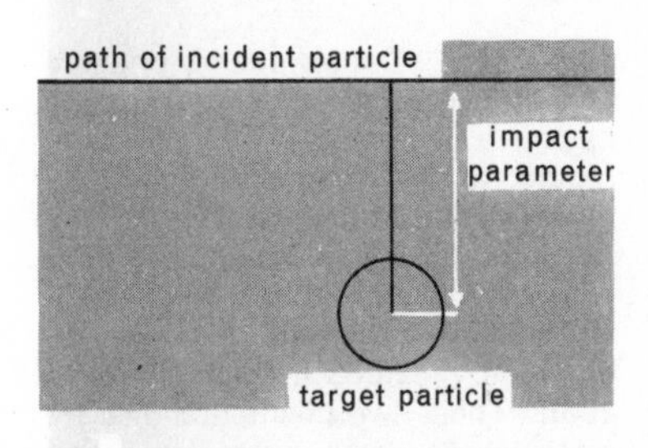

Impact parameter

prior to interaction.—In a head-on collision the impact parameter is zero. This quantity is used in a semi-classical analysis of interaction between particles. This idea enables approximate solutions to collision problems to be found. An exact analysis of the phenomena of interactions between particles is only possible by means of a quantum mechanical calculation.

parapositronium, positronium in which the spin of the negative electron and of the positive electron have opposite directions.

parent, the first element of a radioactive series or family, formed by consecutive disintegrations of unstable nuclei.—Uranium 238 (92 protons, 146 neutrons) is the parent of a radioactive series which, by a series of fourteen consecutive disintegrations, leads to lead 206 which is stable (82 protons, 124 neutrons). (See **series.**)

parity. The parity of a particle system is equal to plus one, if the functions defining the system remain unchanged in the transformation which modifies all the co-ordinates of the system by changing them into their inverse with respect to their point of origin, ie changing sign but not magnitude of cartesian co-ordinates. Parity is equal to minus one, if the functions are changed into their opposites in this transformation, called *parity operation*. The laws of classical physics remain unaltered in the parity operation, with proper allowance for rotation and magnetic effects. To visualise this fact, it may be said that a physical system possesses the same properties as the physical system that is its mirror image. The same property was at first applied to particle systems and it was deduced from it that a system should preserve its parity whatever its transformations, such as reactions, disintegrations, etc. Parity was then considered as

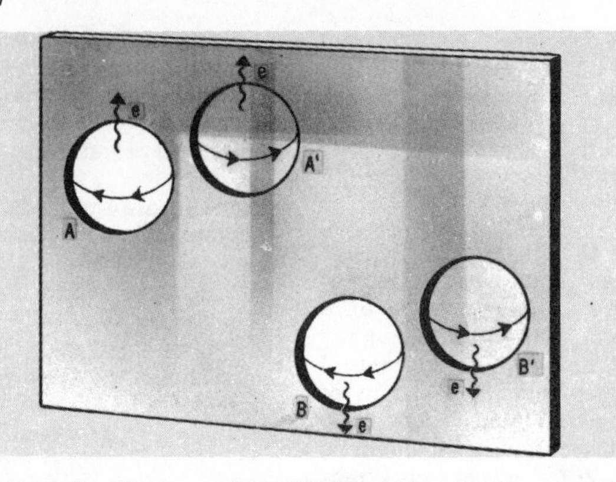

Non-conservation of parity in neutron disintegration. Observe the two neutrons A and B, whose spins have been set in the same direction. These spins correspond to a rotational motion and this is shown by a double arrow on each of them. Does the direction along which the disintegration electron leaves, have any connection with the sense of the spin? In a mirror representing the 'parity' process A has as an image A′ and B an image B′. In the process, the direction of the spin is reversed, that of the electron remains unchanged. If parity were conserved, A′ would have as much chance of materialising as A. Now A′ represents the same case as B, because it is sufficient to turn A′ by 180° to apply it on to B. A and B would therefore be produced with the same frequency. The experiment demonstrates, on the contrary, that of the two possibilities A or B, only one materialises, which proves that parity is not conserved in this disintegration.

an invariant, and the parity transformation as having no influence on the energy of the system. However, in 1958 Lee and Yang tried to solve the problem of the K meson, which had remained incomprehensible within the framework of the conservation of parity: two neutral particles of the same mass, which therefore appeared to be identical, disintegrated into two systems with opposite parity. They formulated the hypothesis of the non-conservation of parity at the same time as they made plausible a symmetrical theory of the neutrino which had previously been abandoned because it did not respect the conservation of parity. A beta disintegration experiment carried out by Mrs Wu was immediately to confirm their hypothesis. Cobalt nuclei, oriented by a magnetic field, emitted electrons having a preferential direction with regard to the magnetic field, this direction being reversed when the magnetic field was reversed. Other experiments carried out on the disintegration of the **mu** (qv), induced by pions, provided the same information. These two disintegrations are also due to weak interactions and these alone do not conserve parity, whereas electromagnetic and nuclear interactions appear to conserve parity, as recent accurate experiments have demonstrated. For particles which have electronmagnetic or nuclear interactions between one another, a relative parity has been defined by agreeing to accept the convention that the parity of the proton is equal to plus one; the parity of the neutron is then also plus one, and that of the pion minus 1.

particle. An *elementary* or *fundamental* particle is an element of matter which cannot be considered as resulting from the composition of lighter elements (eg the nucleus, the result of a composition of protons and neutrons, is not a particle, whereas the proton, which cannot be decomposed into elements, is a particle). —Most of the fundamental particles are unstable and disintegrate; the proton, antiproton, electron and antielectron alone are stable. Photons and neutrinos do not disintegrate. They may be considered stable, although the idea of their duration has no meaning; these particles travel at the speed of light and it is not known how to define an appropriate time for them, starting with measurable time. All other particles disintegrate by emitting lighter particles. Thus the neutron emits a proton, an electron and a neutrino. The pion emits a mu and a neutrino, etc. To each particle corresponds an **antiparticle** (qv) of the same mass but of opposite electric charge. The neutral pion and the photon have no electric charge and are their own antiparticle. Actually 15 other particles and 15 corresponding antiparticles have been counted, giving a total of 32. The question of the fundamentality of the particles is, however, delicate, so that some arguments tend to consider the eta mesons, the omega and f-zero, etc, as particles, although their lifetime is even shorter than that of the preceding ones. Particles, of which a list is to be found on page 180, may be classified according to their mass and properties, into three main groups:
1) *The baryons:* these are heavy particles with a mass at least equal to that of the proton. They may be divided into two groups; nucleons (neutrons and protons), constituent particles of the atomic nucleus, of zero strangeness number; and the hyperons (lambda, sigma and xi), strange particles heavier than the nucleons. All the baryons are fermions; they have a 1/2 spin.
2) *The mesons:* these are particles of intermediate mass. They are considered to be the vehicles of nuclear forces. They may be divided into two groups: the pions, of zero strangeness number; the K mesons, *strange particles*. All these mesons are bosons. They have a zero spin.
3) *The leptons:* these are light particles; the electron and the muon, which cannot exist except in the electrically charged form, and the neutrinos, electrically neutral particles of zero rest mass. All the leptons are fermions. They have a 1/2 spin. They are not subject to nuclear interactions. Finally there is the photon, which, although it is of zero rest mass, is more related to the mesons. It is the vehicle of the electromagnetic field and is a boson. Experimental research on fundamental particles is directed to their intrinsic properties (mass, disintegration method, mean life, spin, etc) and on the properties of the interactions which take place between them. Theoretical studies bear on the classification of particles and on their interactions as well as on the reasons for their existence.

● **particle of the field,** see **field.**

path length or **range,** the distance travelled by a particle in matter until it stops, is absorbed, or produces a reaction.—Alpha, beta and gamma

TABLE OF FUNDAMENTAL PARTICLES

	Name	Symbol	Mass	Spin	Modes of Disintegration	Mean Life
	photon	γ	0	1	stable	stable
leptons	neutrino	$\nu_e, \overline{\nu_e}$ $\nu_\mu, \overline{\nu_\mu}$	0	1/2	stable	stable
leptons	electron	e^+, e^-	0.511 ± 0.000	1/2	stable	stable
leptons	mu	μ^+, μ^-	105.66 ± 0.00	1/2	$\mu^\pm \rightarrow e^\pm + \nu + \nu^-$	$(2.200 \pm 0.02) \times 10^{-6}$
mesons	positive pions	π^+, π^-	139.58 ± 0.02	0	$\pi^\pm \rightarrow \mu^\pm + \nu$ $\rightarrow e^\pm + \nu$	$(2.55 \pm 0.03) \times 10^{-8}$
mesons	neutral pion	π^0	134.97 ± 0.02	0	$\pi^0 \rightarrow \gamma + \gamma$	$(1.78 \pm 0.34) \times 10^{-16}$
mesons	positive ks	K^+, K^-	493.78 ± 0.17	0	$K^\pm \rightarrow \mu^\pm + \nu$ $\rightarrow \pi^\pm + \pi^0$ $\rightarrow \mu^\pm + \nu + \pi^0$ $\rightarrow e^\pm + \nu + \pi^0$ $\rightarrow \pi^\pm + \pi^+ + \pi^-$ $\rightarrow \pi^\pm + \pi^0 + \pi^0$	$(1.229 \pm .008) \times 10^{-8}$
mesons	neutral ks	K^0_1	497.7 ± 0.3	0	$K^0_1 \rightarrow \pi^+ + \pi^-$ $\rightarrow \pi^0 + \pi^0$	$(0.88 \pm 0.01) \times 10^{-10}$
mesons		K^0_2		0	$K^0_2 \rightarrow \mu^\pm + \pi^\mp + \nu$ $\rightarrow e^\pm + \pi^\mp + \nu$ $\rightarrow \pi^+ + \pi^- + \pi^0$	$(5.77 \pm 0.59) \times 10^{-8}$
baryons antibaryons / nucleons	proton	$p, \overline{p}$	938.26 ± 0.01	1/2	stable	stable
baryons antibaryons / nucleons	neutron	$n, \overline{n}$	939.55 ± 0.01	1/2	$n \rightarrow p + e^- + \nu$	$(1.01 \pm 0.03) \times 10^3$
baryons antibaryons / hyperons	lambda	$\Lambda^0, \overline{\Lambda^0}$	1115.44 ± 0.14	1/2	$\Lambda \rightarrow p + \pi^-$ $\rightarrow n + \pi^0$	$(2.61 \pm 0.03) \times 10^{-10}$
baryons antibaryons / hyperons	positive	$\Sigma^+, \overline{\Sigma^+}$	1189.4 ± 0.2	1/2	$\Sigma^+ \rightarrow p + \pi^0$ $\rightarrow n + \pi^+$	$(0.79 \pm 0.03) \times 10^{-10}$
baryons antibaryons / hyperons	sigmas	$\Sigma^-, \overline{\Sigma^-}$	1197.20 ± 0.14	1/2	$\Sigma^- \rightarrow n + \pi^-$	$(1.58 \pm 0.05 \times 10^{-10}$
baryons antibaryons / hyperons	neutral sigma	$\Sigma^0, \overline{\Sigma^0}$	1192.3 ± 0.2	1/2	$\Sigma^0 \rightarrow \Lambda^0 + \gamma$	$< 1.0 \times 10^{-14}$
baryons antibaryons / hyperons	positive xi	$\Xi^-, \overline{\Xi^-}$	1320.8 ± 0.2	1/2	$\Xi^- \rightarrow \Lambda^0 + \pi^-$	$(1.75 \pm 0.06) \times 10^{-10}$
baryons antibaryons / hyperons	neutral xi	$\Xi^0, \overline{\Xi^0}$	1314.3 ± 1.0	1/2	$\Xi^0 \rightarrow \Lambda^0 + \pi^0$	$(3.05 \pm 0.50) \times 10^{-10}$
baryons antibaryons / hyperons	omega	Ω^-	1675 ± 3	3/2	$\Omega^- \rightarrow \Xi^0 + \pi^-$	$(1.3 \pm 0.7) \times 10^{-10}$

particles emitted in natural radioactivity each present certain path length peculiarities:

a) Alpha rays lose their energy by tearing off electrons and by exciting the atoms of the material through which they pass. Alphas are heavy particles with a double charge so that small thicknesses of matter, such as a few centimetres of air, for instance, are sufficient to stop them. To the alpha disintegration of a given nucleus corresponds a definite path length for the emitted particles. However, some radioactive bodies emit alpha rays with two or more energies to which correspond different path lengths.

b) Beta rays, which are electrons, are emitted in natural radioactivity with variable energies, therefore with path lengths variable between two limits. They are said to form a *continuous spectrum*. Furthermore, there exist fluctuations of the path length which are considerable even for electrons of identical energy. (See **fluctuation of range.**)

c) Gamma rays are absorbed in a proportion depending on the thickness of the matter through which they pass and also on their energy. When they are of high energy, the phenomenon of pair-production is preponderant. When they are of lower energy, they lose their energy by scattering of the atoms by the atomic electrons. (See **● Compton effect.**) A *mean free path* is defined as corresponding to a 63 per cent absorption of gamma rays.

Particles such as protons, neutrons and mesons have, in general, a path length determined by their interactions with the nuclei of matter when they are of very high energy. Stopping by ionisation and excitation affects only charged particles of lower energy. The majority interact with nuclei well before they stop. A **mean free path** is likewise defined for nuclear interactions.

● mean free path, the average distance travelled by particles of the same nature and velocity when passing through a substance. When particles pass through a substance they may interact with the atoms of which the substance is constituted. The number of reactions induced by these particles in a certain thickness of matter is given by the laws of chance (statistical laws). For an assembly of particles having the same mass and velocity, the mean free path may be defined as being equal to the average distance travelled by the particles before they have undergone a reaction in matter. Calculation then shows that in a beam which contains a large number of particles 63 per cent undergo reaction before passing through a mean free path, 87 per cent undergo them before passing through two mean free paths, etc, so that the strength of the beam diminishes progressively.

PAULI, Wolfgang (1900–58) Swiss physicist of Austrian origin. With Heisenberg he elaborated the quantum theory of fields. To him we owe the exclusion principle which bears his name and the prediction of the existence of the neutrino. He received the Nobel Prize for Physics in 1945. *See illustration on p. 182.*

● Pauli's exclusion principle, a principle expressed by Pauli in 1925, asserting that two electrons cannot be found in an identical quantum state. (Among the quantum numbers which describe their movements, one at least must possess a different value for one or other of the two electrons.) Used to elucidate the properties of

Wolfgang Pauli (Photo Keystone)

complex atoms which contain several electrons, this principle has been extended to all those particles which, like the electron, are fermions, that is to say, which possess a half-whole spin (1/2, 3/2, etc). Bosons, particles whose spin is whole (0, 1, 2, etc), do not obey this principle. The exclusion principle may be deduced from the more general properties which must be possessed by functions describing a physical system. This relates to the fact that two identical particles which have the same mass, same electric charge, same spin, etc, are indistinguishable. The idea of *indistinguishability* has no equivalent on the ordinary scale, in which two identical objects with the same properties may always be located by an indicator which has an insignificant effect on their properties. Such a distinction is impossible on the microscopic scale. Pauli's principle is of universal application with reference to fermions; it appears, for example, in the structure of the nuclei of the atom which consist of fermions (neutrons and protons), and in the structure of atoms.

penetrating, any radiation capable of passing through an appreciable thickness of matter.—This word is mainly used to describe the *showers* produced by the nuclear reaction of a primary particle of cosmic radiation with an atomic nucleus. Unlike the cascade showers in which gamma rays and electrons are alternately produced, penetrating showers contain particles capable of passing through 15 to 20 cm of lead.

PEREY, Marguerite (1909–) French chemist. She discovered the element **francium** (qv).

period, another name for the term **half-life** (qv).

periodometer, an apparatus enabling the time-constant of a reactor to be measured directly.—Its principle is based on the use of a detector which measures the growth of the neutron flux per second in the reactor. It may be used to release a safety device in the event of this growth being too rapid.

PERRIN, Francis (1901–) French physicist, son of Jean Perrin. In 1939, with F. Joliot-Curie, he established theoretically the possibility of maintaining nuclear chain reactions and of obtaining energy from them.

PERRIN, Jean (1870–1942) French physicist. A theoretician as well as an experimenter, he did notable work on X-rays, on emulsions, on Brownian movement and on the atom. He was the first to liken the atom to a microscopic solar system. In 1908, he gave an exact value to the Avogadro num-

Professor Francis Perrin and Irène Joliot-Curie in front of the control panel of the first French nuclear reactor (Photo Keystone)

ber. He contributed greatly to the foundation of the National Centre for Scientific Research, and created the *Palais de la Découverte*, in Paris. He received the Nobel Prize for Physics in 1926. *See illustration on p. 184.*

phantastron, an electronic assembly employing a single valve which provides electric pulses at a high frequency.—It is used in constructing apparatus for the electronic detection of particles.

phantom, a model, particularly of the human body. (See **ghost.**)

phase, an interval separating two periodic phenomena which are produced with identical frequencies.—The phase is usually measured in degrees, one complete period corresponding to 360°; two periodic phenomena are said to be *in phase* when their relative phase is zero. For example, in a circular particle accelerator, the accelerating electric

Jean Perrin (Photo APF)

voltage is alternating. The particles have to appear in the accelerating gap for a half-period only, so that they may keep together; their phase must be contained between −90° and +90°.

● **phase stability.** An accelerating impulse is given at each revolution to particles in a circular accelerator. This impulse is due to the action of a high-frequency electric field which therefore fluctuates very rapidly. All the particles must pass into this field at the moment when it possesses a certain value, therefore they have to be grouped in time, in some way forming packets inside the tube of the accelerator. In mathematical terms, it is said that they must be *in phase.* It has been shown that phase stability is automatically achieved in circular accelerators within certain limits, without it being necessary to provide a supplementary device. In fact, late particles find themselves more accelerated than early particles so that in a well designed accelerator the particles oscillate with respect to the steadily accelerating centre of the bunch without falling away from it.

phosphorescence, an emission of light by a substance having previously absorbed light or another radiation, with a shorter wavelength.—Contrary to fluorescence, phosphorescence continues, though with decreasing intensity, after the exciting radiation has ceased. (See **luminescence.**) Phosphorescence is produced in various crystals such as zinc sulphide.

photodisintegration, a reaction in which the nucleus is dissociated into lighter nuclei, into protons or neutrons, by an incident photon. For example, a gamma ray with an energy higher than 2.2 million electronvolts may dissociate the deuterium nucleus which consists of one proton and one neutron. A gamma ray with an energy higher than 1.7 MeV may dissociate a beryllium nucleus by ejecting a neutron.

photo-electric effect, a phenomenon in which an electron is ejected from an atom by a photon.—In this case all the photon's energy is transmitted to the electron. The photon disappears. The ejected electron therefore possesses an energy equal to that of the photon, less the binding energy of the electron in the atom. The photo-electric effect can only take place on a bound electron, and not on a free electron. It is thus a different phenomenon from the *Compton effect.* It occurs strongly with X-ray photons whose energy corresponds exactly to the binding energy of the electrons in the atoms (some tens to some thousands of electronvolts). If one takes X-rays of variable energies, strong absorptions may be

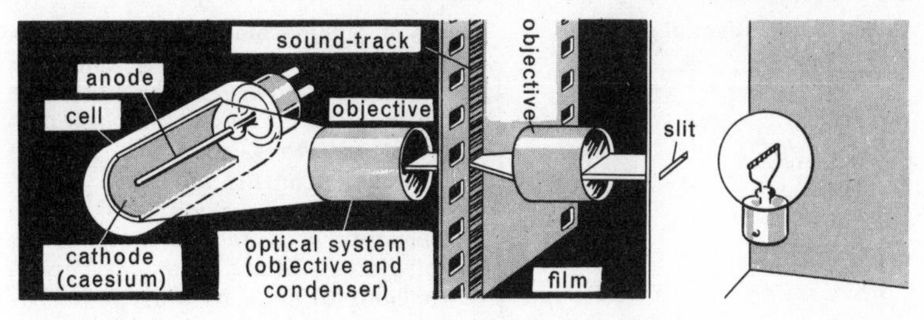

Reading a sound recording track by means of a photo-electric cell

observed for certain distinct energies which correspond to the binding energies of the electrons of the various shells of the body through which they pass. The working of photo-electric cells is based on this effect, as well as that of the photomultipliers which are used for the detection of very low photon concentrations.

photo-electron, an electron torn from an atom by an X-ray or a gamma ray in the **photo-electric effect** (qv).

photomultiplier or **multiplier tube,** an electric valve used in the detection of radiation.—The particles to be detected pass through a **scintillator** (qv) in which they induce an emission of light. One of the electrodes of the photomultiplier tube, called a *photocathode* as it is sensitive to photons, receives the light emitted by the scintillator either directly or through the medium of a light guide. The photocathode is achieved by depositing a sensitive layer, usually metallic, on the upper part of the glass bulb. An alloy of antimony and caesium ($SbCs_3$) is often used for the photocathode. It is sensitive to blue and yellow, and insensitive to red. An alloy of antimony, Li 56, is also used, sensitive to blue only. The efficiency of the photocathode is approximately 0.1, ie one photon in ten coming from the scintillator manages to tear an electron from the photocathode by photo-electric effect. When a particle passes through 1 cm of scintillator, some thousand photons are emitted. A few hundreds reach the photocathode, thereby producing some tens of electrons. So as to obtain a measurable electric current, that is to say some thousands of electrons at least, it is, in consequence, necessary to increase considerably the number of electrons available for measurement. This is achieved in the following manner. Ten or so consecutive electrodes are placed in the photomultiplier tube along which a high electric field is established. An electron arriving at one of these electrodes induces through secondary emission the ejection of two or more electrons (up to ten electrons). Each of the secondary electrons is accelerated by the electric voltage and, striking the next cathode, induces at it the emission of several electrons, etc. It is then possible to collect several million electrons on the final electrode, which represents a measurable electric signal. The multiplication of electrons on each of the electrodes depends on the voltage applied and, this being a cumulative phenomenon, a slight variation in voltage produces

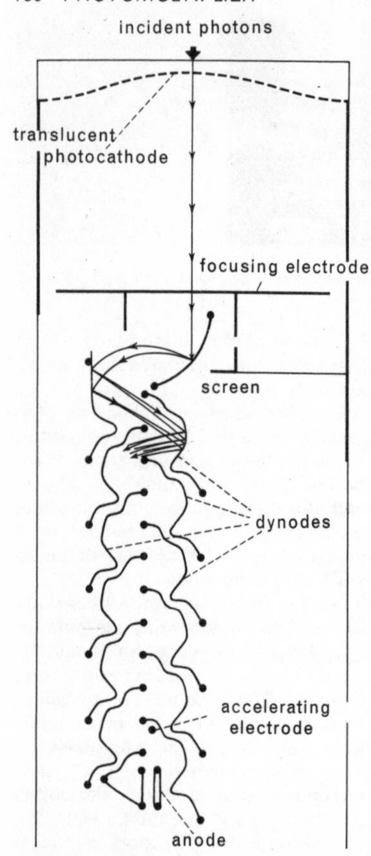

Diagram showing the operation of a photomultiplier

a substantial variation in the measured electric current. The working of a photomultiplier tube necessitates a voltage source stable to a few parts in ten thousand. Use of the photomultiplier tube involves other precautions. It has to be protected from light, which would leave an impression on the photocathode, and it has to be used outside magnetic fields which would have the effect of deflecting the electrons between the electrodes in the valve. The electric pulse provided by the valve has a duration depending on the utilisation circuit, being generally much less than a millionth of a second, so that the photomultiplier tube can count millions of particles a second. The photomultiplier tube is used as much in the study of alpha and beta radioactivity as for the detection of high-energy particles produced by accelerators.

photon, a particle of the electromagnetic field. The photon has no electric charge, no rest mass and travels at the speed of light. Its spin is equal to one. The energy of a photon is proportional to the vibration frequency of the electromagnetic field. The wavelength of a photon, which is the distance between two points of the same vibratory state, varies in inverse ratio to the frequency, and also, in inverse ratio to the energy. The photon is the constituent particle of the various electromagnetic radiations. Radio-electric waves possess wavelengths which vary from some hundred metres to some centimetres. Light waves possess wavelengths of 0.4 to 0.8 thousandths of a millimetre. X-rays emitted by excited atoms have wavelengths of less than a millionth of a centimetre; gamma rays emitted by excited nuclei have wavelengths of less than a billionth of a centimetre. The idea of the photon was foreshadowed by Planck in 1900 to account for the laws of radiation. It was completed in 1905 by Einstein to account for the photo-electric effect in which a particle of light ejects the electron of an atom; this phenomenon shows the corpuscular aspect of light.

During the first decades of the twentieth century, the identity of the nature of various electromagnetic radiations appeared progressively as their properties were discovered.

photoneutron, photoproton, photomeson, a neutron, proton or meson, produced by a reaction in which a nucleus is bombarded by a gamma ray.—A gamma ray with an energy of some millions of electronvolts may extract one of the protons or one of the neutrons from the nucleus. A gamma ray with an energy above 150 million electronvolts may induce formation of a pion in a nucleus.

photonuclear, referring to the action of a photon on a nucleus.—A photonuclear reaction may have several results:

a) A photonuclear reaction on a *single nucleon*; the photon may react on a single particle of the nucleus and induce the ejection of a proton or a neutron.

b) A photonuclear reaction on the *assembly* of the nucleus. In certain cases, and in particular when the photons are of low energy, it is possible to regard the energy contributed by the photon as distributed to the assembly of the nucleus, this being raised to an excited state. Sometimes the photon may induce the evaporation of a few nucleons or nuclear fragments.

c) A nuclear reaction of *photofission*. The excited nucleus may also be completely dissociated into two or more lighter nuclei.

photoproduction, the production of particles by photons. For example, a pion may be formed in the reaction of a gamma ray on a nucleus:

gamma + nucleus *gives* pion + nucleus.

photosource, a source of particles in which the incident radiation consists of photons.—The photosource principle is most commonly employed for neutron production because these cannot be directly produced in an accelerator. For the majority of nuclei, extraction of a neutron requires a minimum energy of 6 to 8 million electronvolts. This is the energy with which a neutron is bound in the nucleus. For nuclei in which the neutrons are lightly bound (such as deuterium, beryllium, etc), an energy of 2 to 3 million electronvolts is sufficient. Natural radio-elements may provide gamma rays having this energy. It is therefore possible to constitute a neutron photosource consisting, for instance, of sodium and beryllium. Gamma rays emitted by *sodium* possess an energy of 2.8 million electronvolts and are capable of extracting neutrons from the *beryllium* nuclei, which are bound with an energy of 1.7 million electronvolts. The neutrons emitted would possess a kinetic energy of about 1 million electronvolts. The importance of a photosource resides in the fact that all the neutrons it supplies have the same energy.

pi, a particle 270 times heavier than the electron.—Its mass being halfway between that of the electron and that of the proton, it is called a meson (from the Greek *mesos*, intermediate). The existence of the meson had been predicted by Yukawa about 1935, to account for nuclear forces. In Yukawa's theory, nuclear forces were due to exchanges of pions between particles in interaction. Nuclear forces possess the particularity of having a restricted range. They only make themselves felt at a short distance. This circumstance implied

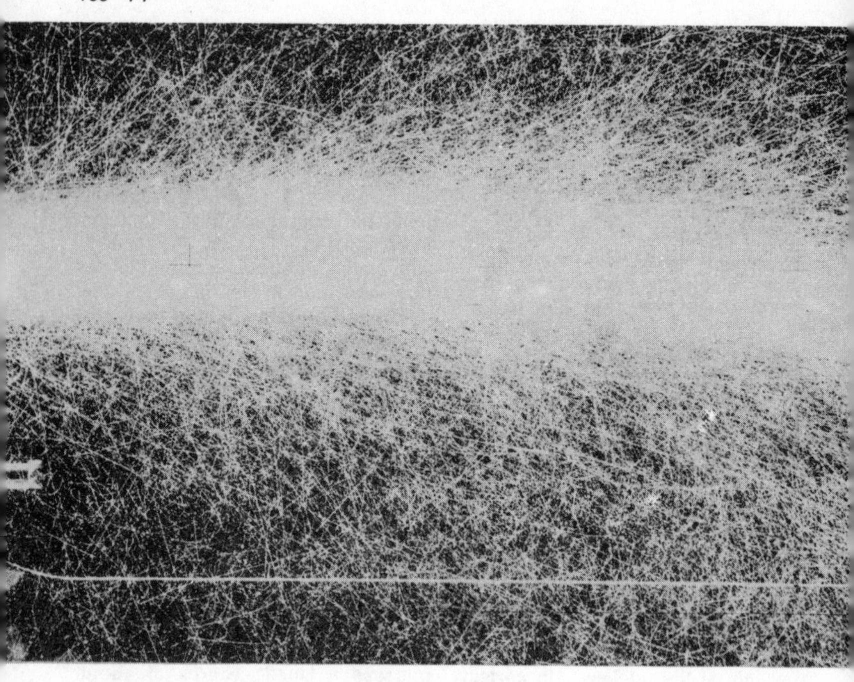

Appearance of a strong beam of negative pi particles in the liquid chamber BP3 at the Leprince-Ringuet Laboratory of the Ecole Polytechnique, Paris

that the particle of the nuclear field should possess a rest mass unlike the photon. Yukawa estimated its value as between 200 and 300 electronic masses. Particles 206 times heavier were in fact discovered in cosmic radiation in 1937 but study of their properties revealed that they had few interactions with matter, contrary to what had been expected of the meson predicted by Yukawa. In 1947 Lattes, Occhialini and Powell discovered, in a photographic emulsion, the pion which disintegrates when giving a mu:

pion *gives* mu lepton+neutrino.

The first pion was discovered in the form of a positively charged particle. It also exists in a neutral and a negative form. The exact masses of the three mesons are as follows:

negative and positive pions:
274 electronic masses

neutral pion:
264 electronic masses.

The negative and positive pions are antiparticles of one another. They have the same mass and opposite electric charges. They disintegrate with a mean life of 26 billionths of a second. The neutral pion is its own

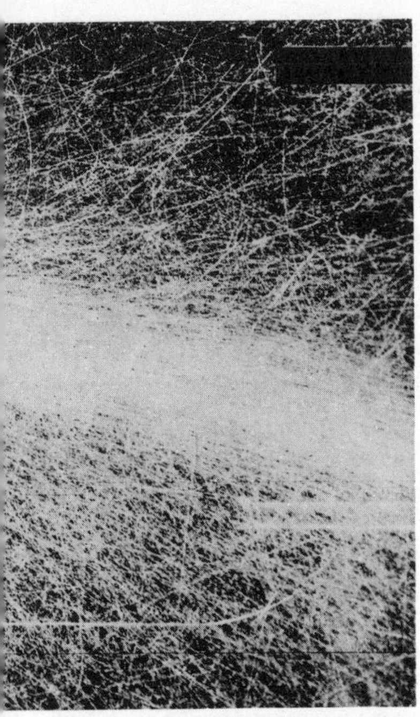

antiparticle. It disintegrates into two gamma rays, with a mean life (still inaccurately known, as it is very short) of the order of 0.1 millionths of a billionth of a second. The three pions have zero spin. Pions are rare in cosmic radiation, except at high altitudes. They are produced in the nuclear reactions of primary cosmic particles, but many of them disintegrate before reaching the ground. Accelerators may provide strong sources of pions, and the latter constitute the most frequently used projectiles for study of high-energy nuclear reactions. Beams of pions are also used for the production of other particles, as pions interact freely with matter.

pile, atomic, the name given to the first nuclear reactors. It is derived from the fact that they were made by stacking bars of uranium fuel in the heart of the moderator.—Since then, reactors have been built whose homogeneous structure no longer justifies the name of *pile*. The adjective *nuclear* is to be preferred to *atomic*, since the energy given off is not at the atomic level but more specifically at the level of the atomic nucleus. The name *atomic pile* therefore tends to be replaced by that of **nuclear reactor** (qv).

● **breeder pile,** a nuclear reactor in which a fissile material is produced, which can later be used in another reactor.—A breeder pile is said to be a *converter* if the fissile material produced is different from that which is consumed. It is said to be *regenerative* if the fissile material is of the same nature as that which is consumed, and a *breeder*, in a narrower sense, if it produces more material than it consumes. (See **reactor.**)

pinch, the aggregation of charged particles in a strong electric current passing through a gas.—When an electric discharge passes through a gas, the electric current sets up a magnetic field. The electrically charged particles which compose the current are themselves immersed in this magnetic field and in consequence are subjected to forces which tend to make them contract into a thin jet of current. Most proposals for the peaceful uses of **fusion** (qv) employ this property to help confine plasma (qv).

pion, the name sometimes given to the π meson.

pitchblende, an ore containing a large part of uranium in the form of oxides. In 1798 the element *uranium* was discovered in pitchblende by Klaproth and given this name because of the discovery recent at that time, of the planet Uranus. The first research on radioactivity was carried out by Pierre and Marie Curie with pitchblende. They revealed that this ore contained other radioactive bodies, *polonium* and *radium* (a highly radioactive element). Pitchblende was the main source of radium production used in the study of radioactivity up to and during the last war. Pitchblende is now used in the production of uranium. It is found in the Congo, in Canada, in the USA and in Czechoslovakia.

PLANCK, Max (1858–1947) German physicist. He received the Nobel Prize for Physics in 1918 for his work on black-body radiation. It was as the result of this research that he formulated the hypothesis of the discontinuity of energy and defined the quantum, one of the fundamental concepts of modern physics.

Max Planck

●**Planck's constant,** a universal constant governing the quantisation of microscopic systems.—It is also called the *elementary quantum*, or *quantum of action*. It has the physical dimensions of action, which is a quantity of energy multiplied by an interval of time, or of angular momentum, a momentum multiplied by a length. Its value is 6.62×10^{-34} joule seconds. The angular momentum of a two-particle system is a quantity associated with the rotation of the particles around each other. It cannot take all conceivable values in a continuous manner, but only takes those which are whole multiples of Planck's constant, divided by 2π. (See **h.**)

planetary, used with reference to Bohr's model of the atom, in which electrons are assumed to gravitate around the nucleus in a manner similar to that in which the planets gravitate around the Sun (eg *planetary electron*).

plasma, a state of matter in which the atoms are completely dissociated into nuclei and electrons. The tearing of electrons from light atoms is complete at a temperature of about 100,000° C. Nuclei and electrons are then agitated by very rapid and unco-ordinated movements, and it is possible to consider plasma as a gas (see **agitation, thermal**), or more precisely as a mixture of the gas formed by the nuclei and that formed by the electrons. It should be possible to achieve a **fusion** (qv) reaction in plasma, at a temperature of several million degrees. The mean energy of the plasma nuclei at this temperature is of the order of a kilo-electronvolt. The energy radiated by the plasma is mainly due to X-rays emitted in the scattering of the electrons by the electric field of the nuclei. This

Model of a Soviet apparatus used for research on plasma

lost energy increases with the density of matter, and with the temperature of the plasma. Fusion reaction induces the release of energy in plasma and this energy also increases with the density of the plasma. For the fusion reaction to be maintained, the plasma must be at a certain temperature, called the *ignition temperature*. Study of plasma is at present directed towards obtaining fusion reactions. Matter found in the interior of the Sun is in a state of plasma, at a temperature of the order of 100 million degrees Centigrade.

plate, nuclear, a photographic **emulsion** (qv) especially sensitive to ionising particles. This kind of emulsion was perfected for the detection of the particle track made visible in the form of silver grains. So as to achieve the greatest possible precision in the measurement of the trajectories, these emulsions have a very fine grain (of 0.1 to 0.2 μ). Unsupported emulsions, in the form of sheets 100 to 1200 μ thick, are sometimes assembled in stacks so that the path of a particle from one sheet to the next may be followed. Ionographic emulsions are at present much used for the measurement of radiations in satellites, because of their low weight and bulk.

plutonium, an artificial element with atomic number 94.—Plutonium may be produced in nuclear reactors from uranium 238, contained in natural uranium. It is a high density metal: 19.25 g per cubic centimetre. It melts at 640° C and may exist in a solid state in five different crystalline forms, according to the temperature at which it finds itself. Its poor mechanical properties make it necessary for care to be taken in the construction of reactors in which it is used. Plutonium 239, a fissile material, is alpha active with a period of 24,000 years. This metal cannot be moved manually in a sizeable quantity because of its radioactivity. Plutonium was dis-

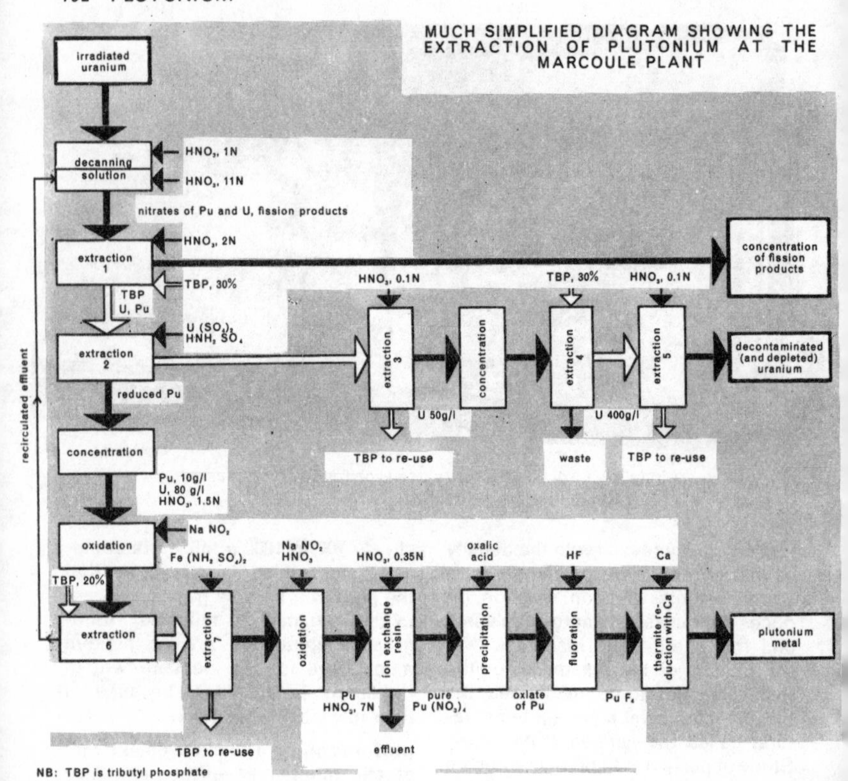

covered in the form of isotope 238 (94 protons, 144 neutrons) by G. T. Seaborg and his collaborators in 1940, in the reaction

uranium 238 (92 protons, 146 neutrons) + deuteron
(1 proton, 1 neutron) *gives*
neptunium 238 (93 protons, 145 neutrons)
+2 neutrons,

followed by the beta disintegration:

neptunium 238 (93 protons, 145 neutrons)
gives plutonium 238 (94 protons, 144 neutrons)
+electron+neutrino.

It is actually prepared in reactors from uranium 238, of which the greater part of natural uranium is composed. Its production is the result of a reaction induced by neutrons of the reactor:

uranium 238 (92 protons, 146 neutrons)
+neutron *gives* uranium 239 (92 protons, 147 neutrons)+gamma.

This reaction is followed by two consecutive beta disintegrations:

uranium 239 (92 protons, 147 neutrons)
gives neptunium 239 (93 protons, 146 neutrons)
+electron+neutrino;
neptunium 239 (93 protons, 146 neutrons)
gives plutonium 239 (94 protons, 145 neutrons)
+electron+neutrino.

Plutonium 239 undergoes fission under the action of slow neutrons, with maximum effectiveness for neutrons with an energy of less than 0.3 electronvolts. Fourteen plutonium isotopes are known, whose mass numbers range from 232 to 246. They are all radioactive. The physical and chemical properties of plutonium have been intensively studied with a view to its military and civilian uses.

poison, fission, an element pro-

General view of the plutonium production plant at Marcoule. On the left, *the reactors G2 and G3;* in the middle, *factory for the extraction of plutonium;* on the right, *the reactor G1.* (Photo P. Jahan-CEA)

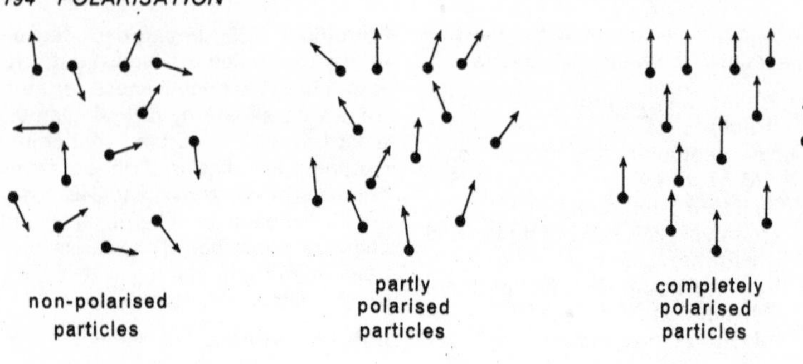

Polarisation: the arrows indicate the direction of the spin

duced in a reactor which hinders it from functioning by the absorption of a great many neutrons. Some elements in fact have a large absorption *cross-section*, the neutrons absorbed being lost for fission reactions. The main ones are xenon 135 and samarium 149. *Xenon 135* may be directly produced in fuel fission. Its production may also result from the radioactive disintegration of tellurium 135, also produced in the fission. Contamination may build up when the reactor is shut down. It is then necessary to wait some tens of hours before starting it up again, until the greater part of the xenon has disintegrated. *Samarium 149* is the result of the radioactive disintegration of fission products; it is stable, and its concentration reaches its limit in the reactor more rapidly the stronger the flux of neutrons in it.

polarisation, the orientation in a preferential direction of particle spins. —Polarisation may be total or partial. Polarisation of a moving particle is said to be *longitudinal* when the spin is oriented along the direction of movement. It is said to be *transverse* when the spin is oriented perpendicularly to the movement.

polonium, one of the first radioactive bodies discovered in 1898 by Pierre and Marie Curie, and named in honour of Madame Curie's country of origin.—It is an element with atomic number 84. The most common is isotope 210, sometimes called *radium F*, as it is produced from radium by consecutive disintegrations in the radioactive series of uranium. Each of the nuclei of isotope 210 contain 84 protons and 126 neutrons. Nineteen polonium isotopes are known, whose mass numbers are from 200 (ie 116 neutrons) to 218 (ie 134 neutrons). All of them are radioactive. Polonium is dangerous to handle, as many of its chemical compounds are volatile and may pollute the atmosphere with radioactivity. It has a half-life of 138 days.

porous barrier, a porous substance used in the process of separation of **isotopes** (qv).—It practically stops the flow of gases. The molecules are obliged to pass through a multitude of tiny holes (of the order of a 100th of a micron). The lightest molecules possess the greater velocity and will pass through the barrier more rapidly. In consequence, the proportion of light molecules is greater after crossing the barrier. This method is used to separate uranium 235 from uranium 238, which is heavier. The gas used is uranium hexafluoride (UF_6), which is highly corrosive. A study had to be made of special substances which could stand up to the action of uranium hexafluoride.

positron or **positon,** a particle of the same mass as the electron, but of an opposite electric charge.—It is also called the *positive electron* and the *antielectron*. Whereas the negative electron, which is a constituent particle of the matter surrounding us, was the first particle to be identified, the positron was discovered in cosmic radiation in 1932 by Anderson. It made a trajectory in a Wilson chamber that was bent by the magnetic field in the opposite sense to that of an electron. Measurement of the energy lost by the positrons when passing through metallic screens demonstrated that they could not be identified with the proton, at that time the only known positive particle. Since then, positrons have frequently been observed, either in beta+disintegration or in the materialisation of gamma rays, which disappear producing a negative and a positive electron. The existence of the positron had been foreseen as early as 1928 by the theoretician Dirac, who established the equation of motion governing the electron. The electron and the positron are antiparticles of one another, that is to say that they have the same mass, same spin, and opposite electric charges and magnetic moments. The positron is a stable particle. However, its existence is restricted in matter by its interaction with the electrons of the atoms:

positive electron + negative electron *gives* gamma rays.

This phenomenon is called *annihilation:* matter disappears while a radiation appears.

positronium, a transient assembly formed by a positron and an electron. Analogously to the hydrogen atom, it is formed by a positive and a negative particle. It may exist in two forms: as orthopositronium in which the spins of the positron and the electron possess the same direction and the same sense, and as parapositronium, in which the spins of the positron and of the electron possess the same direction, but opposite senses. The two forms of positronium disappear by annihilation, on emitting gamma rays. Orthopositronium is annihilated into three gamma rays with a mean lifetime of the order of 0.1 millionths of a second. Parapositronium annihilates into two gamma rays with a mean lifetime of less than a billionth of a second.

potassium, an element with atomic number 19.—Potassium is a metal with a fairly low fusion point: 62.3° C. Absorbing few neutrons, it has been put forward as a coolant in reactors, it is a good vehicle for heat. It is particularly interesting in the form of a liquid alloy with sodium, possessing a low fusion point, 19° C. Use of this alloy raises important technological problems, as it cannot come in contact with the air without danger of oxidation, and has to be contained in a chemically resistant system of pipes made of stainless steel or nickel. It appears that this alloy could be used in the reactors of nuclear-propelled submarines.

Aerial view of Windscale and Calder Works, Cumberland (Copyright UKAEA)

potential barrier, a repulsive potential energy of interaction between two particles. (See **barrier.**)

potential well, a region of attraction. —Protons and neutrons within a nucleus lie in the nuclear potential well.

POWELL, Cecil Frank (1903–) English physicist. We owe to him the use of the photographic emulsion method in the study of nuclear reactions. It enabled him to discover the **pion** (qv). This work earned him the Nobel Prize for Physics in 1950.

power, moderating, see **moderating power.**

power. Nuclear power can in theory be obtained from radioactive decay, fission or fusion reactions. Small amounts of electrical power can be obtained, at high cost, from the activity of eg, fission products, for transmitters on artificial satellites. Fusion energy is so far available only in bombs. Large amounts of electrical power are obtained by using the heat from fission reactors in conventional generating plants, the reactor and heat exchangers being the only specialised components. The reactor may have a solid or liquid moderator, liquid or gas coolant, and a few have the fuel mobile suspended or dissolved in the moderating fluid. Efficiency is limited by the temperature at which corrosion or deformation in the reactor becomes dangerously rapid, and by the high power consumption (quarter of the total electrical output for a typical reactor with graphite moderator and gas cooling) of the circulators for the cooling system. The economics of nuclear power are not yet clearly established. Early plants were designed to produce plutonium (for military purposes) as a valued by-product, but as plutonium stocks have built up, these stations run their fuel longer (say 3000 megawatt days per tonne for graphite moderation) and burn much of the plutonium as it is produced. Further economy in the use of fuel depends on the success of breeder reactors such as the prototype 250 Mw (electrical power) at Dounreay in the UK. Most existing stations have a capital amortisation period (expected useful life) of twenty years, but recent UK results suggest that several of them may run successfully up to thirty years. The safe and economical disposal of large amounts of **radioactive** wastes (qv) is not a fully solved problem. Improvement of thermal efficiency depends primarily on raising the operating temperature in the re-

General view of the nuclear power plant at Chinon at the beginning of 1963. From left to right the power plants EDF1; EDF2; EDF3. (Photo Alain Percival)

Nuclear power station/Dungeness B
(Copyright UKAEA)

1. Visitors' viewing balcony
2. Main control room
3. Data processing room
4. Instrument room
5. Active extract filter room
6. Tank floor and heating and ventilating plant
7. De-aerator
8. Visitors' charge face viewing room
9. Fuelling machine
10. Fuelling machine maintenance crane
11. Maintenance area
12. Fuelling stand pipes
13. Pre-stressed concrete reactor vessel
14. Boiler
15. Gas circulator
16. Gas circulator maintenance crane
17. Essential supplies room
18. 440V battery room
19. Active waste handling bay
20. Active effluent plant area
21. Cooling pond
22. Flask handling area
23. Loading bay
24. Turbo-generator
25. Turbine unit maintenance crane
26. Evaporator plant.

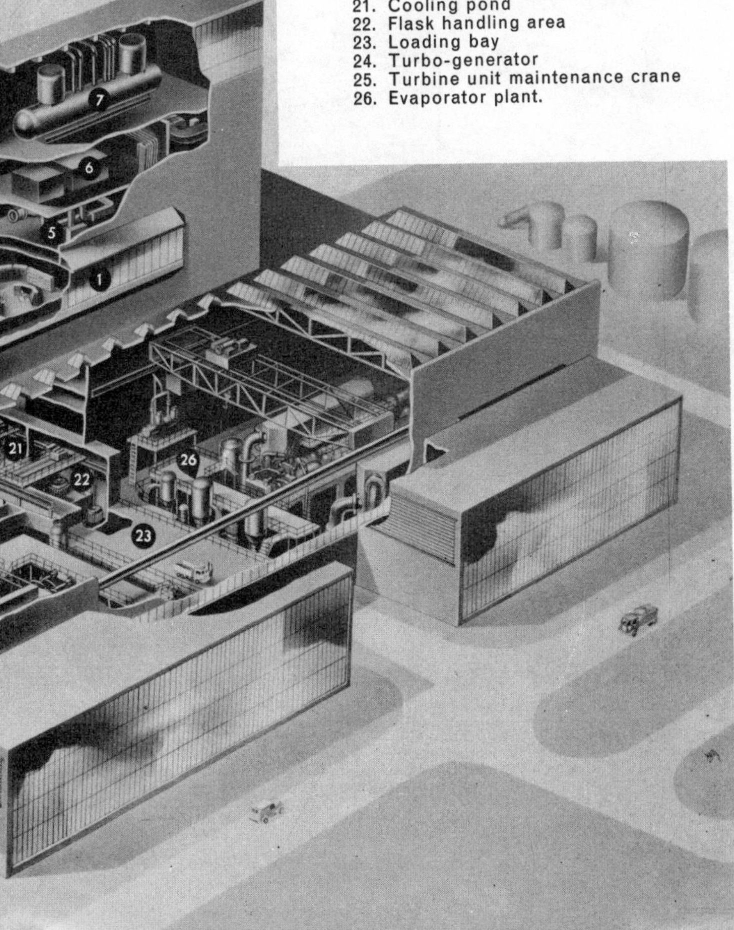

NUCLEAR POWER STATION

1. Concrete reactor shield
2. Pressure vessel
3. Reactor core (graphite moderator)
4. Supporting floor
5. Core roofing
6. Guide pipe for control rod
7. Control rod well
8. CO_2 inlet
9. CO_2 outlet
10. Heat shield
11. Main loading machine
12. Intermediate chamber
13. Castle
14. Castle gantry
15. Connecting carriage for air and electricity
16. Fuel element holder
17. Transporter
18. Intermediate chamber maintenance carriage
19. Control room
20. Electronic racking
21. Switchgear
22. Leak detector outlet pipes
23. Thermocouples
24. Shut-off valve

EDF3 AT CHINON

25. Blowers
26. Auxiliary turbine
27. Superheated steam for auxiliary
28. Turbine steam return
29. Heat exchanger CO_2 outlet
30. Heat exchanger CO_2 inlet
31. Reheater
32. Superheater
33. Economiser
34. Evaporator
35. Steam drum
36. Reheated steam offtake
37. Superheated steam offtake
38. Valves
39. Reheated steam to main turbine
40. Main turbines
41. Alternator
42. Transformer
43. Reheat point
44. Condenser
45. Ejection pumps
46. 'Bonna' piping
47. 60 ton transporter crane
48. Fuel element 'cooling' pond

actor, which depends in turn on improved mechanical behaviour of the fuel. Maximum internal fuel temperatures over 2000° C are expected in reactors under construction, and over 40 per cent thermal efficiency may be reached by combining gas-turbine circuits with the conventional steam-raising plant. (See **DRAGON.**)

power of a reactor, the energy released in a nuclear reactor per unit time.—This power, which may be weak (1 kW, for example) in an experimental reactor, may reach tens of thousands of kilowatts in a high-power reactor. The Centre at Marcoule, France, provides 70,000 kW to the electric grid. It is necessary for 30 million uranium nuclei to fission per second in a reaction for its power to attain 1 kW. It increases proportionally with the following quantities:

—the concentration in fissile nuclei (for example, the number of nuclei of uranium 235 per cubic centimetre)

—the bulk of the reactor

—the neutron flux, or number of neutrons passing through 1 cm^2 per second in the reactor

—the effectiveness of the fuel, assessed with the help of the *fission cross-section*.

Of all the energy released in a reactor in the form of heat, only part can be used for the production of electric energy. Commercial reactors are designed to make this as high as possible.

power, separating, see **separation of isotopes.**

power, stopping, see **stopping-power.**

primary. In a reaction between two particles, the incident and target particles are called *primary*, in contrast to the particles produced in the reaction, which are called *secondary*. In cosmic radiation, particles coming directly from extra-terrestrial space and having undergone no reactions in the Earth's atmosphere, are called *primary*, in contrast to those produced by reactions in the atmosphere, which are called *secondary*.

probability of transition, see **transition probability.**

product of fission, or **fission product,** a nucleus resulting from the fission of heavy nuclei.—The fission of a nucleus of uranium 235, which consists of 92 protons and 143 neutrons, induced by a slow neutron, usually produces 2 and sometimes 3 light nuclei at the same time as it releases 2 or 3 neutrons. When the uranium nucleus undergoes fission, it seldom happens that the two fission products have comparable masses. In 97 per cent of the cases, on the contrary, one of the nuclei contains from 85 to 104 protons and neutrons, the other from 130 to 149 protons and neutrons: it is then said that the fission is *asymmetrical*. About forty fission methods have been counted, leading to different fission products. Chemical analysis has permitted the identification of fission products, about 90 in number, varying from zinc 72 to gadolinium 158. Fission products appear as ionised atoms. Ions thus constituted are atoms which have lost, on average, some twenty electrons. *Heavy* fission products which have a strong electric charge and a not very high velocity are quickly stopped in matter; a few millimetres in the air, a few thousandths of a millimetre in a nuclear reactor. Their arrest in matter is accompanied by a release of heat which contributes to the power a nuclear reactor may provide.

production, associated, a nuclear reaction producing two strange particles simultaneously.—Some particles possess the property of being unable to appear separately, these are the lambda hyperons, sigma, xi and heavy K mesons. The following nuclear reactions do not take place:

pion+proton
gives K meson+proton;
pion+proton
gives pion+lambda.

On the contrary, the following reaction may be observed:

pion+proton
gives K meson+lambda.

It is said that the K mesons and the lambda hyperon are emitted in associated production. The hypothesis of associated production, advanced by Pais, does not take into account all the properties of strange particles. For example, the following reaction does not take place:

proton+proton *gives* lambda
+lambda.

Conversely, lambdas produced separately may be observed in the following reaction:

K meson+proton
gives pion+lambda.

A number called the **strangeness**

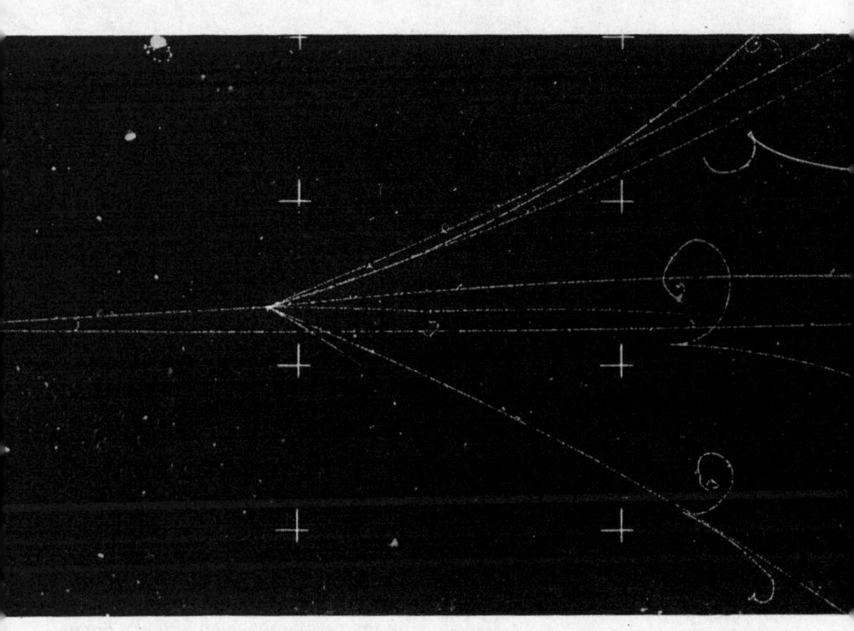

Shower of particles produced in a collision between a negative pion and a nucleon (Photo Ecole Polytechnique)

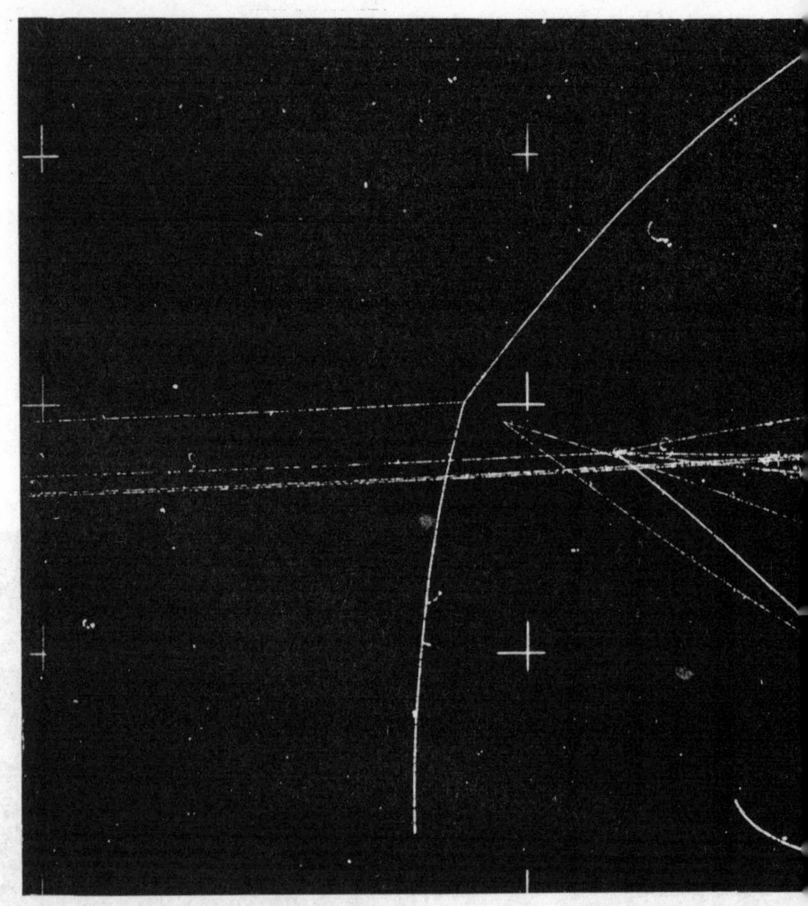

Associated production of neutral k meson +lambda hyperon by a negative pion of 18 billion electronvolts. On the photograph the pion arrives from the left and interacts giving rise to two charged particles (visible) and to two (invisible) neuter particles which disintegrate into visible charged particles. Disintegrations which correspond to a k meson and to a lambda appear on the photograph in the form of a V. The picture was obtained by means of the BP3 bubble chamber.

number (qv), which must remain identical before and after the reaction, has been introduced by Gell-Mann to account for the observed constraints on the reactions which actually occur with strange particles.

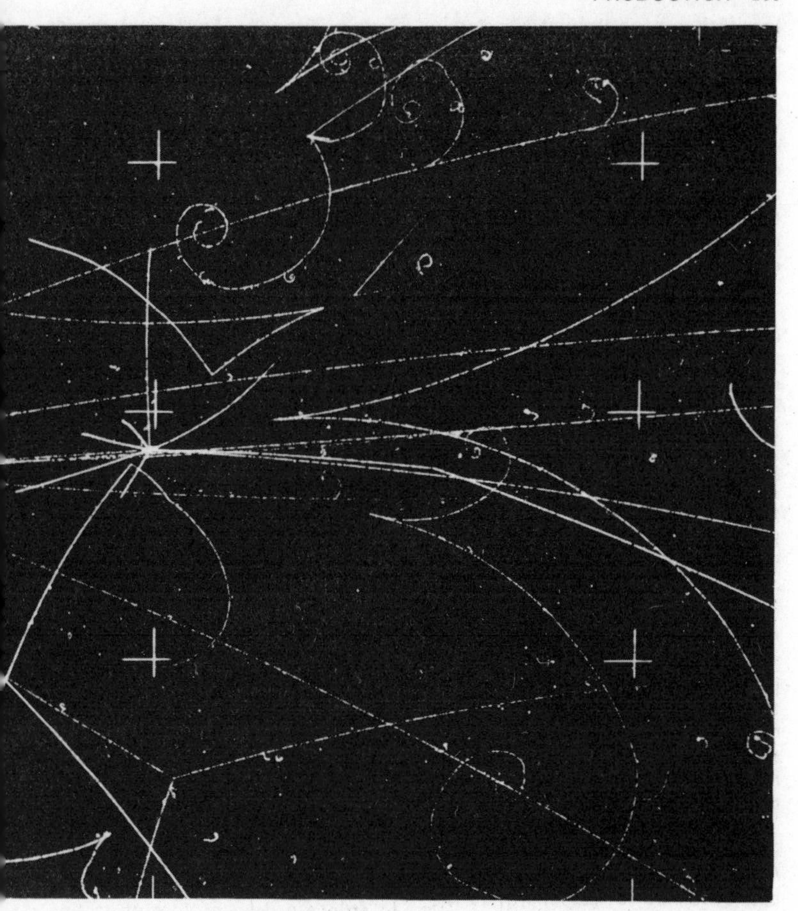

● **multiple production,** a nuclear interaction produced by a very high-energy particle (of several giga-electronvolts). It generally gives rise to a great multiplicity, ie many mesons are formed in the interaction as well as particle-antiparticle pairs such as the proton and the antiproton. It appears in a bubble-chamber in the form of a **star** (qv) consisting of numerous energetic X-rays. *See illustration on p. 203.*

prometheum, an element with atomic number 61.—Each of its nuclei contains 61 protons. Eleven prometheum isotopes have been identified whose mass number varies from 141 to 151, ie the number of neutrons in the nucleus varies from 80 to 90. They are all unstable, either through beta disintegration (emission of a positive or negative electron), or through emission of a gamma ray. They are obtained as fission products in nuclear reactors or by nuclear reactions induced by accelerated particles. The fact that all prometheum isotopes are unstable agrees with their absence from the natural state. Prometheum belongs to the **rare earth** series (qv).

propulsion, nuclear. This has been developed especially in the naval field. The great weight necessitated by reactor installations and, above all, the shielding which guarantees biological protection are not, in this case, an impossible drawback. In the case of the submarine, the absence of an oxygen demand for propulsive power permits a prolonged period of submersion. Such ships are in large measure self-contained in fuel. Thus many vessels are equipped with a reactor using nuclear fuel, among them the ice-breaker *Lenin* and the submarines *Nautilus* and *Seawolf*, etc. Plans are being studied (ANP, *Pluto, Rover, Snap*) in the USA for the application of nuclear energy to the propulsion of missiles or rockets.

prospecting by radioactivation, use of a neutron source to induce radioactivity in mineral samples.—The period and energy of the decays observed aid in identifying and assaying constituents of the mineral. (See ● **neutron logging.**)

protoactinium, an element with atomic number 91. Each of its nuclei contains 91 protons. Eleven protoactinium isotopes have been identified, with mass numbers varying from 225 to 144, that is to say, a number of neutrons in the nucleus of between 134 and 144. All of them are unstable. Protoactinium 233 appears in the preparation of uranium 233 from thorium. Isotope 231 was separated in 1917 by O. Hahn and L. Meitner; it disintegrates by alpha emission into actinium 227, hence its name. Isotope 234 is sometimes called *brevium* because it has a short life: its half-life is 1.2 minutes.

proton, a fundamental particle 1836 times heavier than the electron.—The proton has a positive electric charge, equal and opposite to that of the electron. With the neutron and the electron, it is one of the components of the matter surrounding us, since it enters into the composition of the nuclei of atoms. Its spin, a quantity related to the intrinsic angular momentum of the particle, is 1/2: therefore the proton is a *fermion*. It acts like a small magnet, possessing a magnetic moment of 2.79 *nuclear magnetons*. It is stable and does not disintegrate. Protons and neutrons of closely allied mass and with similar nuclear properties are called *nucleons*. Protons are the particles most frequently used in accelerators. It is, in fact, sufficient to strip a hydrogen atom of its one electron to leave nothing more than its nucleus, which is a proton. Protons, which may be accelerated by an electric field, since they are electrically charged, have numerous interactions with the nuclei of the matter through which they pass. Once they have been accelerated, they may be used directly as projectiles for the study of nuclear reactions or be sent

Two nuclear-propelled naval vessels. Above: the American aircraft carrier Enterprise *(85,000 tons) put into service in 1961. Below: the first atomic submarine,* Nautilus, *built by the United States in 1954, of 3200 tons, 98 m in length and 8.5 m wide, with a range of almost 200,000 km. It is the first vessel to have passed over the North Pole under its ice-cap.* (Photo USIS)

Two nuclear propelled merchant ships. Above: The Savannah, *an American mixed cargo vessel of 22,000 tons, launched in July 1960, capable of carrying 10,000 tons of freight at a speed of 20 knots.* (Photo USIS) Below: *the Soviet ice-breaker* Lenin *of 16,000 tons, the first civilian atomic ship, launched in 1957.* (Photo BSI)

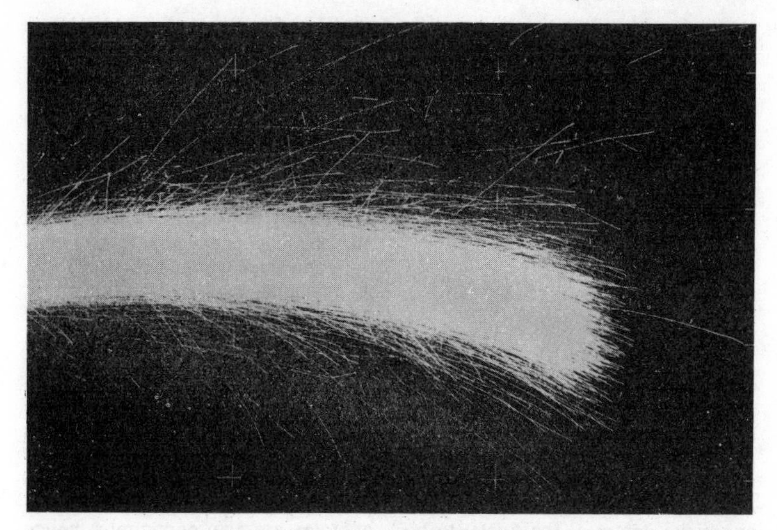

Appearance of a very strong beam of protons of 800 MeV/c stopping in the liquid of the bubble chamber BP3 at the Ecole Polytechnique, Paris

on to a target in which the nuclear reactions they induce are the source of different types of particles, such as the pion, K meson, antiproton, etc. These are then formed into secondary beams, whose reactions with matter are studied. Whether it is the protons, or the secondary particles emitted in the proton reactions, which form the *projectiles*, it is frequently an advantage for a proton also to form the *target particle,* firstly because this appears to be a fundamental particle and secondly for reasons of simplicity, reactions on heavy nuclei being more complex. Hydrogen, the nucleus of which is formed by only one proton, is frequently used in gaseous or liquid form in detection equipment, for instance in bubble-chambers with liquid hydrogen. The proton appears in nuclear reaction cycles which are the source of stellar energy and of the natural distribution of heavy nuclei. (See **cycle.**)

Q

quadrupole. 1) An electric moment of four equal charges on a small parallelogram, any two consecutive charges being of opposite sign. Measurement of the electric dipoles of the nuclei demonstrates that these are all zero; from this it is deduced that the nucleus appears symmetrical with respect to the plane normal to the rotational axis. In next approximation, the nucleus is assigned the shape of an ellipsoid of revolution whose symmetry axis is the axis of spin. The manner in which the electric charge is distributed inside this volume gives some idea of the

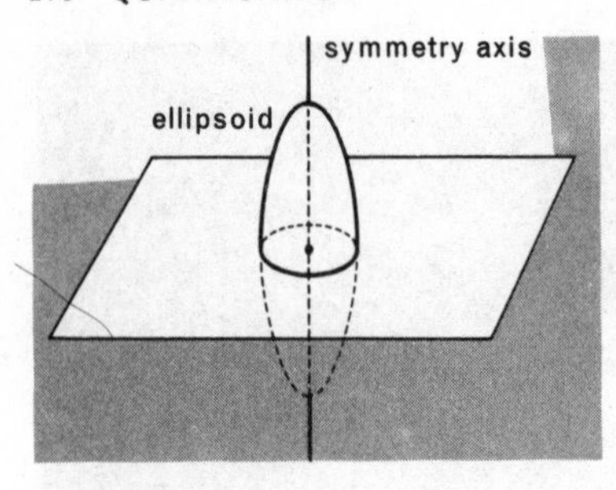

A quadrupole

distribution of electrically charged protons inside the nucleus. The electric characteristic of the quadrupole is associated with the ellipsoidal form. Measurement of the quadrupole moment enables the sphericity defect of the nuclei to be assessed. Nuclei which correspond to the magic numbers, and which have complete neutron and proton shells, are almost spherical, the remainder having a fairly elongated form (see figure above). The measurement of high quadrupole moments for certain nuclei indicates that several nucleons are in connected motion in the nucleus. This finding reinforces the hypothesis of the collective movement of protons and neutrons inside the nucleus. ‖ 2) An instrument employed in the technique of handling beams of electrically charged particles. A quadrupole consists of hyperbolically shaped pole pieces, whose magnetisation is maintained by coils through which an electric current passes. This device enables particles to be deviated in a manner similar to that in which light rays are deflected when passing through a (non-spherical) lens, when the density of particles in the beam is determined by two dimensions, horizontal and vertical. A double lens is usually necessary. Generally speaking, an ordinary magnet acts as a prism on the horizontal plane and as a lens on the vertical plane. *See also illustration on p. 211.*

quantisation, distribution procedure restraining the values of a physical quantity, classically able to take continuous values within a certain range, to a smaller range of values either discontinuous or continuous.—For example, the energy of an electron in the presence of a proton can take only discontinuous negative values and continuous positive values (negative energy, the electron is bound to the proton; positive energy, the electron is free and moves away from the proton). Classically the negative energies are also continuous, hence the classical electron should collapse on the proton. In quantum theory this is shown not to be the case.

quantum, used as an adjective to describe whatever pertains to **quantisation** (qv). ‖ The term as a noun refers to a fundamental quantity which occurs in the quantisation of a physical system.—Quantisation of all physical quantities involves the Planck constant, also called the *fundamental quantum* or *quantum of action*, whose symbol is h. More generally, every indivisible physical quantity (of energy, of angular momentum, etc) is called *quantum*. In the quantum theory of electromagnetism, a radiation of frequency n may be represented as being composed of quanta, each possessing the energy $E=hn$. In the theory of fields, there exists a particle which is responsible for each type of physical interaction. The photon is the quantum of the electromagnetic field, the meson that of the nuclear field.

A quadrupolar electromagnet (Photo P. Jahan-CEA)

● **quantum defect.** Hydrogen-like atoms have their bound state energies defined with a parameter n. Unlike the position in hydrogen, this parameter is not exactly an integer. The difference to the nearest integer is called quantum defect.

● **quantum jump,** the abrupt change of state of a system of particles.—In a quantum jump the system passes from one state to the next by jumping the intermediary states. This peculiarity is due to the fact that certain physical quantities of systems of particles may possess only discontinuous values. Thus, when an atom emits an X-ray, the energy of this X-ray is released by the passage of an electron from a shell of the atom to another shell, ie in this passage the energy of the electron changes by a quantity to be found precisely in the energy of the X-ray. The passage is not carried out in continuous fashion by passing through intermediate energy states, but directly from one state to the next.

● **quantum mechanics,** a theory which describes the systems of particles which are subject to quantisation.—All systems are, in fact, subject to quantisation, but the more massive they are the closer are the discontinuities in the physical quantities. Hence, for macroscopic objects, quantum mechanics is a useless refinement. The uncertainties connected to position and speed become more and more negligible as the masses increase. Development of the theory started at the beginning of the century and is still continuing. It affords an explanation of a considerable number of phenomena whose existence in nature remained hidden in classical physics. The field of application of this theory is enormous: the emission and absorption of light and radiation by molecules, atoms or nuclei; the theories of heat, of magnetism and of the structure of solid bodies; the physical and chemical properties of atoms; the structure of nuclei; nuclear reactions, etc. It overlaps and to a great extent includes the field of classical physics, in which only the macroscopic aspect of phenomena had been studied. This theory originated in work carried out on black body radiation. It is to Max Planck, in 1900, that the first quantum explanation of radiation phenomena is due. He assumed that light was emitted or absorbed by materials in discrete quanta or lumps whose energy E depends on the frequency n according to the law E=hn, where h is Planck's constant. In 1905 Einstein, advancing another step, assumed that not only did the emitting or absorbing material undergo a quantised energy change, but that light itself really existed in the form of particles or photons, and thereby explained the *photo-electric effect*. The work of de Broglie, proposing to connect a wave description with a particle of matter, completed in some sense the work of Planck and Einstein. It became as possible to attribute a wave nature to a particle of matter as to attribute a particle nature to a wave of light. Schrödinger went considerably further in finding the wave equation for particles and the energy levels of hydrogen. Heisenberg and Jordan reached the same results independently from de Broglie and Schrödinger. It was found afterwards that the two formalisations were equivalent. Later Born established the probabilistic interpretation of the wave. In 1928 Dirac introduced the laws of relativity into quantum mechanics, thereby explaining the spin of the electron and the existence of the positive electron. Quantum electrodynamics, elaborated by Schwinger, Kramers, Bethe and Dyson, is the most evolved form of quantum mechanics. The results obtained with it are remarkable for their precision in the atomic field. In the field of the nucleus and of nuclear forces no quantum theory is, as yet, satisfactory.

● **quantum number,** a distinctive number, which may assume either whole or half-whole values. It fixes the value of one of the physical quantities which describe the particle system, ie energy, spin, etc. A good quantum number is one which remains unaltered in an interaction between particles or in the course of the evolution of a system of particles. Thus, the parity of a system which may assume the values plus one or minus one, is a good quantum number for the nuclear interactions which leave it unaltered, but it is not a good quantum number for weak interactions such as beta disintegration.

quark, from *Finnegan's Wake* by James Joyce.—Some theories regard the familiar stable particles as themselves compound. Gell-Mann has suggested as a more fundamental entity this particle, with charge one-third of the electron charge. If charge conservation is valid, separate quarks should be very hard to produce, but very slow to annihilate. The quark has been energetically hunted, but not found.

R

RABI, Isaac Isidore (1898–) American physicist. He received the Nobel Prize for Physics in 1944 for his work on the spin and on the electric and magnetic properties of the atomic nuclei.

rad, a unit of radiation dose which corresponds to a certain quantity of energy, viz 100 ergs, yielded by radiations in 1 gramme of the irradiated body. The rad and the rep are allied units, both corresponding to an absorption of energy. (See **dose**.)

radiation, a wave or particle in motion.—The term *radiation* was first applied to waves, and more specifically to electromagnetic waves, such as light. It was extended to particles, since they too possess a wave aspect, just as the waves possess a particle aspect.

● Cerenkov radiation, light emitted when a fast charged particle passes through a refractive and transparent medium (see **● Cerenkov effect**).

● characteristic radiation, a radiation emitted as an atom de-excites, whose energy makes it possible to identify the nature of the atom. When an electron of an atom passes from a high-energy shell to a lower energy shell, the difference in energy is emitted in the form of radiation. The energies of the different shells of the atoms being known, it is possible to deduce the nature of the atom from the radiation energy emitted during the passage of an electron from one shell to the next.

● cosmic radiation, radiations which originate outside the Earth.—It is believed that the main sources are the Sun and the galaxies. Above the Earth's atmosphere, *primary cosmic radiation* consists principally of atomic nuclei and above all of protons. Some may attain very high energies which correspond to 1000 billion volts. Some rarer particles may attain an energy a thousand or even a million times greater. *Secondary cosmic radiation* is produced by reactions of the primary radiation with the nuclei or electrons of the Earth's atmosphere. In this way mesons and high-energy photons are formed. Electrons, protons and neutrons belonging to atmospheric atoms are themselves ejected in reactions and also acquire a high energy. At sea-level cosmic radiation consists essentially of secondary radiation. *See illustration on p. 214.*

● effects of radiation, actions induced by radiation, particularly on living matter.—Many physicists and radiographers have felt the effects of radiation before realising their importance. Becquerel, who discovered radioactivity and was in the habit of carrying a radioactive source

The Pic du Midi Observatory at Bigorre, France. On the right the magnet-cooling apparatus for the Wilson chamber of the Leprince-Ringuet Laboratory, which enables cosmic radiations to be detected. (Photo Ecole Polytechnique)

in the pocket of his waistcoat, had already remarked a swelling of the skin in the vicinity of the source. The growth of modern atomic plants, and the risks of military uses of atomic energy, have led specialists to extend their knowledge of the biological effects of radiation. These effects are mainly due to the energy which is transferred to the tissues by radiation passing through them. This energy is transmitted by ionisation, ie by the dissociation into ions and electrons of the atoms of which the tissues are composed. Two kinds of effects may be distinguished:

1) Irradiation caused by radiation passing through the body or a part of the body.

2) Contamination produced by the deposit of a radioactive body either outside on the skin, or inside in the digestive or respiratory tract. The radioactive body may then be retained in certain parts of the body, to be more or less rapidly eliminated by subsequent chemico-biological processes.

What takes place at various levels of biological organisation?

a) On the level of the living cell, radiations can produce a functional disorder which may go so far as to completely transform the cell, causing it to reproduce itself in a disordered manner, which constitutes cancer. Mutations may also appear on the level of the cell, modifying its characteristics in a definitive, and often lethal, manner. Finally, heavy irradiation is directly lethal.

b) On the level of tissues, phenomena are differentiated according to the nature of the tissue. Reproductive tissues or those in active growth are the most *radio-sensitive* (skin, blood, glands, genitals). According to the strength of the radiation red patches may be observed on the skin; there is loss of hair, loss of patches of skin and death of tissue. Radiation may also induce cataract of the eyes. In bone-marrow, irradiation destroys the balance of blood-corpuscle formation, which leads to an alteration in the number of red or white corpuscles. In particular, irradiation may induce leukemia, known as *cancer of the blood*, in which the number of white corpuscles in the blood shows an abnormal increase. The genital glands are very sensitive to radiation. This may produce hormonal maladjustment and possibly sterility. The most dangerous effect is certainly that of the mutations which the chromosomes may undergo. If the effect becomes hereditary, it may produce definitive malformations. Muscles and bones are less sensitive to radiation.

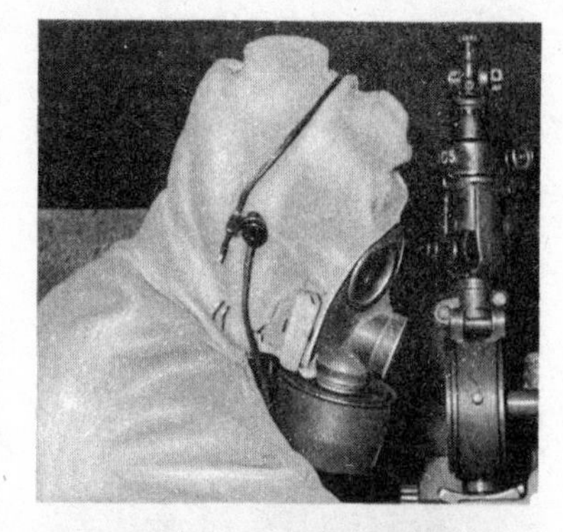

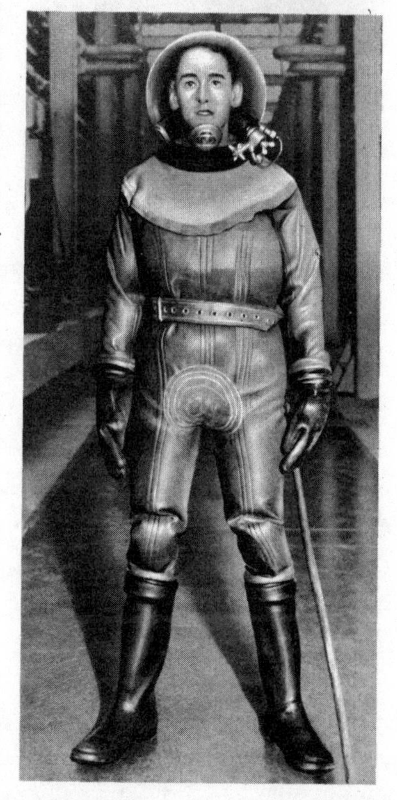

(above) *Protective mask worn against radioactive radiations.* (below) *A protective outfit against radioactivity: this enables the wearer to breathe in a closed circuit and to avoid contamination completely* (Photo C. A. Harwell)

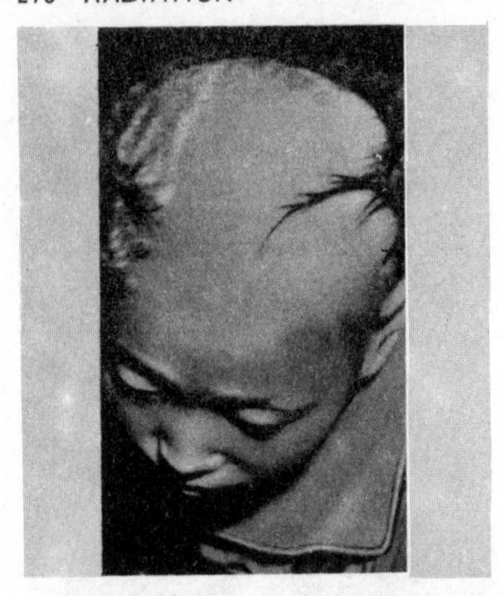

Loss of hair caused by gamma radiation from the Hiroshima atomic bomb

c) The total result of all these transformations is apparent on the human level in a manner difficult to relate exactly to the foregoing elementary effects. In the case of strong general irradiation, troubles start with a state of debility, nausea, vomiting and diarrhoea. After several days, during which the transformation takes root in the tissues, more serious disturbances make their appearance. Haemorrhages, vomiting, loss of hair, a serious decrease in the number of white corpuscles in the blood, extreme debility and eventually death after some ten days. If the irradiation is merely localised, there is only ulceration or destruction of the affected part of the body, unless the irradiation is sufficiently strong or repeated sufficiently often for cancer, which may become generalised, to develop. Hereditary effects, if they should exist, are insufficiently known because of the short time which has elapsed since strong irradiations have been sustained by human beings. These phenomena, which could become catastrophic, inspire all the more caution since the presence of radiation passes unnoticed in the absence of perfected detection appliances. In protection from radiation it is recommended to try and protect the organs in the following order: glands, bone-marrow, eyes, skin. Permissible doses of radiation for these organs are very low. Ingestion by way of the oral or respiratory organs is to be avoided, as this might lead to the fixation of radioactive sources in the organism. Finally, it should be taken into account that several spaced out irradiations are less dangerous for the same total dose sustained than one single irradiation. The small number of accidents recorded in atomic plants compared with injury at work in other employments demonstrates that a controlled use of radiations is perfectly possible. On the other hand, protection of a population in case of nuclear warfare appears to be extremely difficult or simply impossible. (See **dose.**)

● **hard radiation,** a ray which is able to penetrate a considerable thickness of matter (10 cm of lead, for instance).

● **soft radiation,** a ray stopped by a moderate thickness of matter. The meaning varies with the context. Thus, a soft gamma ray might be a fairly hard X-ray.

radiation length, a length by the end of which a charged particle of high energy, which is passing through matter, has lost 63 per cent of its energy.—By the end of two radiation lengths, the particle has lost

$$63+37\times0.63=86 \text{ per cent}$$

of its energy, etc. These energy losses take place through radiation (see **bremsstrahlung**). They are especially important when the particle is light. Thus the radiation length for very fast electrons is 0.5 cm in lead, 8.9 cm in aluminium and 3.30 m in air. The basic principle of interaction length also enables us to calculate the fraction of gamma rays which have materialised, by forming a pair of positive and negative electrons, when passing through a given thickness of matter. For very high energy gamma rays, the materialisation length is equal to 9/7 of the radiation length in air. After passing through one materialisation length, 63 per cent of high-energy gamma rays have materialised; after two materialisation lengths, 88 per cent have materialised, etc.

radiation sickness, an illness induced by an irradiation by ionising radiations (alpha, beta, protons) or by means of neutrons, X-rays or gamma rays.—It is characterised by nausea, vomiting, diarrhoea, alteration in the composition of the blood, loss of hair, infection and psychic depression. It may be fatal. (See **• effects of radiation**.) According to the dose received, the disturbances are as follows:
—0 to 20 röntgens: no damage.
—20 to 40 röntgens: slight alteration in the blood formula, which returns rapidly to normal, without intervention.
—40 to 200 röntgens: nausea and vomiting. Cure takes place within the month following the irradiation.
—200 to 400 röntgens: the damage is more serious, the irradiation may cause death.
—400 röntgens: serious damage, causing death in 50 per cent of cases.
—600 röntgens: serious damage, causing death in three out of four cases.
—1000 röntgens: death practically certain for all cases.

Such remedies as are known for preventing the effects of radiation still do not appear to be very effective. Some results have been obtained on the one hand by the absorption, before irradiation, of certain biochemical substances; on the other hand, by the grafting of bone-marrow after irradiation.

radiative, referring to radiation. For example, energy losses undergone by charged particles through radiation (see **bremsstrahlung**) are called radiative, as they are accompanied by a gamma ray emission.—A disintegration is said to be *radiative* if it produces a gamma ray. Capture of a neutron by a nucleus is said to be *radiative* if it is accompanied by the emission of a gamma ray.

radioactive, said of a nucleus which disintegrates in the phenomenon of radioactivity.—For example, uranium being alpha radioactive, a uranium nucleus which decays emits an alpha particle. Aluminium 28 being beta radioactive, an aluminium 28 nucleus which decays emits a negative electron.

• radioactive affiliation, see **affiliation, radioactive.**

• radioactive chain, a series of consecutive disintegrations leading from one member to another of the same family, or radioactive series. (See **series, radioactive.**) There is a radioactive chain leading from radium 226 and lead 214 (known as radium B), both of the uranium series. The links consist of three successive alpha decays.

● **radioactive charge eliminator,** see **charge.**

● **radioactive decay,** see **decay.**

● **radioactive effluent,** see **effluent, radioactive.**

● **radioactive equilibrium,** see **equilibrium, radioactive.**

● **radioactive family,** see **series, radioactive.**

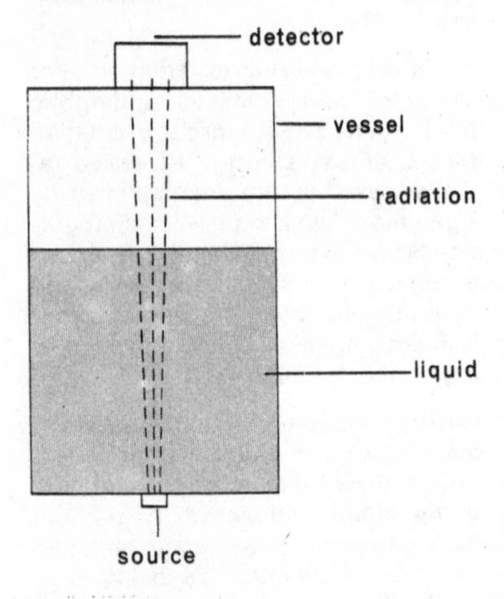

Radioactive level indicator

● **radioactive level indicator,** instrument which permits the measurement of a level by means of a radioactive source.—Inside a water-tight container holding a corrosive liquid or liquid under high pressure, it is convenient to measure the level by means of an appliance outside the container. This may be achieved by a radioactive source and a detection apparatus such as the Geiger-Müller counter.
There are two possible arrangements:
1) The radioactive source may be placed on a float. The detection apparatus, which is fixed, would register fewer radiations the further away the float.
2) The radioactive source may be placed at the bottom of the container. The detection apparatus, placed above the container, would register fewer radiations the more liquid these have to penetrate. In both cases, calibration would enable the level of the liquid to be measured.

radioactivity, the transformation of an atomic nucleus, accompanied by an emission of particles by the nucleus.—In nature there exist substances which are radioactive. Their radioactivity is said to be *natural.* On the other hand, it is possible to induce a radioactivity by bombarding naturally stable nuclei with neutrons, protons, gamma rays, etc. These stable nuclei are transformed into unstable nuclei by the bombardment. This is notably the case for heavy artificial elements which do not exist in nature, because they are unstable, and which are artificially manufactured by bombardment by uranium or other heavy nuclei. These artificially manufactured elements are radioactive.
Natural radioactivity (see **disintegration**) appears in three forms.
1) *Alpha radioactivity* in which a particle consisting of two protons and two neutrons is expelled from the atomic nucleus. It is mainly the heavy elements, which have a large number of protons and neutrons in their nuclei, which undergo this. The residual nucleus has two protons and two neutrons less than the initial nucleus. Thus

radium 228 (88 protons, 140 neutrons)

gives radon 224 (86 protons, 138 neutrons)+
alpha particle (2 protons, 2 neutrons).

2) *Beta radioactivity* in which a negative electron is emitted. In this case, the number of protons of the nucleus increases by one unit, and the number of neutrons decreases by one unit. The simplest beta radioactivity is the following:

neutron *gives* positive proton +negative electron+neutrino.

Beta radioactivity in which a positive electron is emitted also exists. In this case, the number of protons of the nucleus decreases by one unit and the number of neutrons increases by one unit. Thus

polonium 218 (84 protons, 134 neutrons) *gives*
astatine 218 (85 protons, 133 neutrons)+negative electron+ neutrino.

3) *Gamma emission*, in which the nucleus does not change its nature, but undergoes decrease of mass. The energy which corresponds to this decrease in mass is emitted in the form of a gamma ray. Thus

(strontium 85)* *gives* strontium 85 +gamma.

Artificial radioactivity appears in the same form as natural radioactivity. However, a few artificial elements, such as californium 254 and fermium 252, undergo spontaneous fission, the nuclei dividing into lighter elements without the fission, as is usually the case with uranium, being induced by an external bombardment of the nucleus.

In natural radioactivity, several kinds of radioactive substances may be distinguished:

1) *Primary radioactive substances*, which disintegrate slowly, their radioactivity still not extinguished since nuclei were formed on Earth. These are, for example, uranium 235, uranium 238, thorium 232, which are alpha radioactive; and potassium 40, lanthanum 138, indium 115, which are beta radioactive.

2) *Secondary radioactive substances*, which disintegrate more rapidly. They are, however, present in nature, being produced in the consecutive disintegrations of primary substances. (See **series, radioactive.**) The radioactive series of uranium, actinium and thorium thus provide several tens of radioactive nuclear species. Finally, some radioactive substances are the products of nuclear reactions: carbon 14, or **radiocarbon** (qv), is produced continually by the bombardment of nuclei of atmospheric nitrogen by cosmic ray neutrons.

radiobiology, a branch of biology whose field is the study of radiation effects on living creatures.

radiocarbon, a carbon whose mass number is 14, each of whose nuclei consists of 6 protons and 8 neutrons.—Natural carbon consists mainly of carbon 12 (6 protons, 6 neutrons). Carbon 14 is produced in the atmosphere from nitrogen 14, by slow neutrons belonging to cosmic radiation, according to the reaction:

nitrogen 14 (7 protons, 7 neutrons) +neutron *gives* carbon 14 (6 protons, 8 neutrons)+proton.

Carbon 14 is radioactive, with a half-life of 5670 years. Living organisms absorb carbon in the form of carbon dioxide; vegetable matter therefore absorbs a quantity of carbon 14. The proportion of carbon 14 absorbed in the organism decreases progressively from the time of death, since

In archaeology, radiocarbon 14 methods enable the age of objets d'art and other things to be assessed. The margin of uncertainty in dating is mainly acceptable when the work dates back some 5 thousand years. (Photo USIS)

carbon 14 is radioactive. The proportion of carbon 14 which remains in dead organisms therefore makes it possible to deduce the period of time that has elapsed since the death of the organism. This method is used in archaeology and in geology, and produces very good results when the material is some 5- to 20 thousand years old.

radiochemistry, the chemistry of radioactive substances, usually applied to very small samples. || The study of chemical reactions by means of radioactive bodies as distinct from radiation **chemistry** (qv).

radiocobalt, cobalt whose mass number is 60. Each of its nuclei contains 27 protons and 33 neutrons.—Cobalt 60 is used in medicine in the place of radium, being less harmful to the tissues surrounding a tumour. It is beta active with a half-life of 5.2 years. Its decay gives a nucleus of nickel 60 (28 protons, 32 neutrons) and a negative electron. The nickel nuclei thus formed are in an excited state and disintegrate by emitting gamma rays. Radiocobalt, for medical purposes, is used in the form of strong sources which are called *cobalt bombs.* It is also used for the radiography of metals. (See **cobalt.**)

radiocolloid, an assembly of atoms with radioactive nuclei in colloidal aggregates.

radiodermatitis, a skin disease which may vary from a rash to a tumour.—It is induced by the action of radiations.

radioelement, a radioactive substance.—Nuclei of the atoms of a simple body or element do not, in general, all possess the same radioactive properties. In fact, a simple body may consist of classes of atoms all of whose nuclei possess the same number of protons, but various different numbers of neutrons; these are isotopes. Nuclear properties are related to the nuclide, a nucleus composed of a certain number of protons and of neutrons, both well defined. The term *radioelement* is, however, frequently preserved for those isotopes which are radioactive. Thus carbon 14 is called a radioelement, although ordinary carbon,

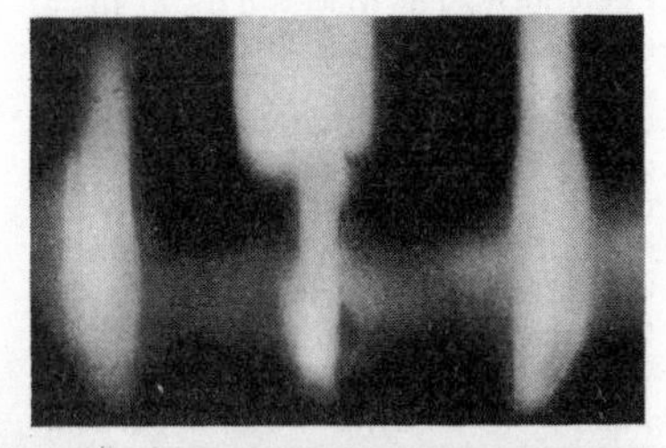

Radiocobalt, apart from its medical uses, is employed in metal radiography.
On the right: *the crankshaft of a diesel motor radiographed with cobalt 60.*
Below: *preparing a metal part for radiographic examination by the introduction of a radiocobalt source.*

consisting of carbon 12 and 13, is not radioactive. A radioelement may be natural, containing isotopes which are radioactive naturally. This is the case of uranium whose three natural isotopes, uranium 234, 235 and 238 are all three alpha radioactive. A radioelement may be artificially prepared, by the addition of a radioactive isotope to the non-radioactive natural isotope. This is the case with iodine 127, which is naturally stable; radioactive iodine 131 is added to it, so that the track of the iodine in living organisms may be followed by means of counters.

radiogenic, developed in a radioactive disintegration.—Uranium ores contain, for instance, lead 206 which is radiogenic, and which is produced during a consecutive series of disintegrations from uranium 238. Uranium ores also contain radiogenic helium, formed from alpha particles emitted in the disintegrations, the alpha particles being the nuclei of helium atoms.

radiography, photography showing the shadows cast by certain substances which absorb more X-rays than others.—The shadows are more strongly accentuated the greater the thickness of absorbing matter through which the rays pass.

radio-iodine, a radioactive isotope of iodine.—The two main ones are radioactive iodine 129 and 131. Each nucleus of radio-iodine 129, for example, contains 53 protons and 76 neutrons, whereas the nuclei of natural iodine 127 contains only 74 neutrons. Natural iodine is stable, radio-iodine 129 is beta radioactive with a half-life of 1.7 billion years. Radio-iodine 131 is beta radioactive with a half-life of 8.1 days. Radio-iodines, and above all iodine 131, whose mean life is shorter and whose radioactivity is greater for the same degree of concentration, are used to study the fixation of iodine in the thyroid gland or in the organism in general. A counter makes it possible to follow the path of the iodine, and to know the speed at which it travels and the percentage of it established in the organisms. Radio-iodines are also used in radio-chemistry.

radio-isotope, the radioactive isotope of an element; eg **radio-iodine** 129 (qv), is a radioactive isotope of iodine. —Radioactive isotopes are usually produced by the exposure of natural elements to the strong flux of neutrons which exist inside nuclear reactors. These neutrons may be captured by the nuclei of the exposed element. This is how cobalt 60 (27 protons, 33 neutrons) is obtained from natural cobalt 59 (27 protons, 32 neutrons). The neutrons of the reactor may equally well induce more or less complex nuclear reactions on the nuclei of the exposed substances. Radioactive isotopes formed may either be produced directly in nuclear reactions, or result from the disintegration of the reaction products. Substances, on which the action of neutrons induces the formation of radioactive isotopes, are placed more or less close to the core of the reactor, according to the velocity of the neutrons chosen to induce the reaction and according to the strength of the neutron flux required. (See **tracer.**)

radiology, a branch of medicine whose field is the application of radiation to the diagnosis or treatment of disease.

radioluminescence, emission of light or, more generally, of electro-

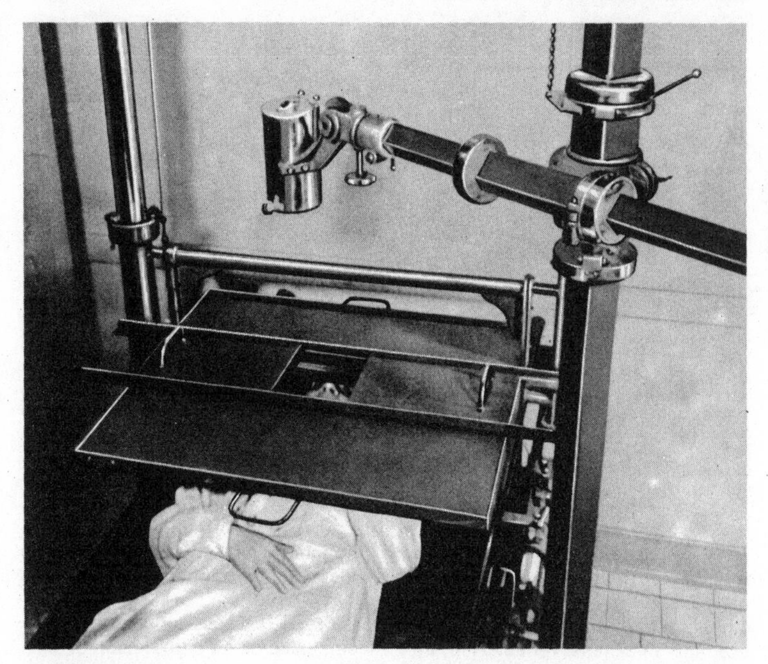

Measurement of the fixation of radio-iodine 131 at the level of the thyroid gland, by means of a Geiger-Müller counter

magnetic radiation, by a substance irradiated by a radioactive source. (See **luminescence.**)

radiometallography, the radiography of metals by means of radioactive sources.—Radiometallography enables deep-seated defects in a bulky part to be detected, such as a cleft in the metal, a bubble of gas or a defect in a weld. Frequent use is made of radiocobalt 60 or radioruthenium 106, radiocerium 144, radiotantalum 182, etc. These radioactive radio-isotopes are manufactured in nuclear reactors, by subjecting natural elements to neutron bombardment. The nature of the radioactive source is chosen according to the thickness of the metal to be examined; the radiation should be the more penetrating the thicker the metal. For thick metallic parts, neutron sources are sometimes used. (See **neutronography.**) The thickness of metallic sheet-iron, paper strip, cardboard and plastic may easily be controlled by a radioactive source; the radiation emitted by the source being more or less absorbed as the thickness of the strip varies. The device may be rendered automatic,

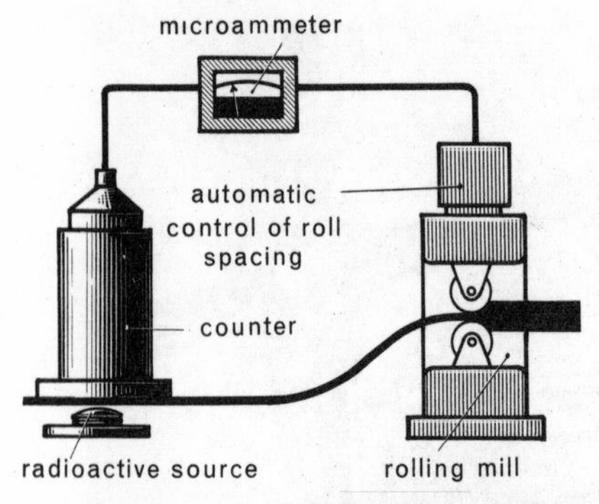

One use of radiometallography: control of the thickness of sheet-iron by a radioactive source. To the variations in thickness correspond variations in the absorption of radiation. The regulating device automatically corrects the separation of the rollers of the rolling-mill.

the system for measuring the thickness acting on the manufacturing equipment so as to readjust it whenever the thickness varies. For thin thicknesses and in the case of light metals, radioactive beta sources of low penetrating power are used. To control larger thicknesses and in the case of heavy metals, more penetrating radioactive gamma sources are generally employed.

radionuclide, a radioactive **nuclide** (qv).—Cobalt 59, which is stable, is not a radionuclide. Cobalt 60, which is radioactive, is a radionuclide. Uranium 238, which is radioactive, is also a radionuclide.

radiophosphorus, isotope 32 of phosphorus.—Each of its nuclei contains 15 protons and 17 neutrons. Natural phosphorus consists of isotope 31, which is stable; each of its nuclei contains 15 protons and 16 neutrons. Phosphorus 32 is beta radioactive with a half-life of 14.3 days. It is used in metallurgy. It has, in particular, made it possible to know the rate at which phosphorus is eliminated from iron and transferred to slag during the processing of the metal. It is also used to study problems of wear on parts which are subject to friction. Radiophosphorus, which has been introduced into the part, is collected in the lubricant and enables the amount of matter removed by friction to be assessed. In medicine, radiophosphorus enables cerebral tumours to be located, since the neoplastic tissues fix the phosphorus assimilated by the organism much more rapidly than normal tissue. In agriculture it has been possible to study the different phosphatised fertilisers by adding radiophosphorus to them. Measurement of the radiophosphorus activity makes it possible to deduce how effectively and with what speed the fertilisers are absorbed. Radiophosphorus has also been used in the treatment of skin affections by external exposure, and in treatment of diseases of the blood by internal irradiation. It is also used as a **tracer** (qv). It is produced from sulphur 32, which enters into the composition of natural sulphur in a 95 per cent proportion. Sulphur is irradiated by neutrons inside a nuclear reactor. The production reaction is as follows:

sulphur 32 (16 protons, 16 neutrons)
+neutron
gives phosphorus 32 (15 protons, 17 neutrons)
+proton.

radioresistance (usually called **radiation resistance**), the capacity of biological organisms to resist the effect of radiation. (This term may also be applied to the behaviour of chemical substances. It possesses a purely qualitative or comparative value.)

radiosensitivity or **radiosusceptibility**, the sensitivity of biological or chemical substances to the effect of radiation. These two terms have merely a qualitative or comparative value.

radiosodium, isotope 24 of sodium.—Each of its nuclei contains 11 protons and 13 neutrons, whereas each of the nuclei of natural sodium 23 contains 11 protons and 12 neutrons. Natural sodium is stable, sodium 24 is beta-active with a half-life of 15 hours. Sodium 24 emits electrons up to 1.39 million electronvolts (and, in an insignificant proportion, electrons up to 4.17 million electronvolts.) Disintegration of sodium 24 produces a nucleus of magnesium 24 in an excited state, so that this disintegration is followed by the emission of two gamma rays, one of 2.76 million electronvolts, and the other of 1.38 million electronvolts, the first corresponding to a passage from an excited to an intermediate level; the second to a passage from an intermediate to a stable fundamental level. Radiosodium is used as a tracer and as a radioactive source. It may be produced by irradiating natural sodium 23 with a neutron flux. A sodium 23 nucleus having captured a neutron is changed into a nucleus of sodium 24.

radiostrontium, a radioactive isotope of strontium.—The most important is radiostrontium 90. Each of its nuclei contains 38 protons and 52 neutrons, while natural strontium consists of several stable isotopes, the most prolific being strontium 88, each of whose nuclei contains 38 protons and 50 neutrons. Radiostrontium 90 is beta-active with a half-life of 28 years. It is produced in appreciable quantities by fission phenomena in nuclear reactors and in bombs. Due to the fact that its radioactivity is lengthy, it is one of the most dangerous isotopes to be produced in reactors and in nuclear explosions. It is, moreover, easily fixed by vegetation and tends to accumulate in bone tissue. It is easily produced in the reactors and having a long mean life, is used as a **tracer** (qv). Another active radioisotope which is fairly common is strontium 89 which is beta-active with a much shorter half-life, 51 days.

radiotherapy, medical treatment based on the effect of radiations.—Treatment of cancer, formerly carried out with the help of radium, is now being effected with the help of radiocobalt which burns the tissues surrounding the tumour much less than radium. Radioactive sources whose radiation is less penetrating than that of cobalt, caesium or tantalum, for instance, are used for superficial affections. Radio-isotopes are sometimes used to re-establish the balance of the blood when there is an excess of red corpuscles. Partial and localised destruction of bone marrow induces a slowing down in the formation of red corpuscles. *See illustration on p. 226.*

radiothorium, the current name for thorium 228, which is alpha radioactive with a half-life of 1.9 years. It belongs to the radioactive series of thorium. Despite the fact that custom attributes the name *radiothorium* to thorium 228 only, it should be observed that all other thorium isotopes are also radioactive.

radium, an element with atomic num-

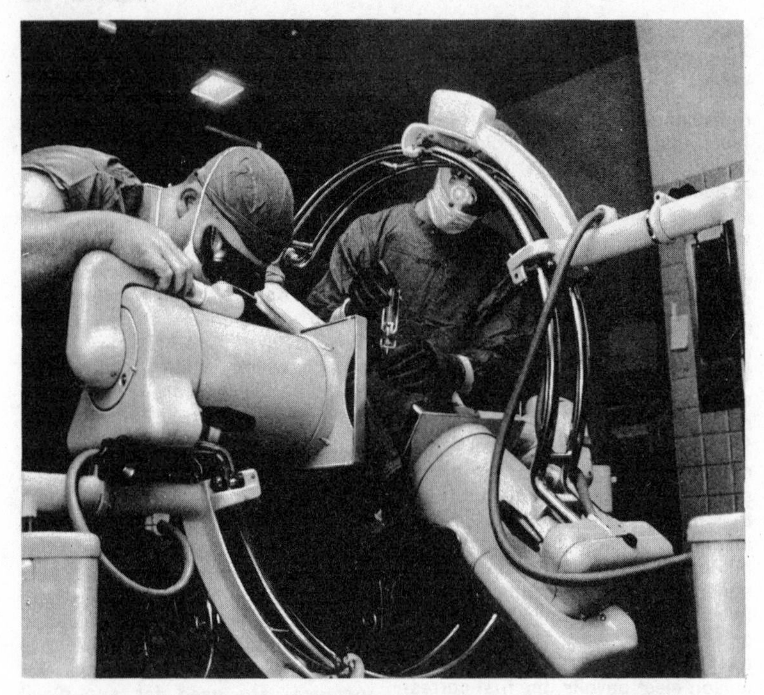

Radiotherapy. On the right: a surgeon with the help of an assistant inserts an implant of radioactive yttrium 90 into the pituitary gland of a patient suffering from cancer. The assistant guides the surgeon's actions by following his movements on a television screen which gives an enlarged picture of the patient's head. (Photo USIS)

ber 88.—Each of its nuclei contains 88 protons. It was discovered in 1898 by Pierre and Marie Curie, in an ore called *pitchblende*, two years after the discovery of the radioactivity of uranium. Isotope 226 (88 protons, 138 neutrons), which was the first to be discovered, is the most prolific. It belongs to the radioactive series of uranium. It is alpha radioactive with a half-life of 1622 years. Thirteen radium isotopes are known; their mass numbers vary from 213 (ie 125 neutrons in a nucleus) to 230 (ie 142 neutrons in a nucleus). They are all unstable, and disintegrate by alpha or beta radioactivity. Between the two World Wars, important research on radioactivity was carried out with the help of radium, which P. and M. Curie, then F. and I. Joliot-Curie had isolated in large quantities. First used in the fight against cancer on account of the destructive action on living cells of the radiations it emits, after the Second World War, radium was replaced in this application by cobalt 60, which is less harmful and can be

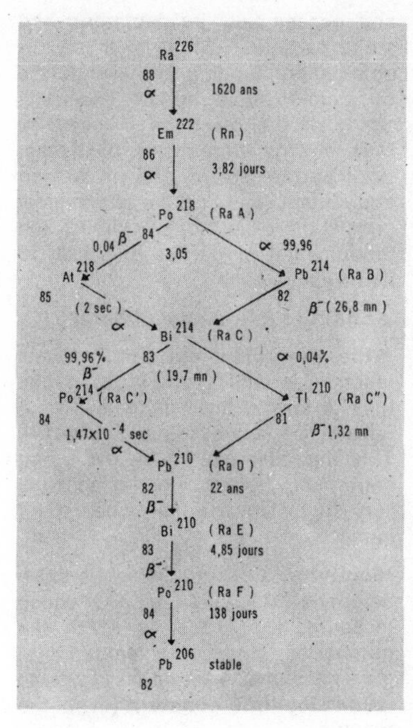

Decay scheme of radium

manufactured in appreciable quantities in nuclear reactors. Radium is still largely used to excite phosphorescence in luminous devices such as watches, etc. Traditionally, the name *radium* is sometimes given to elements of the radioactive series of uranium, which are in fact of a different nature. Radiums A, B, C, C′, C″, D, E, E″, F and G, are respectively, polonium 218, lead 214, bismuth 214, polonium 214, tellurium 210, lead 210, bismuth 210, tellurium 206, polonium 210 and lead 206. They are all unstable, except the last, lead 206, which is the end product of the radioactive series of uranium.

radon, the traditional name for emanon 222, a gas produced in the radioactivity of radium 226.—It is alpha active with a half-life of 3.82 days. The term *radon* is sometimes applied to emanon 219 and to emanon 220, which are gases emitted in the actinium and thorium disintegrations respectively. The latter are more often called *actinon* and *thoron*.

RAMAN, Sir Chandrasekhara Venkata (1888–) Indian physicist. He received the Nobel Prize for Physics in 1930 for his discovery of the effect which bears his name, according to which movements of molecules in a scattering body alter the frequency of the incident light. (See **band.**)

range, see **path length.**

rare earths, a series of elements whose atomic number varies from 57 to 70 and which possess allied chemical and physical properties. (See **Lanthanides.**) The Actinide series is sometimes called the *second series of rare earths*.

rare gas, see **gas, rare.**

ratio, branching, the ratio of the frequencies with which different disintegrations of the same unstable body are produced. Thus:

1) Radon 221 undergoes beta decay in 80 per cent of cases, alpha decay in 20 per cent. The branching ratio $\frac{\text{beta}}{\text{alpha}}$ is of $\frac{80}{20}=4$.

2) The *lambda hyperon* disintegrates into a proton and a negative pion in 2/3 of cases and into a neutron and a neutral pion in 1/3 of cases. The branching ratio $\frac{\text{proton}+\text{pi }(-)}{\text{neutron}+\text{pi }(0)}$ is of $\frac{2}{3}/\frac{1}{3}=2$.

●**gyromagnetic ratio,** the ratio between the magnetic moment and the angular momentum for a particle or a nucleus. This number connects magnetic properties, which may be associated with circulating electric currents, and the properties of rotational motion. If this idea is applied to an isolated part, measurement of this ratio may provide some information on the way in which the electric charge is distributed.

ray, a term of wide significance used to describe any particle in motion. Rays emitted in natural radioactivity (see **disintegration**) are:

—*the alpha ray*, which is the nucleus of a helium atom. It consists of two protons and two neutrons formed between them

—*the beta ray*, which is a positive or a negative electron

—*the gamma ray*, which is a photon, a particle of identical nature to those which constitute light.

For rays of particular types see **radiation** and **particle.**

RBE, symbol of relative biological **effectiveness** (qv).

reaction, interactions between particles modifying their speeds, directions and possibly their natures. —*Disintegration* is a special form of reaction, in which the initial particle fragments to produce two or more secondary particles. The term *reaction* may be reserved for those interactions which involve the intervention of nuclear forces; these are *nuclear reactions*. They are induced by interaction between a particle in motion called a *projectile*, and a stationary particle called a *target*. Important nuclear reactions are those produced on the nuclei by nuclear components, protons and neutrons, and occasionally by deuterons and alpha particles. Study of these enables understanding of the structure of atomic nuclei to be extended. Study of the reactions induced by high-energy elementary particles, such as the proton, pion, K meson and antiprotons, on targets mainly consisting of protons, enables the fundamental properties of matter to be investigated.

●**chain reaction,** see **chain.**

●**thermonuclear reaction,** nuclear reaction in which two light nuclei fuse to form a heavier nucleus by a release of energy (see **fusion**).—This may take place with hydrogen, deuterium, tritium, etc, raised to a very high temperature, whence its name.

reactivity, a quantity which is characteristic of a reactor and which measures the factor by which the number of neutrons present is multiplied per unit time.—It varies in inverse ratio to the **time-constant** (qv) of the reactor.

reactor, nuclear or **atomic pile,** an installation in which fission reactions of atomic nuclei are self-maintained.—Nuclei of certain *fissile* substances, like uranium, possess the property of dividing into several lighter nuclei through the action of neutrons. In this division (see **fission**), two or more neutrons are released from the initial nucleus and are in turn capable of inducing fission in other nuclei of the fissile material. There is therefore a possibility of maintaining fission reactions inside a fissile material. For this to take place, certain conditions have to be fulfilled, relating to the size and composition of the installation containing the fissile material; these are called the *critical* *conditions*. If these conditions are not fulfilled, the neutrons produced in a fission are unable to induce enough new fissions for the reaction to be maintained, and it dies out naturally. In each fission reaction, energy is released. This assumes several forms. On the one hand gamma rays are emitted; on the other, light nuclei produced in the fission, as well as the neutrons released, possess energy of motion due to their velocity. Finally, the radioactivity of fission products is another source of energy, which persists for some time after the fission phenomenon. The energy released finally appears in the form of heat, and it is this energy which may be employed for the production of electricity by a thermal Power Plant. Only some of the energy may be used to produce electricity. Thus, the EDF 1 reactor at Chinon possesses a thermal energy of 300,000 kW, but the electric power which it can supply is only of 60,000 kW. Electricity supplied to the French grid by nuclear reactors, especially at Chinon and Marcoule, still costs more than electricity supplied by coal-burning or hydraulic power plants. However, recent research appears to demonstrate that, for large installations of some hundreds of thousands of kilowatts, the cost of the nuclear kilowatt-hour is comparable to the cost of the standard kilowatt-hour, on condition that the power station functions for at least three-quarters of the time.

The key parts of a nuclear reactor are as follows:

1) *Fuel material* in which fissions are produced.
2) *The moderator* whose role is to slow down neutrons produced in fission to a speed at which they are particularly effective for the production of further fissions.
3) *The reflector* whose role is to prevent absolutely a leak of neutrons towards the outside of the reactor. It consists of a material from which the neutrons bounce back after one or more impacts. Neutron loss obviously cannot completely be prevented, but may be considerably reduced.
4) *Shielding* placed around the reactor, its role is to protect personnel and installations from the neutron flux which escapes from the reactor and the radioactivity induced by fission products.
5) *The cooling system* whose role is to extract the heat produced at the core of the reactor by fission, so as to maintain a reasonable working temperature (some low power reactors have no special cooling system) and to recover heat and use it in the turbines of power reactors.

The materials used to build a reactor are as follows:

1) The fuel may consist of natural **uranium** (qv), which contains uranium 235, which is fissile, and uranium 238 which is non-fissile. Uranium 235 exists in a 0.7 per cent proportion in natural uranium. So as to reduce the size and critical mass of the reactor, some reactors are actually built with uranium enriched in the uranium 235, the only one of use. (See **separation of isotopes.**) This type of reactor is principally studied in the United States, where factories for the separation of uranium have been functioning for several years. Uranium 238 may, however, take part in fission reactions if the neutrons are sufficiently fast. It is less effective than uranium 235 with slow neutrons, and a reactor in which fissions of uranium 235 with slow neutrons were

not used, would require a substantially high neutron flux. Another effective material for fission production is **plutonium** 239 (qv) which, unlike uranium, is not found in the form of an ore, but is produced in uranium reactors by the following reaction:

uranium 238 (92 protons, 146 neutrons)
+neutron *gives* uranium 239 (92 protons, 147 neutrons)
+gamma.

This reaction is followed by two consecutive disintegrations:

uranium 239 (92 protons, 147 neutrons)
gives neptunium 239 (93 protons, 146 neutrons)
+electron+neutrino.
neptunium 239 (93 protons, 146 neutrons) *gives*
plutonium 239 (94 protons, 145 neutrons)
+electron+neutrino.

A uranium reactor may therefore be used to manufacture a fissile material for subsequent re-use. Thorium 232 has also been considered as a nuclear fuel, since it is very plentiful in nature. Unfortunately, its ability to produce fission is poor, and at present it is planned to use it as a breeding material. In fact it is possible to produce from thorium a fissile material which is effective with slow neutrons, uranium 233. Uranium 233 is not present in nature, it is produced by the following reaction:

thorium (90 protons, 142 neutrons) +neutron
gives thorium 233 (90 protons, 143 neutrons).

This reaction is followed by two consecutive disintegrations:

thorium 233 (90 protons, 143 neutrons) *gives*
protoactinium 233 (91 protons, 142 neutrons)
+electron+neutrino;

thorium 233 being radioactive with a period of 22 minutes;

protoactinium 233 (91 protons, 142 neutrons) *gives*
uranium 233 (92 protons, 141 neutrons.
+electron+neutrino;

protoactinium 233 being radioactive with a half-life of 27 days. However, this method for the production of uranium 233 is subject to technical difficulties induced by the need to separate the uranium 233 from thorium and from the fission products of thorium, etc.

2) The **moderator** (qv) must be a light element for the slowing down of neutrons to be effective. Water is frequently used (a cheap process); but the drawback with water is that it captures a fraction of the neutrons circulating in the reactor. Heavy water is almost as good a moderator as ordinary water, and it captures neutrons to a lesser extent, but its cost is high. Graphite is a material which can be obtained in large quantities in an excellent state of purity. It is less good as a moderator than water or heavy water, but it possesses the advantage of capturing few neutrons. Beryllium, a light metal, is sometimes used as a moderator, in the form of beryllium oxide.

3) *The reflector* must have the same properties as the moderator, without necessarily being a light element. It consists frequently of ordinary water, heavy water, graphite or beryllium oxide.

4) *Shielding* is composed of hydrogenous materials, the commonest of which is water, to slow down the neutrons. For shielding against radiation and especially against gamma rays, heavy materials such as iron, tungsten and tantalum are used. Concrete, which contains light elements (10 per cent water) and heavy elements such as calcium and possibly barium, is a universal shielding material.
5) The most frequently used *coolants* are water and carbon dioxide. Metal liquids which conduct more heat for the same volume are also studied, in particular an alloy of sodium and potassium, which liquefies at normal temperatures.
Generally speaking, materials used in a reactor have to satisfy severe conditions. In particular, they must not contain any impurities capable of neutron absorption, and they must resist, both chemically and physically, the effects of radiation. Although a reactor, unlike a bomb, is incapable of producing a nuclear explosion, it is essential to control the neutron flux inside the reactor and not to allow this flux to reach a level at which the heat and radioactivity generated would render the reactor unusable. A regulating system enables a constant neutron flux to be maintained inside the reactor. It consists of **rods** (qv) containing boron, cadmium or hafnium, materials which absorb neutrons. An automatic control enables the rods to be submerged more or less deeply into the reactor. In this manner they absorb a controlled number of neutrons. Apart from these, absorbent safety rods are available to be plunged automatically into the reactor in the event of an accident. There are many kinds of reactor and they are distinguished by the following terms:

Breeder Reactor—a regenerative reactor in which the amount of fissile material produced is greater than the quantity of fissile material employed. It is of particular interest for the complete and rational use of world reserves of uranium, enabling the complete transformation of non-fissile uranium 238 into fissile plutonium 239 to take place. A reactor which transforms thorium 232 into uranium 233 may also be a breeder, if the amount of uranium produced is capable of providing a greater energy than that expended on its manufacture.
Critical Reactor—a reactor whose characteristics respond to the critical conditions in which the fission reaction is maintained.
Enriched Reactor—a reactor whose fuel is natural uranium enriched to fissile uranium 235.

Model of the fast neutron reactor Rapsodie (Photo library CEA)

Experimental or *Test Reactor*—a reactor intended for the experimental study of the working conditions of a certain type of reactor, for instance, one operating with fast neutrons.
Fast Reactor (fast neutron reactor)—a reactor in which the chain reaction is sustained without need for a moderator, eg a fission bomb. Fission is maintained predominantly by fast neutron. The phenomenon of delayed neutron emission makes it possible to construct controlled fast reactors, which are at present the only reactors to have enough spare reactivity to serve as breeders. Cooling is by liquid metal.
Heterogeneous Reactor—a reactor in which the fuel and the moderator are placed side by side without being mixed. The fuel is generally in the form of rods surrounded by the moderator.
High-Flux Reactor—a reactor in which there is a high flux of neutrons. A reactor frequently possesses a neutron flux of several thousand billion neutrons per square centimetre and per second. A high-flux reactor may possess, for instance, a flux which is a thousand times higher.
Homogeneous Reactor—a reactor in which the fuel and the moderator are mixed. It is usually a liquid solution

Homogeneous reactor. The neutron moderator and the biological shield consist of ordinary water in which the uranium bars are submerged. Light emitted at the bottom of the vat is due to excitation of the water by very intense radioactive radiations.

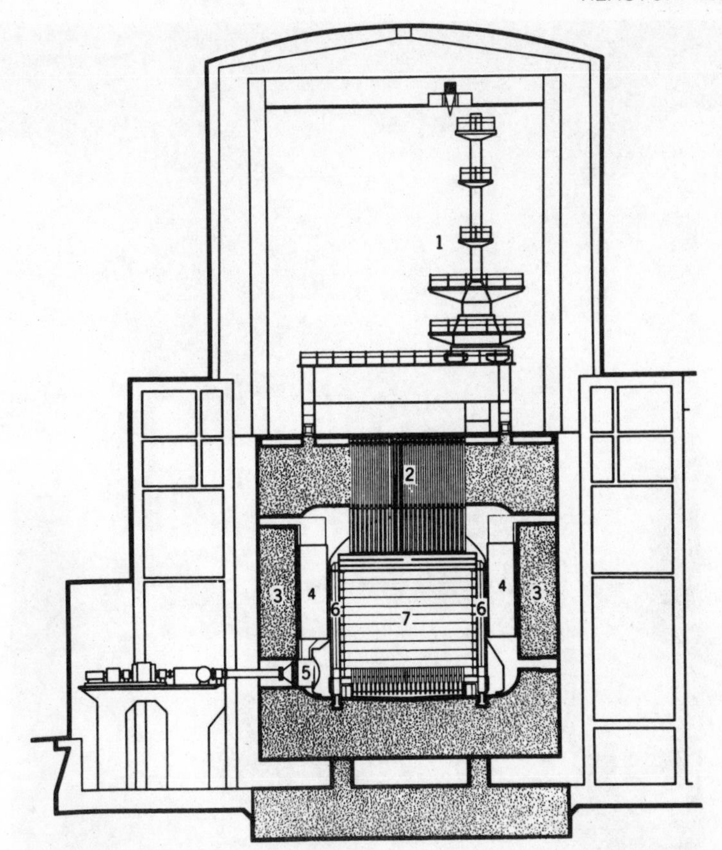

Key: 1. Fuelling machine; 2. Fuelling standpipes; 3. Pressure vessel; 4. Boilers; 5. Gas circulator: 6. Side shields: 7. Core

Power reactor: diagram showing the Dungeness B Nuclear Power Station reactor building (Copyright UKAEA)

or a suspension of metallic fuel or of uranium oxide in ordinary or in heavy water.

Intermediate Reactor—a reactor in which fissions are induced by neutrons possessing speeds half-way between slow and fast neutrons.

Power Reactor—a reactor whose principal aim is the production of electricity.

Production Reactor—a reactor in which plutonium, a fissile material, is produced from uranium 238 present in the fuel. The transformation takes

View of the pile cap of the Advanced Gas-cooled Reactor at Windscale showing the charge/discharge machine in the background and the heat exchanger on either side of the picture (Copyright UKAEA)

View of the charge/discharge floor of Chapelcross Nuclear Power Station showing a fuel element guide being lowered into the core (Copyright UKAEA)

The experimental and test reactor EL3 at the Saclay Centre for Nuclear Research (Photo Larousse)

place through the effect of a bombardment by the neutrons of the reactor.

Regenerative Reactor—a reactor in which a fissile material is produced, in the bombardment of a non-fissile material by neutrons of the reactor. A production reactor is regenerative. A reactor in which uranium 233 is produced from thorium 232 is regenerative, it being possible to use uranium 233 as a fuel in a fresh reactor.

Research Reactor—a reactor intended to provide neutrons for the production of radioelements, and for the carrying out of experiments on materials, on protection, etc.

Sub-Critical Reactor—a reactor which does not fulfil critical conditions.—The terms *lattice* or *sub-critical assembly* are more often used. In it fission reactions are not, of themselves, maintained. It is used for study of the operating conditions of a reactor.

rearrangement, atomic, a phenomenon which is produced when one of the electrons of the atom, other

View of the reactor charging floor of the production reactor at Calder Hall: a basket of fuel elements is being guided into the charge machine (Copyright UKAEA)

than those found on its periphery, is torn off.—One such electron of an atom may, in fact, be ejected from the atom by various mechanisms, such as the action of an X-ray, or the nucleus of the atom which transfers surplus energy to an electron, etc.—Electrons are bound in the atom with different energies. If there is an electron in the atom which is less bound than the one ejected, the first tends to take the place of the second. The electron which changes place becomes more bound, and the difference in energy is emitted in the form of X-rays.

recoil. In a reaction in which several particles come into play, the greater part of the available energy may be carried off by light particles, and only a small part by heavy particles. Thus, in reactions which take place at a nucleus, it acquires little energy because it has the highest mass. It is called a *recoil nucleus* by analogy with the recoil of a gun when the shell is ejected. The nucleus also has a certain recoil in beta or gamma disintegrations, the particles being lighter than the nucleus.

recombination, the reunion of an ionised atom which lacks an electron, and a free electron. Recombination is produced by the action of electric forces, the ionised atom, or ion, being positively charged and the electron negatively charged. This may take place equally well between an electron and an atom which lacks two or more electrons, or again between two ions of a molecule, the one negatively, the other positively charged. In a liquid or gaseous medium, recombination tends to be produced spontaneously because of the electric attractive forces, the ions and electrons being animated by the random movements of thermal agitation. In apparatus in which it is desired to avoid recombination, an electric field enables the positive and negative ions to be removed from each other's vicinity, by driving them in opposite directions.

reflector, material placed around a reactor and intended to reflect inwards neutrons moving outwards which would otherwise be lost to the operation of the reactor.—The reflector must scatter neutrons effectively and not absorb them. The effectiveness of the reflector increases with its thickness, but after a certain thickness the increase is small. The reflector usually consists of ordinary water, heavy water, graphite or beryllium oxide.

regeneration, production of fissile matter which may serve as a fuel from non-fissile matter in a reactor.

regenerator, see **reactor.**

regulation, a system which makes it possible automatically to maintain the normal running of an installation at a constant value.—In a nuclear reactor the *regulation rods* consist of materials which absorb neutrons, and which are submerged more or less deeply inside the reactor, so as to regulate the number of neutrons circulating inside it. They are intended for rapid and precise short range adjustment; the *control rods* enable slower and more extended adjustments to be made.

relativity, a principle which postulates that laws describing physical phenomena should be the same for systems in translation relative to one another. The phenomena should be described by the same laws for observers in translation in relation to one another.—The theory of relativity was developed by Einstein in two stages; the special theory of relativity is applied to systems whose relative motion is rectilinear and uniform; the theory of general relativity is applied to systems whose relative motion is general. The theory of gravitation established by Newton was also based on the principle of relativity: between two bodies with a rectilinear and uniform motion it is impossible to decide which is in motion and which is stationary, only the relative motion counts. However, conclusions drawn from this reached a contradiction when Maxwell expressed the general laws which govern electric and electromagnetic phenomena. For Maxwell's laws to remain valid for all systems, it is necessary for the speed of light to be constant, the same in all systems. The transformation of physical quantities when one passes from one system to the next, in translation, a transformation which retains Maxwell's laws and which therefore corresponds to the principle of relativity, is called Lorentz's transformation. The transformation used in Newton's mechanics is only an approximation to it, valid at low speeds. The experiments of Michelson and Morley, about 1890, had confirmed that the speed of light was not influenced by the speed of the system in which it was measured. Lorentz's transformation is the one which should also be applied to the laws of mechanics. Notions of time and space are modified by it, for it is not possible to define time and space separately. For example, two events which to one observer appear to be simultaneous are, generally speaking, not so for another observer in translation relative to the other. This is a necessary consequence of the existence of a maximum limiting velocity, which is in fact equal to that of light. Time and space are therefore closely connected and constitute what is called the *quadridimensional universe of relativity*. Special relativity has been very fertile, as much from the conceptual point of view as from the point of view of experimental results. In particular, it has made it possible to predict the variation of the mass of bodies with velocity, and the equivalence between mass and energy, both properties which are constantly verified in particle physics. The theory of general relativity whose aims are more ambitious and whose formulation is much more complex, has found fewer applications, yet it has enabled general laws of gravitation to be established. In this theory, gravitational interactions between massive bodies are equivalent to a slight distortion in the space surrounding each weighty body. To employ an approximate image, a massive body forms around itself a kind of cavity which distorts space; into this will fall any other massive body. The theory of general relativity has been tested several times in the field of astronomy.

rem (*r*öntgen *e*quivalent *m*an), a unit of radiation dose which produces the same biological effects on man as those induced by a rad of X-rays of 250 kV.—The dose in rems is equivalent to the dose in rads, multiplied by the relative biological efficiency. (See **RBE.**)

rep (*r*öntgen *e*quivalent *p*hysical), a unit of radiation dose corresponding to an absorption of energy equal to that induced by one röntgen of X-rays in 1 g of water (ie about 93 ergs per gramme of tissue).—The rep, used to measure the same dimension as the rad, has not been officially recognised.

resonance, momentary formation of a compound system in the bombardment of a target particle by a projectile particle.—When a thin target is bombarded by neutrons, these may induce a great many reactions according to their exact energy; this phenomenon is due to the fact that at particular energies the neutron and the nucleus with which it reacts form a compound nucleus with a relatively long, though still short, lifetime. There exist several possible resonances for each nucleus. The existence of resonances is important in reactor physics. Indeed, neutrons must be prevented from being captured by the resonances. This is achieved by slowing them down rapidly, so that most of them jump from a higher energy to one that is inferior to that of the resonance. Just as there are resonances for the nuclei, elementary particles also possess resonant states whose lifetime is very short, of less than a millionth of a second. They may, however, be considered particles in so far as they possess characteristics independent of the way in which they are produced, such as mass, electric charge, spin, etc. A great many such resonances have been discovered in recent years.

● **magnetic resonance,** a phenomenon in which a radio-frequency field induces transitions between the energy levels corresponding to different orientations of the magnetic moment of an atom, atomic nucleus or other particle in a steady magnetic field.

rocket, nuclear. Propulsion of a rocket by nuclear energy has not yet been of practical use. Many plans have been advanced, however, among which two main tendencies may be distinguished:

1) *The utilisation of nuclear reactions:* The propulsion of a standard rocket is carried out by ejecting gas towards the back at a very great speed. This process can be used in the Earth's atmosphere as well as in cosmic space. Here nuclear reactions would present two advantages. One of them is that the amount of energy which 1 g of nuclear fuel can provide is much greater than that provided by 1 g of standard fuel and the other, that the speed of the particles emitted in a nuclear reaction may be greatly superior to the speed attained by gas issuing from a reaction engine. The idea was then advanced of employing particles emitted in induced radioactivity, which is produced by the preliminary bombardment of part of the rocket by primary particles provided by a reactor or an accelerator. But the problem of achieving a bombardment that was sufficiently strong, as well as directing the particles emitted in the radioactivity does not appear to be close to solution yet.

2) *The utilisation of a nuclear reactor:* This would pose two important problems: that of the radioactivity given off by the reactor, from which the navigating personnel must be protected and the question of weight, which is generally very high with a nuclear reactor. One way of reducing radioactivity without imposing a prohibitive increase in weight due to shielding would be to attach the reactor to the spaceship at a considerable distance. The weight of the reactor itself could be considerably reduced by using enriched uranium. In the case of a rocket moving through the atmosphere, the air could

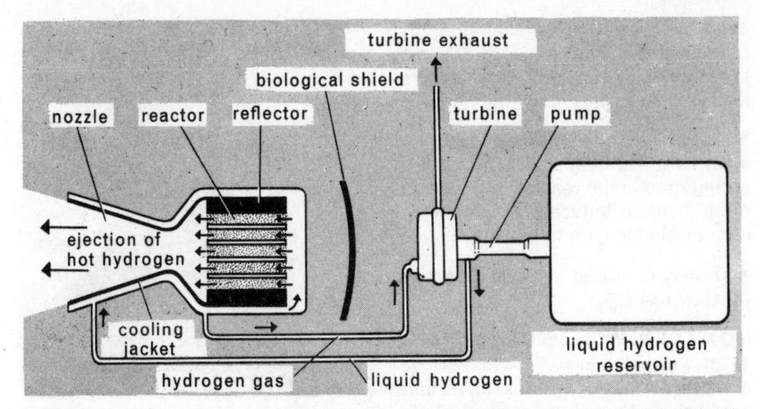

Diagram of the working of a nuclear hydrogen rocket. Propulsion is achieved by the release of hydrogen compressed and heated inside the reactor. The hydrogen, stored in liquid form, is set in motion by a pump driven by a turbine. It cools the outside of the reflector and the nozzle before being introduced at the rear of the reactor. A portion removed before it enters the cooling system is used to feed the turbine.

be raised to a high temperature when circulating through the reactor and then expanded as is done in a standard nozzle, so as to acquire great speed. In the case of a space rocket, it would be necessary to have a sufficient supply of gas available so as to ensure the working of the outlet. Finally, accelerating and slowing down manoeuvres during which a variable power would be required of the reactor are not really conceivable with present reactor techniques in which, on the contrary, power must remain at a stable level.

rod, the name given to several elements which enter into the construction of atomic piles and which have a long, rigid shape.

● **absorbent rod,** the activity of a reactor may be controlled by means of an absorber. This captures some of the neutrons produced and thus prevents chain reaction from diverging too quickly. The most frequently used materials are cadmium and boron for thermal reactors.

● **control rod,** the rod which controls the activity of a reactor.—Instead of using as a control rod an absorbent rod which would cause the loss of a certain number of neutrons, rods of fertile metal are sometimes employed. These can be for example of uranium 238 which produces plutonium 239 by capture of a neutron. A fissile material is then recovered which can, in turn, be used in a reactor so that a saving of neutrons will be achieved.

● **regulation rod,** a control rod which is used for rapid and precise regulation.—Regulation is obtained by plunging the control and regulation rods into the interior of the reactor to a greater or lesser degree, so as to absorb a larger or smaller quantity of neutrons. The name *control rod* is reserved for heavier rods which are less rapidly and exactly adjustable.

● **safety rod** or **shut-off rod,** an absorbent rod destined to be quickly submerged in the reactor in the event of an incident inducing an otherwise uncontrollable gain in activity.

● **shim rod,** fine adjustment or ● **regulation rod** (qv).

RÖNTGEN, Wilhelm Conrad (1845–1923) German physicist.—In 1895 he discovered X-rays, the most important properties of which he studied. This discovery gained him the Nobel Prize for Physics in 1901.

● **röntgen,** a unit of radiation dose defined from X-rays.—It is usually valid for low energy gamma rays. The röntgen is the quantity of X-rays which releases in 1 cm^3 of dry air under normal conditions of temperature and of pressure, an electric charge equal to one electrostatic unit. This electric charge is released by the dissociation of molecules of the air into ions and electrons. In other words, 1 röntgen induces in 1 cm^3 of air, the release of some two billion positive electric charges and two billion elementary negative electric charges equal to those of the electron. The röntgen is a comparatively large unit, and the *milliröntgen* or thousandth of a röntgen is frequently used.

RUTHERFORD, Ernest, 1st Baron Rutherford of Nelson (1871–1937) English physicist.—A student under J. J. Thomson, in 1919 he succeeded Thomson in the Cavendish chair at Cambridge and was appointed Director of the Cavendish Laboratory, after holding professorships at Montreal and Manchester Universities. His principal work deals with the composition of matter and nuclear reactions. In 1899 he discovered the radioactivity of thorium. With Soddy, he elaborated the law of radioactive transformations. In 1906 he measured the ratio between the charge and mass of alpha particles, so demonstrating that they were helium nuclei. In 1919 he achieved the first transmutation of the atom by transforming nitrogen into oxygen by means of bombardment by alpha particles. He predicted the existence of the neutron whose mass he determined. He elaborated a model of the atom in the shape of the solar system, according to which, electrons would find themselves at a considerable distance from a small massive nucleus. In 1908 he received the Nobel Prize for Chemistry.

Ernest Rutherford

rutherford, a little used radioactive unit.—It corresponds to one million disintegrations per second. The official unit is the *curie.*

Rydberg's constant, occurs in an

empirical law linking the frequency values found in light emitted by an excited atom.—The theoretical derivation of this constant was first given in Bohr's theory of the atom.

S

safety or **shut-off rod,** see **rod.**

saturation of nuclear forces, the tendency possessed by nuclear forces to act only between two neucleons (neutron or proton) in the nucleus.—In the case of interactions taking place between electric charges, on the contrary, the forces between two charges do not depend on the presence of other electric charges. When several charges are present, the forces acting between them are the same as the forces acting independently between each couple of charges; they do no more than add to them. The property of nuclear forces is somewhat similar to those of chemical forces. If one carbon atom is united with four hydrogen atoms to form a methane molecule, there is no longer any room for a fifth hydrogen atom. Carbon has four available electrons and shares each of them with a hydrogen atom. In the same way, neutrons and protons in the nuclei are all bound with the same energy, whatever their number. It would therefore seem as though the adding or subtracting of nucleons in a nucleus does not alter the forces to which protons and neutrons are subjected. In fact, this property is not hard and fast, and nucleons are less bound in very light nuclei and slightly less bound in very heavy nuclei than in nuclei with an intermediate number of nucleons. It is precisely the differences in binding energy which may be released in transmutations, which are the sources of nuclear and thermonuclear energies.

Saturn, a synchrotron type of accelerator, operating at the Centre for Nuclear Research at Saclay.—In France this is the accelerator which produces particles of the highest energy. It accelerates protons to an energy corresponding to three billion volts. It has enabled important research to be carried out on the properties of elementary particles.

scanning, the repeated periodic exploration of a physical phenomenon during a given interval of time in an experiment. Scanning is used, for instance, in the cathode ray oscilloscope. (*See figure, p. 244.*)

scattering, interaction between two or more particles between which there is an exchange of energy. The incident particle yields some of its energy to the particle on which it scatters, and its speed is modified in direction. Having acquired energy, the particle which was stationary is set in motion. The energy yielded by the incident particle is all the greater the greater its mass is relative to that of the target particle.

• **Coulomb scattering.** Scattering is said to be Coulomb when it is due to electric forces acting on charged particles. It takes place mainly on the nuclei and, to a lesser degree, on the electrons of the atom. The first experiments were carried out by Geiger and Marsden in 1909. Alpha particles were deflected at angles which were occasionally very considerable, up to 90° when passing through very thin sheets of heavy metal. It could be shown in particular by varying the thickness of the scattering foils, that these large deflections could not be caused by a number of

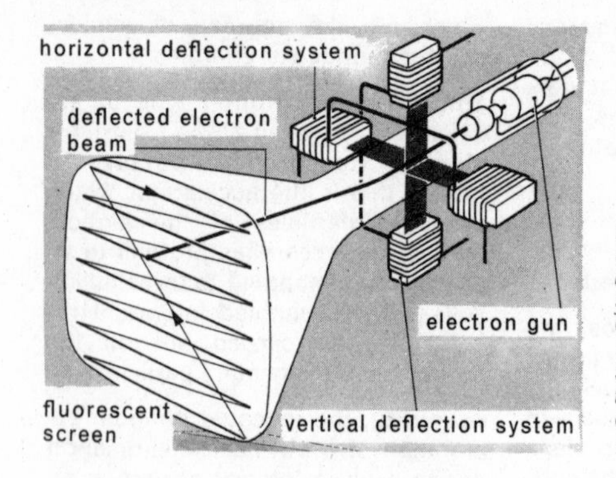

Television scanning. At the transmitter, the camera breaks down the image into horizontal lines. This image is reconstructed on the screen by the electronic beam which first scans the uneven lines: 1, 3, 5—in 1/50 of a second and then the even lines: 2, 4, 6—reproducing the complete image in 1/25 of a second.

successive deflections of the alpha particles. In consequence, in the Geiger-Marsden experiment each alpha particle only interacted with *a single nucleus*. In this case, it is said that the scattering is *simple*. In 1911 Rutherford explained these large-scale scatterings by assuming that the entire positive charge of an atom was concentrated in a small volume, a nucleus. It had previously been thought that the electric charges were distributed throughout the atom, in which case they would not have been able to induce such deviations. The same experimental principle was used to determine the electric charge of various nuclei and, in consequence, the number of protons they contained. This was among the first methods used to classify the elements.

● **elastic scattering.** The scattering of two particles is elastic in the laboratory **system of reference** (qv) when the two particles do not change their nature. Part of the energy is yielded by one particle to the other, but the total kinetic energy of the system does not change. In the centre of mass system there is no change in energy: particles are deflected; the kinetic energy of each particle is conserved.

● **inelastic scattering,** the scattering of two particles is inelastic if a fraction of the energy appears in the shape of newly formed particles, or excited states of the same particle.

Thus:

proton+proton *gives* proton +neutron+positive pion

or:

nickel 60 (28 protons, 32 neutrons) +alpha particle (2 protons, 2 neutrons)
gives zinc 64 (30 protons, 34 neutrons) excited.

The mass of the zinc nucleus produced in this manner is greater than that of a nucleus of natural zinc; the difference in mass corresponds to a certain amount of energy absorbed in the reaction.

● **multiple Coulomb scattering.** When a charged particle passes through a large thickness of matter, it is subjected to Coulomb scattering throughout the length of its path. If its speed is high enough there is a small angle corresponding to each scattering so that the path is slightly wavy. In the case of an electron whose mass is low, the path is very tortuous if the electron has little energy. Measurement of the windings of the path permits calculation of a quantity related to the mass and velocity of the particle. This technique has often been used as an element for determining the nature of a particle in photographic emulsions. Another element is required to identify it completely, for instance, the distance travelled by the particle until it stops in the emulsion.

● **nuclear scattering,** scattering induced by nuclear interaction, also described as *strong*. It is only possible with nuclei or particles having strong interactions, such as protons, neutrons, pions, etc. The electron, mu lepton, photon and neutrinos do not undergo specifically nuclear scattering. Nuclear scattering may be either elastic or inelastic.

SCHRÖDINGER, Erwin (1887–1961) Austrian physicist. A specialist in theoretical physics, he was one of the founders of quantum mechanics. He established firmly quantisation of energy, using the concept of wave mechanics of L. de Broglie to discover the equation which bears his name. In 1933 he shared the Nobel Prize for Physics with Dirac.

scintillation, an emission of light induced by the passage of an electrically charged particle in a **scintillator** (qv).

scintillation counter, see **counter.**

scintillator, a substance in which the passage of electrically charged particles induces the emission of visible or ultra-violet radiation.—These substances are employed to detect particles, usually in association with **photomultiplier tubes** (qv), whose role is to amplify the electric signal induced by a luminous radiation, which is always weak. Scintillators are divided into two categories in which the phenomena responsible for the emission of light are different, viz *organic scintillators* and *inorganic scintillators*. *See illustration on p. 246.*

● **inorganic scintillators,** consist of crystals such as sodium iodide NaI, potassium iodide KI, caesium iodide CsI, etc. The presence of impurities in these crystals, usually a few parts per thousand of thallium, is essential. An electron is displaced in the crystal by the excitation due to the loss of energy of the charged particle in motion. The gap left travels in the crystal until it reaches an impurity which then becomes a positive ion, an atom which lacks an electron. Electrons also travelling because of

Erwin Schrödinger

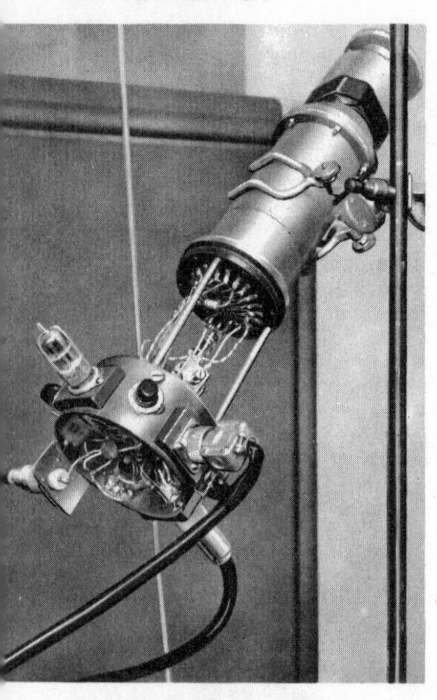

A scintillator used in association with a photomultiplier tube, as a monitor for gamma rays and fast neutrons.

thermal agitation end by rejoining the impurity and an electron, recombining with an ion, forms an excited state which becomes stable by emission of a luminous radiation. The phenomenon is slower than in organic scintillators and possesses a time length of the order of a millionth of a second. In these scintillators the presence of certain impurities which extinguish the emission of light and transfer the energy into heat instead has to be avoided.

● **organic scintillators.** In these substances the charged particle in motion yields a small part of its energies to the molecules. The molecule, which is found in an excited state, returns to its normal state by an emission of luminous radiation. This phenomenon takes place in a very short period of time, of the order of 0.01 millionth of a second. The main substances used, which should be transparent for the radiation they emit, are benzene and its derivatives: napthalene, anthracene, etc. These bodies may be obtained in the form of monocrystals. In this case, the excitation state is transmitted from molecule to molecule in the crystal. If some foreign molecules enter the crystal, they may also acquire an excitation energy and emit light. They emit a light of a distinctive colour, different from that of the basic substance. Sometimes this fact is used to obtain a radiation of a distinct colour adapted to the photomultiplier tube. It is, however, necessary to control strictly the presence of foreign molecules, as some of them, such as oxygen, extinguish the luminous radiation and must be excluded.

screen, a thickness of matter generally composed of a thin metallic plate, used for slowing down, by a given reduction of energy, or for stopping particles. (See **shielding.**)

screening. An effect by means of which protons and neutrons close together in the nucleus serve to conceal one another. On account of this effect, a particle which arrives on a nucleus does not *see* all the neutrons and protons, but only those on the surface of the nucleus. The greater number of nuclear reactions on a nucleus will take place on the surface and not in the bulk of the nucleus. From this it results that the number of reactions is not proportional to the number A of the nucleons of the nucleus, but to the number of those on the surface (ie proportional to $A^{2/3}$). This law is only approximate.

SEABORG, Glenn Theodore (1912–) American chemist. In 1941 he discovered plutonium in collaboration with McMillan; in 1945 americium and curium, and in 1950 berkelium and californium. In 1951 he received the Nobel Prize for Chemistry which he shared with McMillan.

secondary, said of a particle or radiation emitted as the result of a reaction between an incident particle in motion and a stationary particle called a *target*. The secondary particle may be of the same nature as the primary particle, or different. Thus in the reaction:

polonium 218 *gives* lead 214
+alpha particle

the nucleus of lead 214 and the alpha particle are secondary particles. This qualification may also be applied to particles emitted in radioactivity. Thus in the disintegration:

proton+proton *gives* proton+proton
+pion

the two protons and the pion emitted are all secondary particles. In the ionisation processes in which the electrons are torn from the atoms, the *secondary electrons* are those which have been torn off by the action of electrons already released through ionisation.

SEGRÉ, Emile (1905–) American physicist of Italian extraction. In 1937 he discovered technetium. He later took part in the procuring of plutonium. With Chamberlain he received the Nobel Prize for Physics in 1959 for having experimentally shown the existence of the antiproton (1955).

selection rule, a rule governing the transformation of physical quantities distinguished by quantum numbers, such as angular momentum, parity, etc, in a reaction or disintegration. For instance, nuclear and electromagnetic interactions are such that the parity of the final system is the same as that of the initial system of particles.

separation of isotopes. Isotopes are elements with the same number of protons in their nuclei, and so also the same number of electrons in their atoms. Their chemical properties are identical, since these are due to the shell of electrons surrounding the nucleus. Isotopes differ only by the number of neutrons in their nuclei. The weight of an atom, practically proportional to the number of neutrons and protons contained in the nucleus, varies slightly from one isotope to the next. Methods of separating of isotopes differ according to whether it is a question of isolating a small amount of isotope for study or for research, or whether, on the contrary, it is necessary to obtain appreciable amounts of the isotope. Natural uranium appears in the form of a mixture which contains principally two isotopes, uranium 235 and uranium 238, the first only being fissile, and therefore usable in a reactor or a bomb. A quantity of some kilograms, the *critical mass* is necessary to the functioning of the reactor or bomb. The proportion of uranium 235 being of only 0.7 per cent in the natural mixture, several hundred kilos of uranium have to be treated. Only an industrial installation can do this. On the other hand, the difference in mass between uranium isotopes is appre-

An isotope separator in the Joliot-Curie Laboratory at the Radium Institute of Orsay, France

ciable, though still weak, the two isotopes being approximately in a ratio of 238/235=1.013. The methods used have to be precise and delicate methods of analysis. The different techniques are:

1) *Centrifuge Methods*—mixtures of isotopes or of identical chemical compounds of the isotopes are subjected, in liquid or gaseous states, to very rapid rotation. Centrifugal force, proportional to the masses, tends to concentrate the heavier isotope on the periphery, whereas the lighter isotope is concentrated on the axis. For the method to be effective, the rotational speed must be very high, several thousand revolutions per second, so that the centrifugal force is incomparably greater than the weight of the isotope. This force must balance the tendency of the

molecules to re-mix by diffusion, the mixture being agitated by random molecular motion dependent on the temperature. Experiments have already been carried out and are being continued in *ultracentrifuges*.

2) *Gaseous Diffusion*—isotopes are used in gaseous form or in the form of gaseous chemical compounds. In the mixture, the molecules are animated by *thermal agitation*. In a gas in equilibrium, energies are distributed in exactly the same way among heavy and light molecules. In this case, evidently, the velocity of light molecules is on average higher than that of heavy molecules. If the mixture is allowed to pass through a barrier pierced by holes of diameters less than the *free path* of the molecules, that is to say than the distance separating two impacts on other gas molecules, the concentration of light molecules increases after passing through the barrier and the proportion of light and heavy molecules alters in proportion to the speeds. The diameter of the holes should be several millionths of a centimetre only. The only stable gaseous compound of

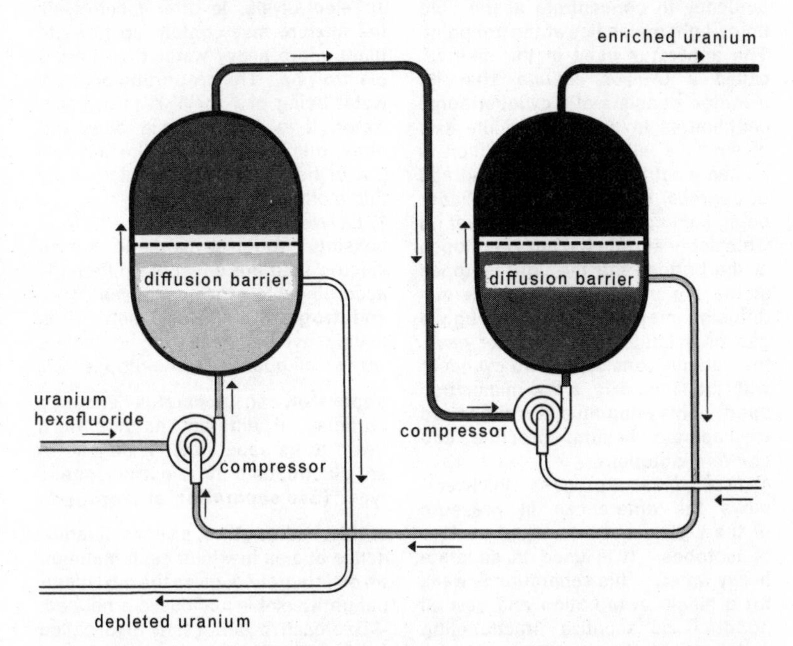

Principle of the separation of uranium isotopes by gaseous diffusion. Enrichment of natural uranium by gaseous diffusion consists in making hexafluoride of uranium pass through porous membranes, called barriers, through which the molecules of hexafluoride of uranium 235 pass more easily than the molecules with uranium 238, since their mass is smaller. By repeating the operation a great many times, one succeeds in increasing the proportion of uranium 235 in the gaseous mixture, to values of the order of 90 per cent. (Diagram CEA)

uranium is hexafluoride, a highly corrosive gas. The enrichment in light molecules is low, a few per cent for uranium, and it is necessary to repeat the operation many times. Diffusion barriers are connected in **cascade** (qv). Substantial plants are necessary, as at Oak Ridge in the USA and at Pierrelatte, in France, when it is desired to obtain the separation of an appreciable amount of isotopes.

3) *Thermal Diffusion*—in certain mixtures subjected to variations in temperature, heavy molecules have a tendency to concentrate at the cold point, light molecules at the hot point. The apparatus used in the method, called a *Clusius column* after its inventor, consists of a cylinder some centimetres in diameter on the axis of which a wire is placed, which is heated electrically to some hundreds of degrees, the sides of the cylinder being kept cold. Currents are set up which concentrate the heavy isotopes at the bottom and the light isotopes at the top of the column. Thermal diffusion may take place through a gas or a liquid. In the latter case, the column consists of two cylinders with the same axis, a few millimetres apart. This apparatus is mainly used to separate helium, bromine and chlorine isotopes.

4) *Distillation*—a process which employs the differences in pressure of the vapour above a liquid mixture of isotopes. It is used to separate heavy water. This separation is weak for a single evaporation and several hundred consecutive fractionating plates have to be arranged to extract heavy water from ordinary water.

5) *Chemical Equilibrium*—the rapidity of chemical reactions relies to some extent on the mass of isotopes entering reaction, thermal agitation of heavy molecules being weaker than those of light molecules. In a reversible chemical reaction, the equilibrium is slightly different for each isotope. This method of separation is used with chemically active substances such as chlorine, bromine and iodine.

6) *Electrolysis*—water dissociated by an electric current is enriched with heavy water, the dissociation energies of molecules of ordinary water and heavy water being slightly different. Enrichment, which must take place at a low temperature, may attain 8 for an electrolysis, ie after electrolysis the mixture may contain up to eight times more heavy water than before electrolysis. The proportion of heavy water being of 1 for 6000 in ordinary water, it is necessary to carry out numerous electrolyses. The first output of heavy water was obtained by this method.

7) *Electromagnetic Separator*—the ions passing through a magnetic and an electric field are deflected differently according to their masses (see **spectrograph**). This method is mainly used in research, to isolate very small quantities of isotopes.

separator, an apparatus enabling particles of different natures in a beam to be separated. It may be of an electrostatic or electromagnetic type. (See **separation of isotopes.**)

series, radioactive, a series of radioactive bodies in which each member, on disintegrating, gives the next member until a stable nucleus is produced. —Radioactive series are also called families, the first member being called the *parent* the following ones the *descendants*, and the final member the *end-product*. There is said to be an affiliation between members of the series. Disintegration of each of the members is characterised by a change in the nature of the nucleus of the atom. The three natural disintegrations which may take place are the *alpha* and *beta disintegrations* and the *emission* of a *gamma ray*. In the alpha disintegration, a particle consisting of two protons and two neutrons is emitted. The mass number of the nucleus, equal to the total number of protons and neutrons, decreases therefore by four units. In the beta disintegration, a positive or negative electron is emitted. The result is the same as though a proton of the nucleus changed into a neutron with emission of a positive electron, or *vice versa*. In this case the mass number of the nucleus remains unaltered. In the gamma emission, a neutral gamma ray, with no rest mass, is emitted. The mass number of the nucleus also remains unaltered. Therefore, for the three kinds of radioactivity either no change is to be observed in the mass number of the nucleus or there is a change of four units. The parent of a radioactive family therefore can only give rise to nuclei whose mass number differs from it by a whole multiple of four units. It can easily be understood from this that four radioactive families may exist. These are: the one whose mass number is a whole multiple of four; the one whose mass number is a whole multiple of 4+1 unit, the one whose mass number is a whole multiple of 4+2 units, and finally the one whose mass number is a whole multiple of 4+3 units. These four series are called respectively (4n), (4n+1), (4n+2), (4n+3). In fact only three series are to be found in nature: the (4n) series or thorium series, the series (4n+2) or uranium series, the series (4n+3) or actinium series. The parents of these three series have

official name	*half-life*
^{235}U	$7.13–10^{8}$y
^{231}Th	25.64 h
^{231}Pa	$3.43–10^{4}$ y
^{227}Ac	22 y
^{227}Th	18.2 d
^{223}Fr	21 m
^{223}Ra	11.7 d
^{219}At	0.9 m
^{219}Rn	3.92 s
^{215}Bi	8 m
^{215}Po	0.0018 s
^{215}At	$\sim 10^{-4}$ s
^{207}Pb	36.1 m
^{211}Bi	2.16 m
^{211}Po	0.52 s
^{207}Tl	4.79 m
^{211}Pb	stable

Radioactive series of uranium. The half-lives are expressed by: y, years; d, days; h, hours; m, minutes; s, seconds.

half-lives of hundreds of millions or billions of years. The half-life is the length of time by the end of which half of the nuclei have disintegrated, the other half remaining radioactive. It has been possible to calculate the length of time that has passed since the formation of some minerals on Earth as some 4 billion years. (See **lead.**) It is therefore natural that radioactive bodies belonging to these three series should still exist at the present time. The reason why the series (4n+1) is not to be observed in nature, is simple. It belongs to the neptunium series, which it has been possible to produce artificially in the laboratory. All its members have radioactive periods of less than several million years. They therefore probably existed at the time nuclei were formed in the universe, but they have since disintegrated much more rapidly than those of the other series. In fact, bismuth 209 is present in nature; it is the end-product of the neptunium series, and is stable. Beside these three natural radioactive series and the radioactive neptunium series, other radioactive series whose nuclei are also of the type

(4n), (4n+1), (4n+2), (4n+3),

have been discovered in the laboratory. Their periods are much shorter than those of the four preceding series, of the order of the hour or minute.

shells. Atomic electrons are distributed over shells called K shell, L shell, M shell, etc. Each shell can only contain a limited number of electrons: K shell, 2 electrons; L shell, 8 electrons; M shell, 18 electrons, etc. When K shell is full, L shell fills up and so on. (See **atom.**) Each atom in a pure body contains a specific number of electrons and it is the number of electrons in the final shell which fixes its chemical properties. When an atom possesses a large number of electrons, the structure is, in reality, rather more complex and the shells sub-divide into sub-shells which contain respectively 2, 6, 10 and 14 electrons. Likewise one can conceive of the atomic nucleus as consisting of successive shells of protons and neutrons. (See **models of the nucleus.**) Nuclei whose final shell is complete are especially stable. They possess numbers (4, 8, 14, 20, etc), which are analogous to the numbers of electrons 2, 10, 18, of the chemically stable bodies.

shelter, anti-atomic. In the event of an atomic attack, shelters in reinforced concrete would provide the best protection. Underground shelters would be the most efficient, as they cut off the effects of blast and

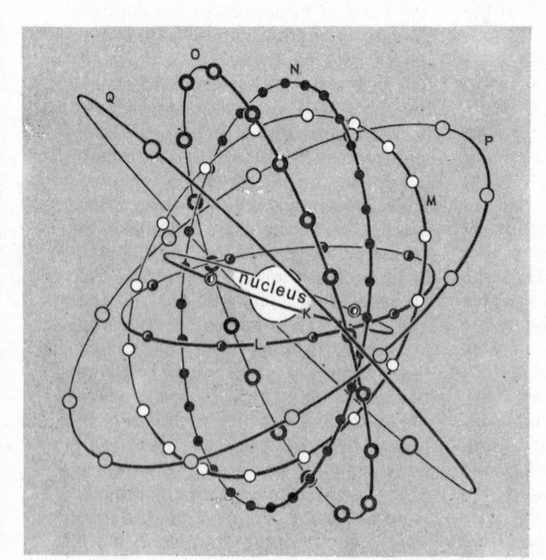

Electron shells of the uranium atom

1st shell	K	2	electrons
2nd ,,	L	8	,,
3rd ,,	M	18	,,
4th ,,	N	32	,,
5th ,,	O	18	,,
6th ,,	P	12	,,
7th ,,	Q	2	,,

Exterior and interior views of an anti-atomic shelter in the USA (Photo USIS)

heat. A thickness of earth can give protection from the effects of neutrons and gamma rays. Contamination of the air and of foodstuffs would remain; this would be unavoidable except in huge air-conditioned shelters.

shield, the protective enclosure of a reactor which prevents neutrons from escaping. The immovable part of the shield may be built of metal or concrete.

shielding, biological, an assembly for the protection of personnel from the radiations of an installation (eg radioactive source, reactor or accelerator). In this manner radiation flux is reduced to an acceptable level for the human organism.—This radiation flux usually consists of four main parts: protons or ions, electrons, gamma rays and neutrons. These radiations are absorbed in different ways according to their nature and energy. Protons, low-energy ions and high-energy electrons are absorbed by a process of energy loss through their impacts on the atoms of the shield. High-energy protons and ions are absorbed by nuclear reactions with the nuclei of the shield. Gamma rays are absorbed preferably by heavy materials in which they disappear by forming electron-positron pairs. Low-energy neutrons may be absorbed by materials which produce **resonance capture** (qv). Absorption of neutrons may be aided by slowing them in light materials in which they gradually lose their energy by undergoing impacts against the nuclei of the moderating substance. High-energy neutrons may, like protons, be absorbed by nuclear reactions.

shower, a group of charged particles produced by the interaction of cosmic radiation with matter.—These particles are generally electrons. It is recognised that a proton is to be found at the origin of a shower which produces mesons through interaction with matter. These particles in turn produce electrons and photons. The electrons generate photons by **brems-**

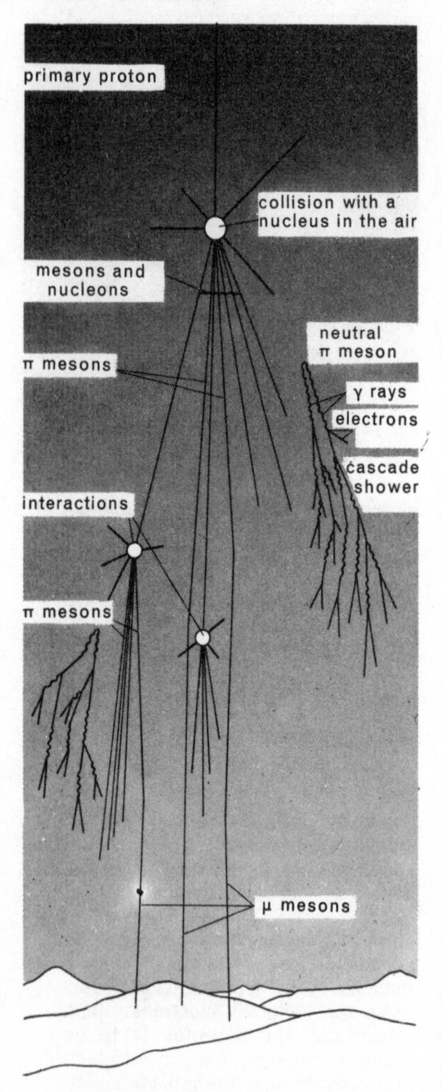

Shower: the successive effects of a primary proton colliding with the nuclei of the air

strahlung (qv) which materialises by electron-pair creation. The cascade continues by bremsstrahlung and pair creation up to an energy at which such phenomena are no longer possible. Very strong showers have been detected in the atmosphere, of the order of a million particles.

skin dose, see **dose.**

slowing down, loss of energy undergone by a particle when passing through matter.—A charged particle is slowed down when it yields its energy through ionisation, and through excitation of the atoms, by **bremsstrahlung** (qv) or by means of nuclear reactions. Neutrons of a nuclear reactor mainly yield their energy on impact with atoms of the moderator.

SODDY, Sir Frederick (1877–1956) English chemist and physicist. He did much work on radioactivity. In 1902 he discovered the law showing the affiliation of radioactive elements, and in 1903 the phenomenon of isotopy. He received the Nobel Prize for Chemistry in 1921.

sodium, an element with atomic number 11.—Sodium is a metal with a fairly low melting point: 98° C. Because it absorbs few neutrons it has been suggested as a coolant in nuclear reactors, as it is a good heat conductor. It is mainly of interest in the form of a liquid alloy with **potassium** (qv) which has a low melting point of 19° C.

SOMMERFELD, Arnold (1868–1951) German physicist and mathematician. —A specialist in theoretical physics, his studies dealt with the application of relativistic mechanics and quantum mechanics to the atom, thereby explaining the atomic and molecular spectrum. He constructed a model of the atom in which the electrons describe elliptical orbits.

source, radioactive, a sample of a radioactive substance.—The source is called *natural* or *artificial* according to whether the radioactive substance is present in nature or whether it has been manufactured in the laboratory by bombardment with a beam of particles. The source is described, according to the nature of the particles it emits, as an alpha source, a beta source (electrons), a gamma source, or a neutron source (see **neutron**).

space-charge, electric charges of the same nature (all positive or all negative), which have accumulated in a certain volume. Since these charges repel each other, results arise from this effect which may be important when the density of the charged particles is high as, for instance, in fusion phenomena, in accelerators and in electromagnetic separators.

spallation, a phenomenon which takes place in a nuclear reaction induced by a fairly high-energy particle (of at least 100 million electron-volts), which reacts on the nucleus of an atom.—In this reaction a certain number of protons and neutrons are ejected from the nucleus. They may be isolated or still associated together, in this way forming lighter nuclei. The ejected fragments are mainly protons, neutrons, deuterons and alpha particles. The spallation phenomenon is qualitatively distinguished from the evaporation phenomenon by the energy of the ejected fragments, which is greater in the first than in the second.

● **spallation fragment,** a nucleus struck by a high-speed particle may emit one or more light particles such as a neutron, proton, alpha particle, etc. These products of emission are called *spallation fragments*.

spark counter, see **counter.**

spectrograph, an apparatus which enables a spectrum to be traced. (See **spectroscope.**)

spectrometer, an apparatus enabling a spectrum to be measured. (See **spectroscope.**)

spectroscope, particle, an apparatus enabling a spectrum to be examined. (The terms *spectrograph* and *spectrometer* are frequently used for this apparatus, the difference referring only to details of use.)—It makes it possible to select from identical particles those which possess different energies, or on the other hand to select particles of different natures. To do this, use is made of the property possessed by electrically charged particles to be deflected by an electric or magnetic field. These two combined effects are almost always used. Generally speaking, deviation induced by the action of the field is greater the greater the electric charge of the particle and the smaller its mass and velocity. Deviations induced by the field therefore differ according to the nature and speed of each particle, thus enabling the particles to be separated. Focusing properties are generally required of a spectrograph, that is to say, it must collect together in a restricted area particles of a certain nature or a certain energy. This area is called the *image*, by analogy with the images obtained in optical systems. In a mass spectrograph, charged particles which issue from the apparatus in different pos-

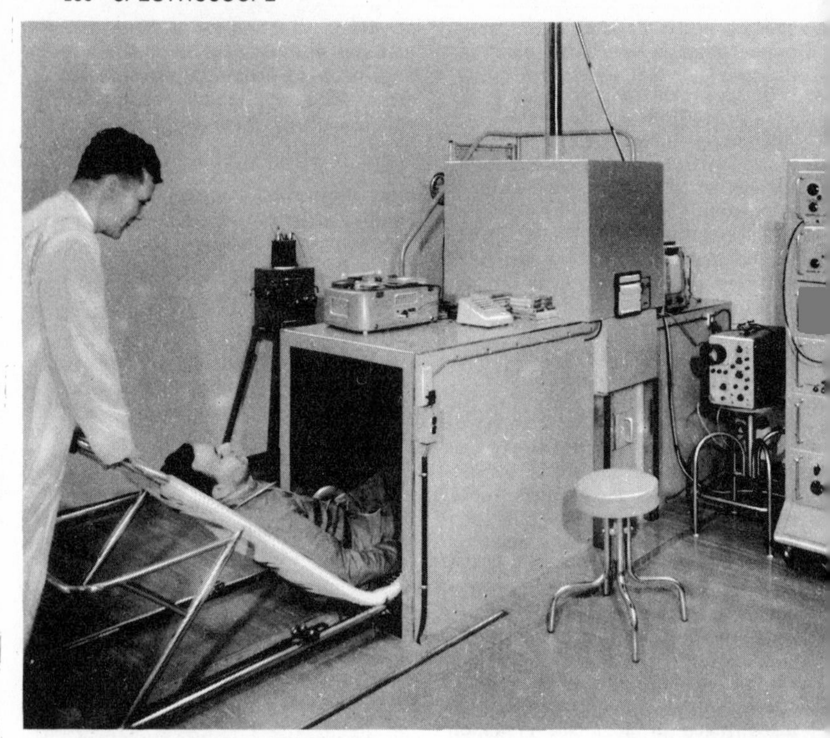

A gamma spectrometer for measuring the radioactivity of the entire human body (Photo library CEA)

itions, will mark a photographic plate in the various places where the images are located. From knowledge of the characteristics of the apparatus and the position of the images, the masses of particles which have passed through the apparatus may be deduced. It is also possible to measure, by means of a spectrometer, the energy of the gamma rays, although they are neutral. For this one uses electrons produced by the passage of the gamma rays through matter, resulting from materialisation or from the Compton or photo-electric effect. These electrons are charged and may be measured in a spectrometer. The first mass spectrograph was built in 1912 by J. J. Thomson, who subsequently used it to show the presence of two isotopes, both nuclei with the same electric charge but of different mass, for neon. Spectrographs have since been considerably developed and have enabled great advances to be made in the study of isotopes. The power of resolution of a spectrograph is in inverse ratio to the relative difference of the mass which may be detected. It is known at present how to build spectrographs with a power of resolution of 50,000; such an apparatus may separate particles whose masses differ by only 0.002 per cent.

spectrum, distribution of the energies of the particles given out in a radiation, in a radioactivity or in a reaction. Thus:

1) In the beta radioactivity of a particular nucleus, the energy of the electrons varies between two definite boundaries, according to whether the fraction of energy distributed to the two other particles emitted in the disintegration, the neutrino and the residual nucleus, is more or less great.

2) Molecules excited by outside action are de-excited on emitting electromagnetic radiations (light, infra-red, ultra-violet). The radiation emitted may possess a variable energy when the values of the energy are distributed in continuous fashion between certain boundaries, in which case there is said to be a *band spectrum*. When the energy values are distributed in a disconnected fashion and only assume definite spaced out values, there is said to be a *line spectrum*.

3) A spectrum may refer to physical quantities other than energy; for example, to the *rest mass* of particles produced in a reaction. In this case, it is called a *mass spectrum*.

spin, intrinsic, the intrinsic angular momentum of a particle (rotation of the particle on itself).—The spin is a quantity which may be conceived in terms of a rotary movement of the (extended) particle upon itself. It has a clearly defined value for each fundamental particle. The value of the spin, expressed in units of $h/2\pi$, can only be whole or half-whole. Particles with a half-whole spin (1/2, 3/2, 5/2, etc) are called *fermions*. They obey the statistical laws of Fermi-Dirac. Particles with a whole spin (1, 2, 3, etc) are called *bosons*. They obey the statistical laws of Bose-Einstein. The spin of a compound particle system may also be defined. For instance, the spin of a nucleus results from the composition of the spins of the different protons and neutrons which it contains, and of the relative angular momenta of the protons and neutrons inside the nucleus. In this case, spin is sometimes called *total angular momentum*. In the present state of the theory in which the structure of a fundamental particle is not described, the spin has no exact intuitive image. Its properties are derived from the complex formalism of quantum mechanics.

spin, isobaric, synonym of **spin, isotopic** (qv).

spin, isotopic, an abstract physical quantity introduced to account for the fact that certain particles, having nearly equal masses but different electric charges, possess corresponding nuclear properties.—Study of nuclei shows that the proton and neutron are subject to similar nuclear forces inside the nucleus. The masses of the proton and neutron differ by only 2 per cent, the proton having a positive electric charge, the neutron a zero electric charge. The proton and neutron are then considered to be manifestations of one and the same particle, the nucleon. The electric charges, which are different for the one and for the other, are considered to result from the different orientation of a quantity called *isotopic spin* whose formal (mathematical) properties are analogous with those of the spin.

spurion, particle identified on apparently sound grounds, either experimental or theoretical, but subsequently found not to exist. || Colloquially, particle announced by a rival physicist.

stability of motion, resistance to forces perturbing a predetermined path. It is particularly important in particle accelerators (see **phase stability** and **focusing, radial**).

stable, said of a particle system whose physical characteristics do not change.—A nucleus or a particle is said to be stable if it does not disintegrate.

standard, radioactive, sample of a radioactive material in which the number of disintegrations per second is exactly known.—It consists of a very pure element, so that the type of disintegration particles is well established. Generally speaking, an element having a very long period is used. For some elements this amounts to billions of years; in this case radioactivity is constant. The radioactive standard enables measurements to be made, by comparison, of sources of unknown strength.

star, a phenomenon visible in nuclear photographic plates, in Wilson chambers and in bubble-chambers. Several tracks can be observed leaving from the same point. The star indicates a nuclear reaction induced by a fairly high-energy incident particle. In this reaction, the nucleus is broken up and protons and neutrons are released; the tracks of ionising protons are seen; the neutrons leave no trace. When the incident particle has sufficient energy, mesons, antiprotons, etc, may also be produced. (See also **spallation.**) Stars may also be observed coming from the disintegrations of the nuclei of a radioactive sample placed in a Wilson chamber or on a nuclear plate. *See illustration on p. 259.*

state of a physical system. An atom or a nucleus possesses properties characterised by certain physical quantities: mass, kinetic energy, electric charge, spin, etc. A similar kind of atom may exist having different characteristics. It is said that it may find itself in several states of mass, of energy, of charge, of spin, etc.

●**excited state,** a state in which a particle has absorbed energy from an outside source.—By virtue of the law of equivalence of mass with energy, its own mass has increased. An X-ray may excite an atom by transferring energy to one of the electrons which surround the atom. A gamma ray may excite a nucleus, in which case it is not possible to say that a single one of the protons or a single one of the neutrons which compose the nucleus finds its energy increased. Rather it is the whole nucleus which absorbs the energy. The nucleus usually returns rapidly to its normal state, called the *ground state*, by emission of a gamma ray which may be detected. Certain nuclear reactions and some disintegrations may also produce nuclei in an excited state directly.

●**final state,** state of a particle system after reaction or disintegration.

●**ground state** or **fundamental state,** a state in which the energy is minimal.—In all other states of a physical system the energy is higher. The ground state is the stable state to which the system tends to revert when it is in another state. States

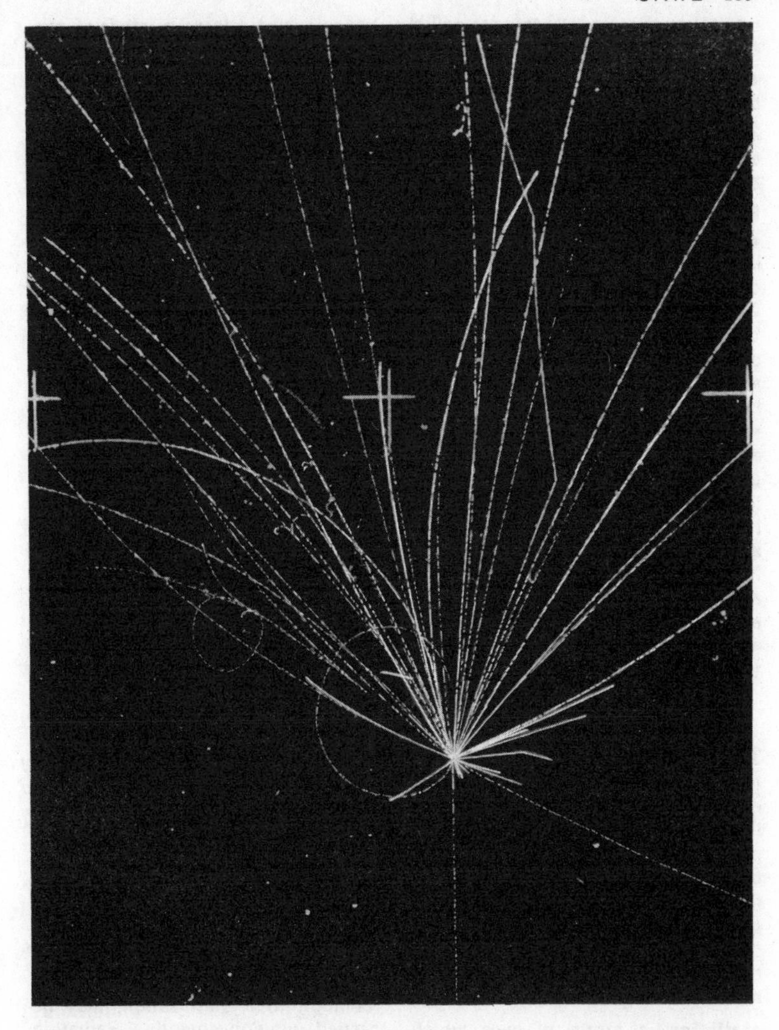

A high-energy negative. meson (18 GeV/c) encounters a nucleus, producing a nuclear star. The picture was taken by means of the bubble chamber BP3 at the Leprince-Ringuet Laboratory of the Ecole Polytechnique in Paris.

other than the ground state are called *excited states.*

● **initial state,** the state of a system before a reaction or a disintegration.

● **metastable state,** a state stable with respect to small perturbations but unstable on sufficiently strong perturbation.

● **virtual state,** a state in which the law of the conservation of energy does not hold. The existence of virtual states may be considered to be related to the fourth *uncertainty principle* of Heisenberg. The time and energy of a particle system cannot be absolutely simultaneously determined. Should the first be completely determined, the second is completely undetermined and *vice versa.* Thus, in theory, states are made to intervene in which energy is subject to variations, on condition that it should be for very short intervals of time.
a) Some nuclear properties may be explained by the emission and re-absorption of one pion per nucleon (proton or neutron):

nucleon *gives* (nucleon+pion) *gives* nucleon

This process, impossible according to the law of the conservation of energy, may be possible because of the *uncertainty principle.*
b) In the same way, the forces between two electric charges may be represented by the emission of virtual photons by one of the charges, and the absorption of these photons by the second charge. ‖ The term is sometimes used for **resonance** (qv).

statistics, a group of laws which govern the behaviour of physical systems which contain numerous elements.—The laws of particle physics are usually statistical, in the sense that they may foresee the general behaviour of a large number of particles or systems, but they cannot foresee the individual behaviour of each of them. The statistical laws the particles obey are those of Fermi-Dirac, for particles called *fermions,* and those of Bose-Einstein for particles called *bosons.* (See ● **Bose statistics** and ● **Fermi-Dirac statistics.**)

sterilisation by radiation, a method of preserving perishable foodstuffs by using radiations.—This method is particularly effective for the preservation of food when it has previously been packaged in a small hermetically sealed bag. In this manner meat, fish, dairy products, fruit, vegetables, cereals, bread, beer, coffee and fats, etc, may be preserved. Radiation possesses the property of destroying taenia (tapeworm) in pork, and insects in cereals. The length of storage time for onions and potatoes may be increased, and sprouting prevented or slowed down. It is also possible to induce interesting mutations by exposing plants to radiation. Radiation may be used against plant worms and wood-worms. In the sterilisation of cloth, radiations have the advantage of wearing out or tearing the cloth less than usual methods. Care should be taken when sterilising, that radiations do not modify the nutritive value, taste or smell of the food. Tests have been made on animals to demonstrate the non-toxicity of the radiations. Pasteurisation, which requires a lower dose of radiation than sterilisation, may be carried out conveniently. Radiation sources used may be natural, such as radium, or artificial, such as cobalt 60. X-rays may also be used, which are produced by a cathode ray tube or by artificially accelerated electrons.

stopping-power, the energy lost by a particle when passing through matter, by unit of length.—An electrically charged particle yields some of its energy to the atoms of the matter through which it passes, through the medium of two phenomena:

a) *Ionisation:* by means of the interaction between the electric charge of the particle and that of the electrons of the atoms the latter may be torn from the atom.

b) *Excitation:* the atoms are raised to a higher state of energy, called the *excited state* (one or more electrons of the atom may change orbit, passing over to an orbit in which their energy is higher).

The phenomenon of ionisation is usually predominant. Stopping power depends on the electric charge, on the velocity of the particle, and on the nature and density of the matter through which it passes. For very low-energy particles, loss of energy by ionisation increases with the speed, it then passes rapidly through a maximum, then decreases with rising velocity to reach a minimum for a particle energy which is equivalent to its mass: about 0.5 million electron-volts for an electron, 1 billion electron-volts for a proton, etc. A particle of this energy is said to be at *minimum ionisation* and a minimal number of ions formed at this energy is in fact observed in detection apparatus. Loss of energy then increases with the energy by an effect of relativity. This phenomenon is called *relativistic raising of ionisation*, and it continues up to very high energies, growing gradually weaker in such a way that the energy lost through ionisation by a very rapid particle is practically independent of its velocity. The particle is then said to be on an *ionisation plateau*. The quantity of energy lost by a particle on the plateau through ionisation is not much higher, for example 1.2 times more, than at the minimum of ionisation. On the other hand, at a lower energy a particle at maximum ionisation may lose 200 times more energy than at minimum ionisation. Light particles such as electrons may also lose their energy through radiation. (See **bremsstrahlung.**) Theory and experiment enable different sources of energy loss to be understood, whose sum provides the stopping power. Understanding the stopping power for a given particle and material enable the range of a particle of given energy to be determined, ie the thickness of the matter through which the particle passes before coming to a stop.

storage-ring, see **accelerator.**

straggling, see **fluctuation of range.**

strange particle. A fundamental particle which has a non-zero value of the quantum number *strangeness*. The name derives from the behaviour of these particles, unintelligible at the time of their discovery and very different from that of the previously known particles; although freely produced in energetic nuclear reactions they appeared very rarely among decay products. Study of these particles showed that they are never formed singly in nuclear reactions (see **associated production**), and that a strange particle can decay into non-strange particles. To describe this behaviour Gell-Mann introduced the new quantum number called *strangeness*, which is conserved in nuclear interactions but not in weak interactions or disintegrations. The strange particles known at present are the K mesons and the lambda, sigma, xi and omega hyperons. Their strangeness, in spite of their name, is now no more (or less) than that of all known particles.

strangeness, a physical quantity introduced by the American physicist Gell-Mann to account for the strange behaviour of certain particles (see **strange particle**). It is a number introduced for K mesons and hyperons to extend a relation, found true for other particles, which relates the total charge, the number of baryons and the isotopic spin. In a strong (nuclear) **interaction** (qv), this quantity is conserved; for instance, from a pion and a proton both of zero strangeness two strange particles may be produced. One, the K meson, will have a positive strangeness, the other, the lambda hyperon, will have a negative strangeness so that the total of both of them is exactly zero. The reaction is as follows:

(negative) pion (strangeness 0)
+(positive) proton (strangeness 0)
gives
(neutral) K meson (strangeness+1)
+(neutral) lambda hyperon
(strangeness−1).

The idea of strangeness explains why strange particles are produced relatively freely by strong interactions, since they are produced in pairs without any alteration in total strangeness. They can disintegrate by a process in which there is a change of strangeness; this is the situation of weak interactions, which explains why strange particles disintegrate relatively slowly. Strange particles are known of strangeness −2, −1, 0, +1.

STRASSMAN, Fritz (1902–) German physicist. A specialist in nuclear chemistry and physics. In 1939, together with O. Hahn, he showed the possibility of nuclear fission.

stripping, a phenomenon by means of which a particle of great velocity provokes the departure of a particle that is attached to a whole. An electron is torn from an atom, a nucleon from a nucleus. || The *stripping reaction* is a reaction produced by a deuteron (deuterium nucleus) on a nucleus. It may be understood as a splitting of the deuterium nucleus into its two components, the neutron and the proton. The proton may be arrested by the target nucleus, while the neutron carries on. This reaction is thus a means of forming an almost mono-energetic beam of neutrons. In an accelerator, neutrons produced in this manner may escape from the electric and magnetic fields which govern it, since they possess no electric charge. In the reaction the neutron carries off almost half the energy of the incident deuteron.

strontium, an element with atomic number 38.—Each of its nuclei contains 38 protons. Stable strontium isotopes are present in nature. These are strontium 84, each of whose nuclei contains 38 protons and 46 neutrons; strontium 86 (38 protons, 48 neutrons); strontium 87 (38 protons, 49 neutrons) and strontium 88 (38 protons, 50 neutrons). The other strontium isotopes are radioactive. Isotope 90 (38 protons, 52 neutrons) is particularly dangerous, since it is fairly abundantly produced in fission reactions. Reactors and nuclear explosions induce therefore, the formation of strontium 90 which has the property of remaining radioactive for a long time, its period being 28 years. Danger lies in the fact that it may be fixed in plants and in the human organism, especially through the medium of milk.

structure, fine, duplication of a line

in the radiation emitted by an excited atom.—The radiation of an atom excited by an outside source of energy contains lines, ie clearly defined radiations of energy. Analysing the lines emitted by alkaline atoms, it has been observed that each of them in reality consists of two closely allied lines. The alkalis are atoms with a solitary electron on their outer shell. The duplication of lines is explained by the idea of *spin*, introduced by Goudsmit and Uhlenbeck. The electron of an atom revolves around the nucleus of the atom, but it also revolves on itself, like the planets around the Sun. Since the electron is electrically charged, its rotational motion around the nucleus causes a magnetic field to appear in the vicinity of the nucleus. To its intrinsic angular momentum on the other hand, corresponds a magnetic moment typical of a small magnet. The magnetic field formed by the movement of the electron around the nucleus acts on the magnetic moment, bound to the movement of the electron upon itself. This magnetic moment may assume two directions, to which two possible energies for the electron correspond. The energy of the radiations emitted by an excited atom being due to the difference in the energies of the electron before and after emission, it is conceivable that two radiations, which correspond to two possible states of energy, may be emitted. In atoms other than the alkaline ones, more complicated effects may lead to a multiplication of the number of lines. It is then said that one has a *line multiplet*. The multiplet is called a *doublet* when it consists of two lines, a *triplet* when it consists of three lines, etc.

● **fine structure constant,** a dimensionless constant whose value is approximately 1/137. It serves to measure the effective strength of electromagnetic interactions. Thanks to its small value, perturbation theory applies usefully in quantum electrodynamics.

● **hyperfine structure,** a duplication of lines in the radiation of an excited atom, connected with the spin of the nucleus.—The multiplicity of lines is greater the higher the spin of the nucleus.

sub-critical, used of an *assembly* similar to a nuclear reactor, but which cannot diverge, ie one in which fission reactions cannot be maintained naturally. (See **reactor.**)

supercritical, said of a nuclear reactor which may fulfil critical conditions in an excessive manner. In it chain reaction develops of itself.

swimming-pool-type reactor, a reactor one of whose components is liquid. (See **homogeneous** and **reactor.**) Generally speaking, it has a moderator composed of ordinary water, open to the atmosphere for reactors of very low power.

synchrocyclotron, a type of circular **accelerator** (qv) in which the high electric voltage which accelerates particles on each rotation is synchronised with the varying duration of their revolutions.

synchrotron, a type of circular **accelerator** (qv) which has been perfected to a higher degree by comparison with the **synchrocyclotron** (qv).—The magnetic field which guides the particles on their circular orbit possesses a value which is variable during acceleration. This value is such that the radius of the orbit remains constant whatever the

Proton source of the CERN synchrotron (Geneva); in the background can be seen a Faraday cage (Photo Ecole Polytechnique)

Proton synchrotron of CERN (Geneva). Above: *optical element of the beam M_2.* Below: *Injection into the synchrotron. In the foreground the shunting electrostatic lens ensuring continuity of the orbit at injection and after the first circuit.* (Photo Ecole Polytechnique)

Above: *General view of the proton synchrotron Saturn at the Saclay Centre for Nuclear Research*

Below: *A glimpse of the protective concrete shielding around and above the accelerator* (Photo J.-P. Sudre-CEA)

energy of the particle. The magnetic field is regulated to synchronise with the high-voltage source.

systems of reference. Laboratory system and **centre of mass system.** These are geometrical references used to study the movement of particles in a reaction or disintegration. The movement of bodies is relative. Therefore, the aspect of this movement depends on the velocity of the observer in regard to the body he is observing. In the case in which the movement of the bodies under study is rectilinear and uniform (of a constant velocity), two especially convenient references are used: the *laboratory system* and the *centre of mass system*. In the laboratory system the observer is stationary in regard to the detection apparatus, and the particles are in motion. In the centre of mass system the observer moves so that the total linear momentum of the physical system observed appears to be zero. The particular importance of the centre of mass reference system lies in the fact that the energy available for reaction in a collision process is the energy measured in this reference system. Quantities related to speed and energy in one of the systems are related to the same quantities in the other system. Passage from one system to the other takes place by means of transformations in which, for high relative speeds relativistic effects have to be taken into account. (See **relativity.**) These are Lorentz's transformations. When speeds are low, this is not necessary.

T

TAMM, Igor (1895–) Soviet physicist. He collaborated with Franck to establish a theory explaining the effect shown by **Cerenkov** (qv). These three physicists received the Nobel Prize for Physics in 1958.

target, a material which is exposed to a beam of particles for the purpose of studying reactions produced by incident particles upon the particles of which the target is composed.—A target may be exposed to the beam of an accelerator, or to the stream of particles emitted by a radioactive source. A target is called *thin* if the average amount of energy lost by an incident particle during its passage is negligible. When the amount is considerable, the target is called *thick*. Interactions which take place in the target are more numerous the thicker the target, whereas the precision of the measurements is greater the thinner the target. According to the object of the experiment, a compromise is made. Very thin targets (metallic deposits of a few microns thick) are used in nuclear low-energy physics. || The name *target* is sometimes used for the stationary particle among those which initiate a reaction.

technetium, an element with atomic number 43.—Each of its nuclei contains 43 protons. It is not present in nature in discernible quantities, but can be produced artificially. It was obtained in 1937 by C. Perrier and E. Segré through bombarding molybdenum, atomic number 42, with deuterons and neutrons. More than twelve technetium isotopes are known, with mass numbers varying from 92 (43 protons, 49 neutrons) to 107 (43 protons, 64 neutrons). They are all unstable, with half-lives of less than a million years, which explains why technetium is not present in nature. The commonest are technetium 99 and 97, which may also be obtained in the shape of fission products in nuclear reactors.

thermal, said of a neutron or any other particle in thermal equilibrium at normal temperatures.—A thermal neutron possesses an energy in the region of 0.025 electronvolts.

thermal agitation, see **agitation, thermal.**

thermalisation, slowing down of neutrons from the energy at which they are produced by fission in a reactor, to the *thermal energy* at which they are in thermal equilibrium as a gas at normal temperature.—Thermal energy is 0.025 electronvolts. The energy possessed by neutrons produced in the fission of a fuel nucleus is such that they are ineffective for reproducing fission in other nuclei of the fuel. In a reactor, the fission reactions must maintain themselves. It is therefore of interest to slow down neutrons until they possess an optimal energy for fission production; ie until they are in the neighbourhood of thermal energy. In a nuclear reactor, neutrons are thermalised by impacts against the nuclei of the **moderator** (qv). The average number of impacts required to thermalise a neutron emitted with an energy of 2 million electronvolts is 19 in water, 35 in heavy water, 115 in graphite and 215 in uranium.

thermonuclear, refers to the phenomenon of fusion, in which two light atomic nuclei combine to form a heavier atomic nucleus.—For reaction to take place (see **fusion**), it is necessary for the light nuclei to be propelled at high speeds so as to overcome the electric forces of repulsion. These high speeds may be obtained by raising the nuclei to a temperature of several million degrees, whence the term *thermonuclear* given to this reaction. A device in which fusion energy is used, is called thermonuclear. (See **bomb** and **cycle.**)

THOMSON, Sir George Paget (1892–) English physicist, son of Sir Joseph John Thomson. In 1927 he discovered the diffraction of fast electrons in crystals, a phenomenon which confirmed the wave mechanics of L. de Broglie. In 1937, with Davisson, he received the Nobel Prize for Physics.

THOMSON, Sir Joseph John (1856–1940) English physicist. A student of Maxwell, he carried out important work on the theories of electricity and electronics. He determined experimentally the ratio of the charge and mass of the electron and, subsequently, the absolute value of this charge. He invented the mass spectrograph which enabled numerous isotopes to be discovered. He invented a first model of the atom. His works brought him the Nobel Prize for Physics in 1906.

Joseph John Thomson

thorianite, an ore consisting of thorium and uranium oxide. It is to be found in the USSR and in India.

thorite, an ore consisting of thorium and uranium silicates.

thorium, an element with atomic number 90.—Each of its nuclei consists of 90 protons and 142 neutrons. It is present in nature and has a mass number of 232. It was discovered in 1828 by Berzelius and its radioactivity was discovered by Marie Curie in 1898. It is a white metal, but blackens when exposed to air. Thorium 232 is alpha radioactive with a half-life of 13.9 billion years. It is the first of a radioactive **series** (qv) consisting of no fewer than thirteen elements which are all radioactive, except the last, lead 208, which is stable. Thorium is fairly plentiful in nature. It is to be found in a proportion of 15 parts per million. It is therefore four times as plentiful as uranium. Deposits of thorium are, however, not very localised. The principal ores are thorianite, monazite and thorite. The exporting countries are India and Brazil. Apart from thorium 232, 12 artificial thorium isotopes are known, whose mass numbers vary from 223 (90 protons, 133 neutrons) to 235 (90 protons, 145 neutrons). Thorium 232 may be used as a fuel in reactors, since it gives rise to fission reactions under the action of a bombardment by fairly fast neutrons (of several million electronvolts). However, its reactions are not very frequent in comparison with those given by uranium 235 under the action of slow neutrons. It may also be transformed into uranium 233, which is an interesting nuclear fuel. (See **reactor.**) Thorium A, B, C, C′, C″, D and X are names traditionally given to the elements of the radioactive series of thorium. These are, respectively, polonium 216, lead 212, bismuth 212, polonium 212, tellurium 208, lead 208 and radium 224.

thoron, a radioactive gas produced in the disintegration of radium 224, in the radioactive series of thorium.—Its official name is emanon 220.

threshold, the minimal energy which a particle must possess to induce a reaction of a given type.—For a pion, for instance, to be produced in the reaction of an incident proton on a stationary proton, the incident proton must have an energy equal to 180 million electronvolts. This energy is slightly higher than the energy equivalent to the mass of the pion formed, ie 140 million electronvolts, as a fraction of the energy of the incident proton is necessarily transferred, through conservation of momentum, to the three out-going particles: the two protons and the pion. Only the initial kinetic energy in the centre of mass system is fully available for particle creation. (See **systems of reference.**)

time-constant of a reactor, the time during which the number of neutrons circulating in a reactor in the absence of regulation is divided by the factor 2.7 when it diminishes, or multiplied by this same factor when it increases. So as to facilitate the regulation of the reactor by means of control bars, which are directed mechanically and oscillate around a mean position, the time-constant of a reactor is usually fixed at a value of the order of a second.

tolerance dose, see **dose.**

tracer, a foreign substance added to a basic substance so as to observe its path and concentration.—The tracer should possess chemical and physical properties, according to the phenomena under study, which are very similar to the basic substance. The isotopes of an element provide a very easy means of tracking the evolution of an element. They consist of atoms, the nuclei of which differ solely by the number of neutrons which they contain. Two isotopes of the same element have, on the other hand, the same number of electrons and the same number of protons in their nuclei. Chemical properties due to the electrons are therefore very similar. Their physical

Tracer: vacuum plant for the synthesis of labelled molecules (Photo J.-P. Sudre-CEA)

properties are also very similar, the masses of isotopic atoms being very close. Isotopic tracers are sometimes called *indicators*. Two kinds of isotopic tracers should be distinguished: *stable* isotopes and *radioactive* isotopes.

1) The addition of an isotope which is artificially manufactured and stable to a natural element enables the latter to be followed through physical transformations or in chemical reactions. So as to assess the quantities of the natural element, the product is analysed, by a mass spectrograph for instance, so as to evaluate the concentration of artificial isotope in it.

2) The addition of an artificially manufactured and radioactive isotope to a natural element makes it possible to follow the latter through every moment of its evolution by means of detectors (radioactivity counters). Improvement of the means of detection

makes it possible to introduce only a small quantity of radioactive isotope into the element studied, so that it is possible to use this method to follow the path of an element even in the human body. This, for instance, is the case with iodine, the fixation of which in the thyroid gland may be studied by means of radioactive iodine, or radio-iodine. Radioactive isotopes are also used in the diagnosis, and occasionally the therapy, of certain tumours which possess the property of fixing elements more rapidly than the rest of the organism. They also make it possible to diagnose digestive troubles. Tracers are used in chemistry, to study the evolution of reactions by marking with a radioactive tracer the pure body or grouping whose behaviour in the reaction one wishes to understand. They are now manufactured commercially. (See **radio-isotope.**)

track, a visible phenomenon induced by a particle when passing through a detection apparatus.—In a photographic emulsion, the track consists of a series of grains impressed by the particle. In a diffusion chamber and in a Wilson chamber, the track is formed by a series of liquid droplets which condense on the passage of the particle through a gaseous medium. In a bubble-chamber, it consists of a series of gaseous bubbles formed during the passage of the particle in a liquid medium. In a spark chamber, it consists of a series of sparks the striking of which is induced by the passage of the particle. In all these devices the path followed by the electrically charged particles may be followed exactly.

trajectory, a line constituted by the series of positions consecutively occupied by a particle in motion.

transition, evolution of a physical system leading to a modification of its characteristics. For example, an alpha disintegration is a transition which leads from a physical system consisting of a nucleus, to a physical system consisting of a different nucleus and of an alpha particle. || *Isomeric transition* is a transition which takes place between two **isomer** nuclei (qv).

transition probability, the probability per unit time that a system of particles should pass from one state to another. For example, the law of disintegration of a radioactive body is a statistical law. Given a large quantity of radioactive nuclei, the proportion of those which disintegrate in unit time (usually per second) is a quantity characteristic of the radioactive body under consideration: it is the *transition probability*. Given a single radioactive nucleus, only the probability this nucleus has of disintegrating in a second is known, this is equal to the transition probability. The exact moment of its disintegration cannot be foreseen. De-excitation of **isomer** (qv) nuclei and disintegration of fundamental particles are also phenomena for which a probability of transition is defined.

transmutation, transformation of a pure body into another pure body.—This transformation may be induced by a nuclear reaction which transforms one nucleus into another nucleus, with a different atomic number. Transmutation was the dream of the alchemists who sought a means of turning vulgar metals into gold. This has become a commonplace today, but it is not an economical process for the production of precious metals.

transparent, used to describe something which does not oppose the passage of radiations by means of absorption; the opposite of **opaque** (qv). This term qualifies a substance when the type of radiation is specified. Bismuth, for example, is transparent to neutrons but opaque to gamma rays. The thickness of the substance must also be specified, the same substance being transparent when thin enough, yet opaque when thick enough.

transuranian, an element with higher atomic number than that of uranium which is 92.—Transuranians are not present in nature. They have been artificially produced by nuclear reactions, in which neutrons, alpha particles, etc, join the nucleus so as to increase its atomic number and its mass. All known transuranian elements possess an unstable nucleus which disintegrates by radioactivity. This explains their absence from nature. At present nine transuranian elements are well known. These are: neptunium (93), plutonium (94), americium (95), curium (96), berkelium (97), californium (98), europium (99), fermium (100) and mendelevium (101). (See **Actinides.**)

tripartition, the bursting of a heavy nucleus into three lighter nuclei in **fission** (qv).—Triple fission is much less frequent than double fission (bipartition).

triplet, a **multiplet** (qv) of order 3.

tritium, a hydrogen isotope of mass number 3.—Each of its atoms contains one electron, and the nucleus consists of one proton and two neutrons. It is sometimes called *extra-heavy hydrogen*, deuterium being called *heavy hydrogen*. Tritium is unstable, its nucleus disintegrates, forming a nucleus of helium 3 and an electron, with a half-life of 12.26 years:

tritium (1 proton, 2 neutrons) *gives* helium 3 (2 protons, 1 neutron) +electron+neutrino.

It is assumed that tritium is formed in the atmosphere by reactions induced by the neutrons of cosmic radiation:

neutron+nitrogen 14 (7 protons, 7 neutrons)
gives carbon 12 (6 protons, 6 neutrons)+tritium
(1 proton, 2 neutrons).

This hypothesis is upheld by the fact that the proportion of tritium in hydrogen is higher in the atmosphere than on the ground. At sea-level the proportion of tritium is of the order of 5 tritium atoms to 1 billion billion hydrogen atoms. Tritium may be used in **fusion** (qv) reactions, particularly with deuterium, with which it gives a reaction releasing a large amount of energy.

triton, a name sometimes given to the **tritium** (qv) nucleus. It consists of one proton and two neutrons and is unstable.

trochotron, an electronic valve enabling the electric pulses provided by a particle detector to be counted.—It requires a high magnetic field and usually consists of ten positions distributed round a circle. When ten pulses have passed into the counter, the trochotron emits a signal which notifies the ten, which may feed another trochotron counter of tens, and so on. A trochotron system may succeed in counting up to 1 million particles in a second.

tungsten, an alternative name for **wolfram** (qv).

tunnel effect, a specifically quantum effect, according to which a particle bound in the nucleus, which the laws of classical mechanics would forbid it to leave, may in fact escape from it.—This process is referred to in the theory of alpha radioactivity established by Gamow in 1928. An alpha particle inside a nucleus is, on the one hand, subjected to the forces of attraction of the other components of the nucleus; on the other, it is subject to movements within the nucleus, that is to say, it possesses kinetic energy. The combination of these two effects cannot cancel the electric forces of the Coulomb barrier of the nucleus, at least not in an orthodox manner. But, from the point of view of quantum mechanics, this particle has a finite chance of tunnelling through the Coulomb barrier during its movements and from this the name *tunnel effect* is derived.

U

uncertainty relations, principle advanced by Heisenberg. They are only concerned with microscopic systems and have no effect at the macroscopic level. They demonstrate that it is impossible to know all the data relating to a corpuscle at the same time. For two quantities called *complementary variables* exact knowledge of the one implies complete ignorance of the other. There is always uncertainty about the simultaneous definition of two complementary variables. The product of the uncertainty of the first with the uncertainty of the second is always greater than a constant quantity, called ● **Planck's constant**. Apart from a numerical factor this is the same constant that Planck introduced into the quantisation of energy.

The *complementary variable* pairs are, first, the position of a particle along a given direction and its momentum along this same direction. The momentum of a particle is the product of its mass by its velocity in standard mechanics. (In relativistic mechanics its definition is somewhat more complex.) It is therefore not possible exactly to define both the position and momentum of a particle along the same direction. If the particles are made to pass through a given point by setting up a very small opening, their momentum will be ill-defined, the more so the smaller the opening. Particles with different directions would be obtained at the output. This behaviour, which is similar to that of light when it is subjected to diffraction, may be understood by realising that matter also possesses a wave nature. Space contains three independent directional axes, therefore there are three uncertainty relations between the position and momentum of a particle. There exists a fourth uncertainty relation on the two complementary variables, time and energy. This makes it possible to foresee that in the case of an excited atom X-rays emitted in the de-excitation do not all have the same energy. There is a slight spreading of energy connected with the mean life of the state which has been excited by the uncertainty relation. This is a general phenomenon for all unstable systems, such as radioactive nuclei and unstable fundamental particles. The longer the mean life of an unstable system the closer the grouping of the energy value.

On the macroscopic level uncertainty relations do not arise because a measuring instrument may always be refined in such a way that it will be sensitive, while yet exercising a negligible influence on the quantities to be measured. At the microscopic level, on the contrary, the measuring instrument reacts with the system to be measured without its being possible to reduce the disturbance below a certain level. Furthermore, this is not foreseeable, so that uncertainty relations always affect microscopic systems. Uncertainty relations, which may be considered *a priori* as a principle, may also be deduced from a more precise formulation of the quantum mechanics used to describe microscopic systems. They assume a wider significance when they are considered within the framework of the idea of *complementarity*. (See **wave-particle duality.**)

univibrator, device of a double electronic valve, enabling electric pulses of regular strength and duration to be obtained from irregular pulses provided by a particle counter.—The electric pulses from a Geiger-Müller counter possess a constant rate of rise. This increase is used to flip the system from one valve to the next, each flip providing a well calibrated pulse. These pulses are then used in coincidence circuits or in counter valves. Such an arrangement enables up to 10 million particles per second to be counted.

unstable, this is said of a physical system whose characteristics evolve in time.—The nuclei with alpha, beta or gamma radioactivities are unstable, the residual nuclei produced having different characteristics from those of the initial nuclei. Fundamental particles, with the exception of the proton, electron, photon and the neutrinos, are unstable. They disintegrate into secondary particles that are less heavy than the primary particle. An atom excited by an X radiation or an ionising radiation is unstable. It may be de-excited, for instance, through emitting an X-ray.

uranides, a series of elements comprising uranium, neptunium, plutonium and americium and possessing allied chemical properties.—The uranides belong to the Actinides.

uranium, an element with atomic number 92.—Each of its nuclei contains 92 protons. Uranium fission is used as a source of nuclear energy in reactors and bombs. Uranium was discovered in 1798 by Klaproth and its radioactivity in 1896 by Becquerel. It is the natural element possessing the highest atomic number. The succeeding elements, called **transuranians** (qv), may be artificially manufactured and are unstable. Uranium is a metal of high density, 18.7 g to the cubic centimetre. It melts at 1133° C and appears in a solid state in three different crystalline forms according to its temperature. Uranium ores are fairly widespread throughout the world. The earth's crust contains about 0.004 per cent of them. In rocks this concentration is ten times lower. However, not all the ores, of which there are more than a hundred, are usable. The principal ones are pitchblende, deposits of which are in Katanga (Congo) and at Great Bear Lake (Canada); and carnobite, in the USA. There are important deposits in France. Natural uranium consists of three isotopes, all of which are radioactive and emit alpha particles:

—uranium 238 (92 protons, 146 neutrons) which has a half-life of 4.51 billion years

—uranium 235 (92 protons, 143 neutrons) which has a half-life of 713 million years

—uranium 234 (92 protons, 142 neutrons) which has a half-life of 240,000 years.

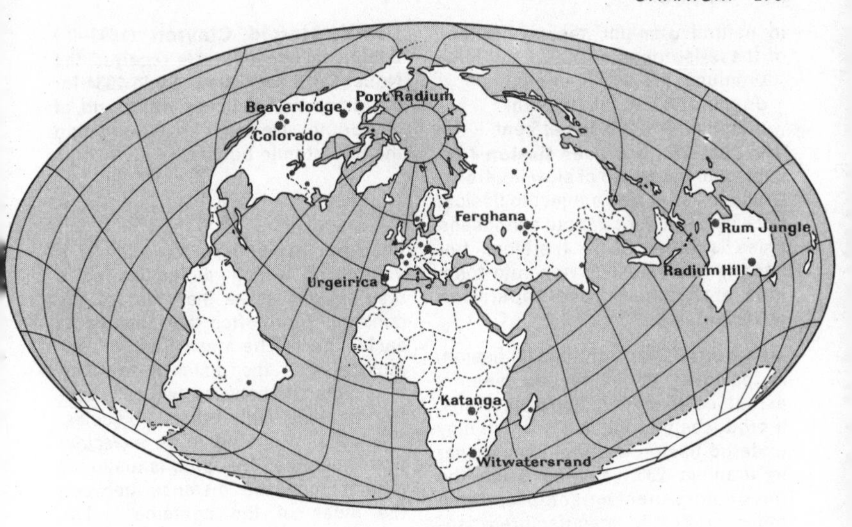

Principal world centres for the extraction of uranium

Forging a uranium ingot which will later be divided into fuel units destined for the reactors (Photo USIS)

In natural uranium, the proportions of these isotopes are:

uranium 238: 99.28 per cent
uranium 235: 0.715 per cent
uranium 234: 0.0058 per cent

Uranium 235 undergoes **fission** (qv) subject to the action of slow neutrons. Uranium 238 is also subject to fission, but with a frequency about a thousand times weaker. It is therefore frequently of interest to separate them from each other. (See **separation of isotopes.**)

● **Uranium 238,** of little use for fission, is, however, an interesting material as, subjected to the action of neutrons, it produces plutonium 239 which may undergo fission in conditions similar to uranium 235. Setting aside the three natural uranium isotopes, eleven other artificially manufactured isotopes are known, whose mass number varies from 227 (92 protons, 135 neutrons) to 240 (92 protons, 148 neutrons). They are all unstable and disintegrate by radioactivity. Uranium 233 also displays a great tendency towards fission, subject to the action of slow neutrons. It may be obtained in considerable quantities in a reactor by the bombardment of thorium 232 with neutrons. Uranium 238 is the first member of a *radioactive series* which consists of no less than 19 elements, all of them radioactive except the last, lead 206, which is stable. *Uranium I* is a common name for uranium 238. *Uranium II* is a common name for uranium 234, a member of the uranium series.

● **uranium X^1, X^2, Y, Z,** are names usually given to elements of the *radioactive series of uranium.*—These are, respectively, thorium 234, protoactinium 234 (or brevium), thorium 231, protoactinium 234 (isomer of uranium X^2).

UREY, Harold Clayton (1893–) American chemist. He received the Nobel Prize for Chemistry in 1934 for the discovery of heavy water and of deuterium. He took part in perfecting the first atomic bomb.

V

vacuum, molecular, the state of a volume in which molecules of a residual gas strike the sides of the container more often than they strike each other.—The mean free path for molecules is the distance travelled by a molecule between two consecutive impacts with other molecules. The vacuum is said to be *molecular* when the mean free path is distinctly greater than the distance between the sides of the container. The pressure which exists in a container subjected to molecular vacuum is at the most some millionths of the atmospheric pressure. The gas density is reduced with pressure in the same proportion as the density of air with atmospheric pressure.

valence, a chemical property of the atoms of an element, measured by the number of hydrogen atoms which may combine with an atom of the element should this be an oxidiser (*negative valency*), or by the number of hydrogen atoms for which it may substitute itself in a chemical compound, if it is a reductor (*positive valency*).—By definition, hydrogen has a positive valency equal to 1. For example, oxygen has a negative valency equal to 2 in water H_2O, which results from the combination of an oxygen atom with two hydrogen atoms. Valence is most frequently a constant for each element. This rule, however, is not absolute.

VAN DE GRAAFF, Robert

Jemison (1901–) American physicist.—Author of many books on nuclear physics, he is very well known in the development of the first electrostatic accelerators of charged particles. One type of these machines bears his name. (See **accelerator.**)

VEKSLER, Vladimir (1907–) Soviet physicist. A specialist in the construction of large accelerators, he proposed a type of electron accelerator called a **microtron** (qv). He also carried out important work on perfecting the **synchrotron** and the **synchrocyclotron** (qqv).

virtual, that which cannot really be observed, because it is contrary to the laws of the conservation of energy. —A particle is said to be in a • **virtual state** (qv) if the available energy is insufficient for its mass to be formed. It may be imagined as existing in a transitory state which violates the law of the conservation of energy to an extent, and for a period, limited by Heisenberg's uncertainty principle. (See **uncertainty relations.**)

W

WALTON, Ernest Thomas Sinton (1903–) Irish physicist. In 1929, with Cockcroft, he perfected an electrostatic particle **accelerator** (qv). In 1932, he established a method of transmutation of atomic nuclei by means of artificially accelerated particles. He shared the Nobel Prize for Physics with Cockcroft in 1951.

waste, radioactive, an unusable radioactive body produced in a nuclear installation, for example, in a reactor.—Elimination of this waste raises an important problem. Some radioactive elements disintegrate rapidly and are eliminated because of this. So the fuel bars of a reactor are stocked for some months, at the end of which time their radioactivity has decreased considerably. However, other radioactive elements disintegrate slowly. Strontium 90, for example, produced in a reactor, has a mean life of 20 years. Since it may be absorbed by living organisms, it would be dangerous to spread it about. Only one method is yet used for disposing of these products with a substantial lifetime. The waste is placed in steel or reinforced concrete containers which are then either buried or submerged. Radioactive gases, such as xenon, are also produced in fuel fission. They are preserved inside the reactor and then eliminated by absorption when the fuel bars are discharged. When the reactor is air-cooled, a certain amount of radioactive argon 41 is formed, during neutron bombardment of argon 40 which is contained in the air-cooling circuit. In this case it is necessary to increase as much as possible the speed of the cooling air, the amount of radioactive argon being greater the longer the time taken by the air passing through the reactor. Gases are evacuated at a sufficiently high altitude, while contamination at ground level is monitored by suitable detectors. Whether radioactive waste is stored in disused mines or dumped in the sea, corrosion of its containers entails a risk of its return to biological circulation. It seems likely that the dangerous isotopes will have to be built into the chemical structure of ceramic or glassy substances which are nearly incorrodible even by sea water at deep-sea pressure, before being dumped.

wave. The concept of wave, related to *light* in classical physics, has been

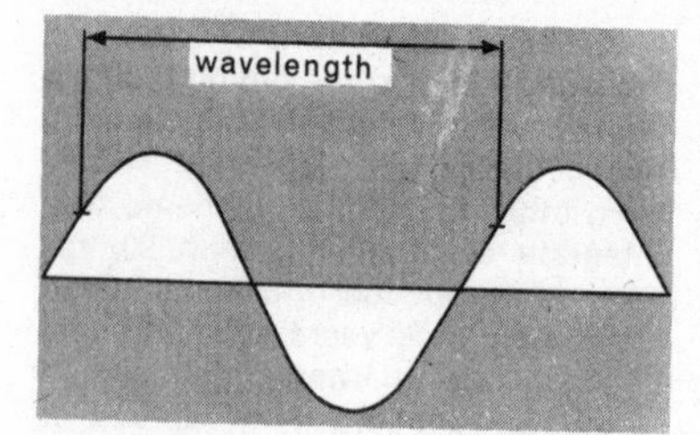

Definition of a wavelength

extended to *matter* in corpuscular physics. Light is constituted by the superposition of electric and magnetic fields vibrating at a specific frequency. This vibration travels at a speed of 300,000 km per second. The wavelength is equal to the distance between two consecutive points in the same state of vibration. A wavelength may also be associated with a particle in motion, the de Broglie wavelength. This quantity varies inversely with the velocity and mass of the particle. Diffraction phenomena, characteristic of a wave, may also be observed in particles such as electrons, neutrons, etc. The wave of matter associated with a particle may be represented by the superposition of waves of different lengths whose interference produces a maximum effect in the region where the corpuscle is localised.

● **wave-function,** a function which represents a microscopic system.—Whereas the evolution of a classical macroscopic system is fully determined by a certain number of data (positions and velocities of the elements of which it is composed), the same does not apply to a microscopic system. It is known merely how to forecast the average behaviour of the latter; several microscopic systems prepared in an identical fashion evolve in different ways. Quantum mechanics makes it possible to foresee with what degree of probability each of the possible results may be obtained, ie that the realisation of a great many experiments upon identical systems gives different results, though with definite frequencies for each of the latter. Each corpuscle or corpuscular system is described by a wave-function, a mathematical quantity from which the relative probability of observing different results is obtained. A simplified statement is that the product of the wave-function with itself gives for the particle the likelihood of finding itself in a certain volume at a given moment. This product is called *probability density*.

● **wave guide,** an extended **cavity** (qv) which is able to conduct electromagnetic waves without damping them.—The name *cavity* is reserved for an enclosure in which the waves are stationary; *wave guide* is the name given to an enclosure in which the waves travel.

● **wavelength of electromagnetic waves.** Study of the properties of light demonstrates that this may be considered the superposition of two fields, one electric, the other magnetic, vibrating at a frequency which decides the colour of the light. Electric field E at at first increases, then diminishes, then changes direction and in the end recovers its initial value. The complete oscillation is called *wave*. Magnetic field H oscillates in the same way but lags, in regard to electric field E, so that the maximum of the one corresponds to the minimum of the other. The fields H and E are both perpendicular to the direction of propagation and perpendicular to each other. The distance travelled

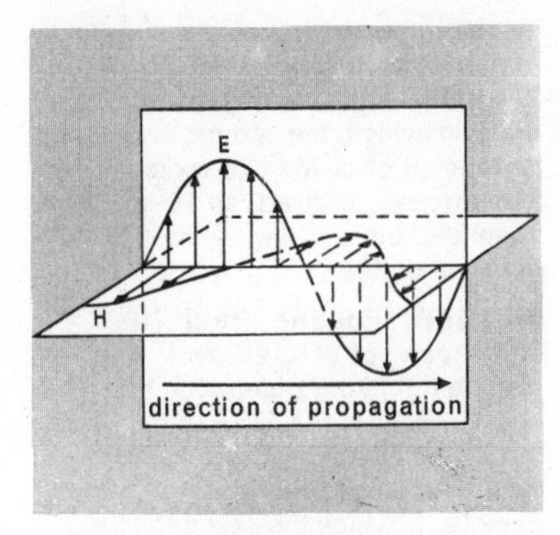

Wavelength

by light during a complete oscillation is called a *wavelength*. It is smaller the greater the oscillation frequency, since the propagation velocity remains the same. Radio waves are of the same nature as light waves. Their wavelengths vary from a few centimetres (very short waves) to some hundreds of metres (long waves). Visible light corresponds to wavelengths contained between 0.4 thousandths of a millimetre (violet) and 0.8 thousandths of a millimetre (red); the wavelengths of X-rays are of the order of a millionth of a millimetre and those of gamma radiation are of the order of a billionth of a centimetre or less.

wave-particle duality, a modern concept according to which matter possesses a dual nature, undulatory and corpuscular.—In classical physics, it was customary to consider the nature of light as undulatory, ie as a vibration to be conveyed. Early discoveries on molecules and atoms caused these to be considered as particles, ie as well-localised grains of matter. The undulatory nature of light and the corpuscular nature of matter in this scheme of things appeared to have no common focus. However, after the discovery of certain physical phenomena—such as the quantification of radiative energy (Planck-Einstein), the photo-electric effect (Einstein 1905: the extraction of an electron from an atom by means of a photon)—it came to be thought that light could also appear in a corpuscular aspect, the photon. On the other hand, experiments carried out by Davisson and Germer in 1927 demonstrated that electrons falling on to a crystal were subjected to the same diffraction phenomenon as that undergone by light, which gives rise to interference. These experiments agreed with the work of de Broglie who, in 1923, proposed to ascribe to each particle a wavelength, like those possessed by light, which would determine a vibration frequency. To sum up, a wave also presents a corpuscular aspect, whereas a particle also presents an undulatory aspect. In the development of quantum mechanics by Heisenberg, Schrödinger and Dirac, this duality appears universal. The uncertainty relations of Heisenberg convey the impossibility of knowing simultaneously the position of a microscopic object (which we will call neither a *wave* nor a *corpuscle*) along a certain direction and the value of its momentum, along the same direction. (The momentum is the product of the mass and speed of the object.) In the same way it is impossible to know with absolute precision the energy and moment of passage at a given point of a microscopic object. Uncertainty relations also reflect the wave-corpuscle duality in the sense that a plane wave of completely definite energy, by which light was described in classical theory, cannot have its position fixed because it extends to all of space. To form a picture of an object of undulatory nature, yet whose extension is reduced in space, a wave-packet must be imagined, which is a superposition of waves vibrating with different frequencies. These waves practically cancel each other out in the whole of space, except in a small volume which determines the locality of the microscopic object. Energy is linked to the frequency, therefore the less well determined in energy the object is, the better it is located in space. The microscopic object thus has two natures simultaneously, the one corpuscular, the other undulatory. However, it is only the kind of experiment that establishes the nature that is being observed. For instance, by making the electrons diffracted at a crystal, their undulatory nature may be observed, whereas in a phenomenon such as the knock-on in which a high-speed electron strikes an atomic electron and ejects it, its corpuscular nature is observed. Both these natures are said to be complementary, in the sense that a microscopic object cannot be described under only one of its two aspects, the equations have to take into consideration the dual nature of the object, ie wave and corpuscle. Quantum mechanics known process for describing this duality.

way, eightfold, classification of fundamental particles due to Gell-Mann, analogous to Mendeleyev's periodic classification of the chemical elements. As with Mendeleyev's prediction of eka-boron, etc, the eightfold way predicted the existence of other particles, such as the Ω^- since discovered by experiment.

weight, atomic, a term commonly used to specify the *atomic mass.*—It may be measured in chemical units in which the atomic weight of natural oxygen (consisting of isotopes 16, 17 and 18) is fixed at 16 g or in physical units in which the atomic weight of isotope 16 of oxygen (8 protons, and 8 neutrons) is fixed at 16 g. The chemical unit is equal to 1.000272 physical units.

WIGNER, Eugene Paul (1902–) American physicist and mathematician of Hungarian extraction; he has worked in the USA since 1930. In 1937 he established the hypothesis of a model of the uniform atomic nucleus, in which the exchange forces of the nucleons are independent of charge and spin. In 1958 he received the Fermi Prize, and in 1963 he shared the Nobel Prize for Physics with Mrs M. Goeppert-Mayer and Hans Jensen. His most important works deal mainly with the discovery and application of the principles of symmetry in quantum theory.

• **Wigner effect.** In a crystallised body, each atom occupies a distinct place in the lattice. A sufficiently high-speed neutron or ion may destroy this structure and eject the crystal atom. The atom is occasionally slowed down in the crystal after being ejected and occupies interstitial position. This effect has proved to be a fairly serious disadvantage for reactor materials. Their mechanical characteristics, especially ductility, are found to deteriorate because of the high flux of neutrons in the reactor, and the energy thus stored may be disastrously released.

WILSON, Charles Thomson Rees (1869–1959) British physicist.—In 1912 he perfected the cloud chamber which bears his name. For his work on beta and alpha emissions he received the Nobel Prize for Physics, with A. H. Compton, in 1928.

wolfram, an element with atomic number 74.—It is a metal whose use is studied for the shielding of reactors. It is particularly effective for shielding against gamma rays on account of its high atomic number and its high density of 19 g per cubic centimetre. Its use would be of interest in reactors operating at a high temperature as its fusion point is high, 3379° C, because lead, with a density of 11.3, melts at 327° C.

X

X-rays, the name of electromagnetic radiations of the same nature as light whose energy is contained between that of ultra-violet rays and that of the gamma ray.—X-rays are photons whose ●**wavelength** (qv) is contained between some millionths of a millimetre and some billionths of a centimetre. They were discovered by Röntgen at the end of the nineteenth century. They are produced by excited atoms, when an electron passes from one shell of the atom to a shell on which its energy is lower, the difference in energy being emitted in the form of an X-ray. Fairly heavy elements are needed to give energetic X-rays; light elements yield only soft radiation. X-rays are also emitted in the form of **bremsstrahlung** (qv). X-rays are used in radiography and for therapy.

Y

YANG, Chen Ning (1922–) Chinese physicist working in the USA. In 1957 he shared the Nobel Prize for Physics with Lee, for his work on the breakdown of parity conservation.

ylem, magma in the form in which, on one set of cosmological assumptions, matter was found before the formation of nuclei and atoms. Various lines of evidence suggest that some billion years have passed since the original ylem, if any, disappeared. (See **lead.**)

YUKAWA, Hideki (1907–) Japanese physicist.—A theoretician and a specialist in nuclear physics, he did much work on the binding forces between nucleons and on the processes of beta radioactivity. He predicted the presence of mesons. These particles were later discovered by Anderson and Neddermeyer. He received the Nobel Prize for Physics in 1949.

Z

ZEEMAN, Pieter (1865–1943) Dutch physicist.—He discovered the variations in optical wavelengths with the magnetic field applied to the source, which is called the *Zeeman effect*. (See **atom.**) In 1907 he shared the Nobel Prize for Physics with Lorentz.

zirconium, an element with the atomic number 40.—It is a metal which may be used in reactors, as it absorbs few neutrons and retains good mechanical properties up to very high temperatures. It melts at 1860° C.

Zoé, the first nuclear reactor built in France in 1948. It is also called EL 1.—This experimental reactor had very low power output and used natural uranium oxide fuel, whence its name: *Z*ero energy, *O*xide of uranium, *E*xperimental. Since it was built, this reactor has undergone modifications.